The RSGB Guide to EMC

Robin Page-Jones, CEng, MIEE, G3JWI

Radio Society of Great Britain

Published by the Radio Society of Great Britain, Cranborne Road, Potters Bar, Herts EN6 3JE.

First published 1992, entitled *The Radio Amateur's Guide to EMC*.
Second edition 1998.

ISBN 1 872309 48 8

Cover design: Jon Stewart.
Illustrations: Derek Cole and Bob Ryan.
Editing and typographic design: Ray Eckersley, Seven Stars Publishing.
Production: Mike Dennison.

Disclaimer
The opinions expressed in this book are those of the author and contributors, and not necessarily those of the RSGB. While the information presented is believed to be correct, the author, contributors, publisher and their agents cannot accept responsibility for consequences arising from any inaccuracies or omissions.

Printed in Great Britain by Black Bear Press, Cambridge.

Contents

Acknowledgements

So many people have contributed to the preparation of this book that it is not possible to thank them all individually. Special thanks are due to the following:

David Lauder, G0SNO, for his contribution to the appendices, and also for his generous assistance in adapting information originally appearing in his EMC column in *Radio Communciation*.

Hilary Claytonsmith, G4JKS, for advice on style and content.

Alan Martindale, G3MYA, and Martyn Culling, G8UCP, for their contributions to the appendices.

My son Michael, G7VZY, for supplying the physicist's point of view in our many technical discussions.

And finally my wife Renée for her assistance in the preparation and checking of the copy.

Robin Page-Jones, G3JWI

1 Introduction

AT FIRST SIGHT, updating the text of *The Radio Amateur's Guide to EMC* for a second edition seemed a simple task – just a question of adding a few bits and pieces, and correcting the odd error that had crept in. The first edition was written in the form of more-or-less independent chapters with specialist appendices so that it could easily be brought up to date in future editions. In fact this has proved to be a great deal more difficult than had at first been anticipated. The original intention was that the chapters would require only minimal revision in later editions, but once work began it was evident that significant changes and additions would be needed to bring things up to date.

Some of the old appendices have been retained with new material added as required. Appendix 1 has been rewritten to reflect a more general picture of PME, and to put it into a practical context. The simple spectrum analyser which was featured in Appendix 2 is now very well known and has appeared in several other RSGB publications. Accordingly this has been dropped from this edition. An aspect of EMC which received little notice is naturally occurring static and a new Appendix 2 on lightning gives some background information on this fascinating subject.

Writing about EMC in the present climate is like trying to hit a moving target which in some cases you can't even see. There is a certain amount of pleasure to be gained from being in the forefront of the battle but it has its disadvantages. This is particularly true in the in the area of regulations, where proposals, drafts and policy statements are coming out in bewildering profusion. Because of this, unattractive statements like "at the time of writing . . ." appear much too often. However, the alternative of leaving out such information altogether, or publishing statements which may turn out to be untrue, would be a great deal more unattractive.

The expansion of the use of radio and electronic devices over the last few years must be unprecedented. Added to this, new ground is being broken in the entertainment industry with digital broadcasting for both sound and TV. The transmission of all these signals to and from the user's premises is a problem in its own right, and one in which the trade-off between cost and EMC considerations will be very significant. It is likely that the coming of digital radio and TV will make a significant difference to the practical application of EMC to amateur radio. Whatever happens the fundamental physical factors underlying EMC will remain the same.

When the first edition was going to press it was expected that the EC EMC regulations would come into force at the beginning of 1992. For various reasons this was delayed until January 1996 but now the regulations are with us. Needless to say, these regulations have not been devised to benefit radio amateurs or any other specialist group. They are framed round broadcast reception and the use of commercial radio and electronic products in a typical domestic environment. Most amateurs wish that the regulations were a lot more stringent but, to be reasonable, one cannot expect the whole radio and electronics industry to gear itself to the needs of a relatively small group. So we must make the best of what we have. The regulations feature frequently in this new edition. Apart from anything else, perusing the regulations gives a good understanding of the background to EMC and what it is all about.

A book of this sort fulfils two requirements – as a quick reference and as a book for general reading. To achieve both these requirements there is, inevitably, considerable repetition as different facets of the same basic facts crop up in different parts of the book. While this may not be ideal, there is no other way to avoid constant cross-reference which would detract from the readability.

The first edition of this book broke away from tradition by dealing with interference as part and parcel of the practice of amateur radio, not just a nuisance to be thought about only when circumstances make some sort of action inevitable. Radio amateurs exist in the EMC environment, and it is an environment that is constantly changing. Because of our special interests and skills, we are well placed to play a part in the shaping of that environment, and the part we play may be far greater than our relatively small numbers would suggest.

2 Radiation – wanted and unwanted

THE ONE THING that links together all radio enthusiasts, young and old, amateur and professional, is electromagnetic radiation. The ability to communicate without any apparent medium has a fascination of its own which never entirely fades, however jaded one may become with the nuts and bolts of radio and electronics.

Natural radio frequency radiation has been around for a very long time. In fact, if the cosmic background radiation really is the remnant of the 'big bang', as current theories suggest, then radio signals have a direct link to the creation of the universe; a good pedigree by any standard. RF radiation is only a small part of the electromagnetic spectrum, which extends from very-low-frequency radio waves right up to gamma rays which have wavelengths of only about 10^{-14} metres. Visible light is a fairly thin slice somewhere near the middle, with wavelengths in the region of half a micron (0.5µm) (see Fig 2.1 overleaf).

Visible light, very roughly, forms the division between non-ionising radiation like radio waves and ionising radiation such as x-rays and gamma rays. Ionising radiation, as its name implies, is energetic enough to have a direct affect on the atomic structure of certain materials and, if this material happens to be a living cell, serious damage can be done. Non-ionising radiation, on the other hand, only causes atoms and molecules to vibrate (without coming apart), giving rise to heating effects. The sunlight which gets through to the Earth includes both features in a more-or-less optimum mix for sustaining life. Information on the biological effects of various types of radiation (including radio frequency radiation) can be found in leaflets published by the National Radiological Protection Board (NRPB). These are available to the public on request [1].

What radiation really is, and how it fits into life, the universe and everything, is a fascinating subject, and anyone interested should read one of the many popular books on the background to modern physics. We shall, however, confine ourselves to the uses and abuses of radio frequencies.

What is RF radiation?

So far as radio frequencies are concerned, radiation is caused by accelerating electric charges, which in electric circuit terms means a varying current in some sort of conductor. A current flow implies both electric and magnetic fields, and it is the interaction of these two fields which gives rise to electromagnetic radiation. Many academic textbooks which deal with antennas and radiation offer an impressive display of advanced mathematics,

Fig 2.1. The electromag-
netic spectrum

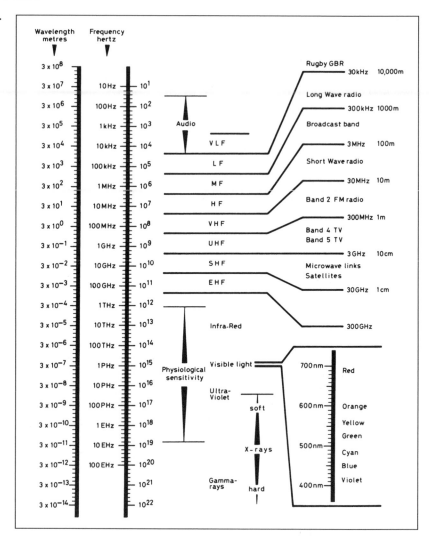

but not much from which the plain man can form a mental picture of what is actually going on. At the other end of the scale, excessively simplified explanations can give a false impression of understanding. The truth of the matter, of course, is that there is no simple picture of the mechanism of radiation, and the best that can be done is to try to get some sort of feel for what is going on, coupled with an appreciation of the magnitude of the effects which are of interest in amateur radio in general, and to EMC problems in particular.

Power density and field strength

These two parameters turn up regularly in EMC literature, and most importantly in the EMC standards for domestic and industrial equipment. These standards set down limits for the immunity to RF fields, and also the limits of permissible radiated interference, for all types of equipment. It is therefore essential that everyone in the radio and electronics world should be at least on nodding terms with them. The relationship between power density and field strength embodies most of what the average man in the street (with an EMC problem) needs to know about radiation, and is nicely illustrated by the following technical day dream.

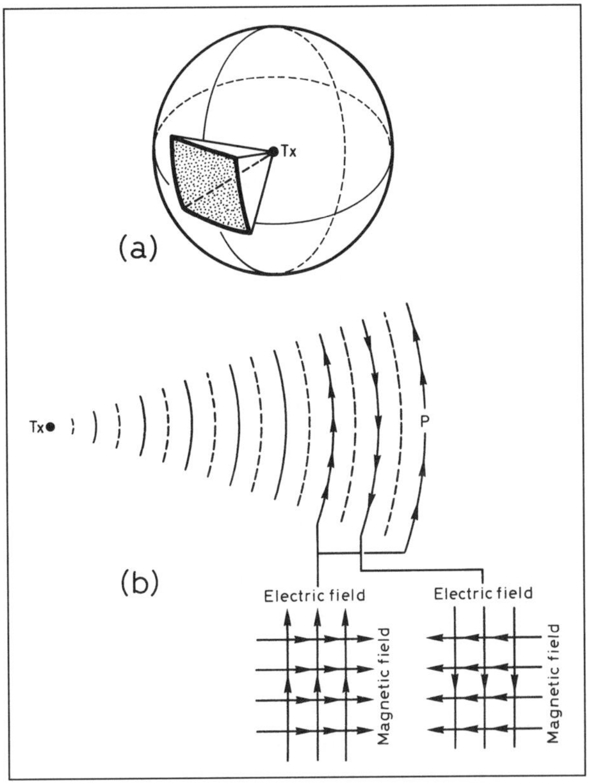

Power density

Imagine a large sphere somewhere out in space, made of magic glass with exactly the same electrical properties as space itself. At the centre of the sphere is a transmitting antenna which is truly isotropic, so that it radiates equally in all directions. Further imagine the surface of the sphere is divided up into squares of one metre side, like the panes of glass in a huge spherical greenhouse (Fig 2.2(a)).

The power density in watts/square metre is simply the fraction of the power which passes through each square. For instance, assuming that the power of the transmitter is 100W and the radius of the sphere is 282m, so that there are a million squares (the surface area of a sphere is $4\pi R^2$), then the power density would be 100µW/square metre.

Fig 2.2. (a) Radiation falling on one square of surface of imaginary sphere. (b) Fields seen by an observer located at point P on the surface of the sphere

Impedance of free space

Now imagine that the sheets of glass are replaced by sheets of conductive material, rather like the conductive foam used for packing CMOS integrated circuits, but having a resistivity of exactly 377Ω per metre square. The foam will absorb all the radiated power and none will be left over, so that the situation, as seen by the transmitter, is indistinguishable from the magic glass condition, ie the radiation seems to be passing out into space. This is analogous to an infinitely long transmission line which, from the transmission end, appears to be terminated in its characteristic impedance, but which can be terminated in its characteristic impedance anywhere along its length without changing what the transmitter sees.

Field strength

For this we have to imagine that we are back in the magic greenhouse, and that all the conductive foam has been cleared away. Think of just one of those metre squares of magic glass, and assume that the polarisation of the radiation is such that the electric field is up and down the square, and the magnetic field is side to side, like the divisions on a sheet of graph paper (Fig 2.2(b)). If we could take a magic voltmeter and measure the voltage between the top and bottom of the square, this would be the field strength in volts per metre. Since this voltage is across the characteristic impedance

5

of free space, which is 377Ω, we can relate this to the power density by the simple power-voltage-resistance formula:

$$P = V^2/R \quad \text{or} \quad V = \sqrt{(PR)}$$

For our 100W transmitter 282m away, the power density is 100µW/square metre, so the field strength is:

$$\sqrt{(100 \times 10^{-6} \times 377)} = 194\text{mV}$$

across one metre of space, ie 194mV/m.

An approximate way of working out the field strength, if we know the power radiated and the distance away, is by taking the square root of the power, multiplying by 5.5, and then dividing by the range in metres. In our case:

$$\frac{5.5 \times \sqrt{100}}{282} = 195\text{mV/m}$$

At this point it is essential to emphasise that it is not practical to use these simple formulas to predict with any accuracy the conditions in the neighbourhood of an amateur antenna. The most obvious thing that comes to mind is that practical antennas are not isotropic, but this is the least of our troubles since a correction can always be made for whichever antenna we are using.

The really serious problem is that amateur antennas are usually fairly close to earth and also surrounded by other obstructions, so the field strength at any point is really the sum of direct and reflected waves. This means that the field strength can vary from zero to at least twice the calculated value, depending on the phase of the received waves. Another problem, which is particularly relevant to EMC investigations, is that at lower frequencies the receiving point is often too close to the source for the calculated figures to have any meaning. All in all, though the calculated figures must be treated with the greatest circumspection, they can be useful in giving an idea of where problems are likely to arise.

Near and far fields

While on the subject of definitions, it is a good time to bring up two more which are important to the understanding of EMC problems. These are *near field* and *far field*.

The near field exists relatively close to the antenna, where the relationship between the inductance and capacitance of the antenna itself, and the fields surrounding it, is the same as it would be in or around actual components; energy flows backwards and forwards between antenna and field (Fig 2.3). In some ways the effect is similar to the space charge around the cathode of a valve, where there is a balance between electrons emitted and those falling back to the cathode. Any conductors, such as mains cables or TV antennas, in the near-field region will be coupled to the radiating antenna by

Fig 2.3. The flow of RF energy around a short dipole antenna

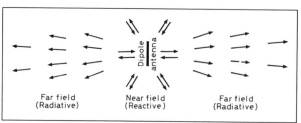

Far field (Radiative)   Near field (Reactive)   Far field (Radiative)

direct capacitive or inductive coupling, and this can give rise to much larger unwanted coupling than might be expected.

The far field, often called the *radiation field*, is the region well away from the source, where the magnetic and electric fields are on their own, and proceed through space at right-angles to one another and to the direction of propagation. Under these conditions the intensities of the two fields are in phase so that, going back to our magic sphere, an observer sitting at a point P (Fig 2.2(b)) on the surface of the sphere would see the electric and magnetic fields sweeping over him out into space. As the fields pass him they increase and decrease, in phase with one another, following the RF cycle. In the far field the electric and magnetic fields cannot exist independently; destroy one and the other disappears as well.

How far from the source does the near field extend? Like so many questions about radiation there is no simple answer. As a rough guide, it can be said that for a half-wave dipole the near and far fields are equal in intensity at a distance of about one-fifth of a wavelength. Inside that distance the near field predominates, but as the distance increases the near field rapidly declines, becoming negligible at a distance of a few wavelengths. At lower frequencies, 3.5MHz for instance, the influence of the near field spreads out quite a long way and may well encompass the home of the amateur and those of his near neighbours as well.

Signal pick-up and capture area

If a conductor is placed in an EM field, the free electrons in the conductor will move under the influence of the field. In other words an RF current flows in the conductor. Whenever current flows in a conductor, radiation takes place, so that the situation is a complicated mixture of energy absorption and re-radiation. Some energy will be dissipated in the losses in the conductor but, more importantly, energy can be coupled out of the conductor to do useful work, such as providing an input signal to a receiver. Calculation of the energy which can be extracted is simplified by the concept of *capture area*. This is a hypothetical area from which energy is available for extraction.

Capture area can be illustrated by looking at a simple case; that of a half-wave dipole in free space placed parallel to the electric field. Looking again at Fig 2.2, the receiving dipole is at point P on the surface of the sphere and the energy is extracted from the space around it. The capture area of a half-wave dipole is approximately 0.13 times the wavelength squared ($0.13\lambda^2$ square metres). If the dipole is correctly matched by connecting a resistor of 75Ω across the terminals, the total power extracted, and appearing at the load, is half the capture area multiplied by the power density. The other half of the power is re-radiated or, as is more usually expressed, is 'lost' in the radiation resistance of the dipole. The really interesting fact is that the capture area of a dipole much shorter than a half wave is almost the same as that of the full-size half-wave dipole, provided that it is tuned to resonance and correctly matched by some form of antenna tuning unit (ATU). The trade-off is that the bandwidth of the antenna system becomes very narrow as the antenna is made shorter, and losses in the ATU become prohibitive.

THE RSGB GUIDE TO EMC

Where the load resistance is smaller than the radiation resistance, a larger proportion of the energy is re-radiated and, apart from losses, a wire with no load will re-radiate all the energy it receives. In practice this means that almost any wire will have a resonance at some frequency or other, and will re-radiate energy if a nearby transmitter happens to be on or near that frequency. This brings near-field conditions into places where they would not otherwise be expected, and is responsible for many of the unpredictable effects which bedevil the investigation of interference problems.

As an illustration of the significance of capture area, it is worthwhile using the simplified view discussed above to look at two amateur bands, the 73kHz band and the 70MHz band. Suppose we have two antennas, one tuned and matched for 73kHz and the other tuned and matched for 70MHz. Since a dipole is a bit impractical at 73kHz we will assume that the antennas are monopoles. (A monopole has about half the capture area of a dipole, and again a short monopole tuned to resonance and correctly matched has almost the same capture area as a quarter-wave monopole.) The wavelength at 70MHz is 4.3m while at 73kHz it is 4.1km, so the two capture areas would be about 1.2 square metres and 1.1 million square metres respectively. If the power density at the surface of our sphere was 1 picowatt per square metre, then the 70MHz antenna could potentially extract 0.6 picowatts, while the 73kHz antenna could deliver 650,000 picowatts (0.65μW). This explains why, in the early days of radio, remarkably long ranges were possible using receivers with no amplification. Very long wavelengths were used with large antenna/earth systems and low-loss antenna tuning units. In practice these seemingly attractive figures for low frequencies are never fully realised. Losses in the ATU and particularly in the earth connection reduce the received signal to a small fraction of what is potentially available in the capture area.

Unwanted radiation

Though the principles underlying all forms of RF radiation are the same, there are two quite different aspects which affect the whole of the radio and electronic world. One is the deliberate radiation of signals from an antenna, where the object is to radiate as much of the energy supplied by the transmitter as possible. Despite the vagaries of imperfect grounds and cluttered gardens, this is a comparatively controlled situation. The other aspect is quite the reverse. This is where unwanted signals are accidentally radiated from some form of equipment which is supposed to be carrying out some completely non-radio function. In the majority of such cases the details of the actual process of radiation is exceedingly complex, involving a large number of unknown variables, so that it is almost always easier to consider the problem as a whole than to attempt detailed analysis. It is perhaps a paradox that the computer, which on the face of it is the symbol of the strictly logical approach, is, under its business-like exterior, a seething mass of unpredictable radiation sources.

Generally speaking, this type of radiation takes place where current is rapidly changing, usually in some form of switched circuit. Nowadays the most common source of interference is from switched electronic circuits such as those in computers and switch-mode power supplies. The amount of energy depends on the current involved and the speed of switching and usually these are related; faster logic devices tend to draw more current. It is well-known that pulses of current can be analysed into a series of harmonically related sine waves and that the steeper the sides of the pulse, the higher the harmonics involved (Fig 2.4).

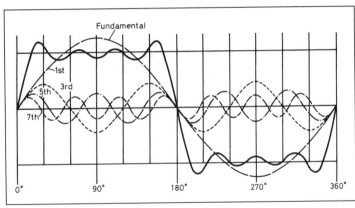

Fig 2.4. A square wave can be analysed into a sine wave plus odd harmonics

A typical home computer generates pulses with edges of only a few nanoseconds, giving harmonics up to tens or even hundreds of megahertz. Because there are so many pulse streams, all with their associated harmonics, the net result is RF energy radiated over a wide spectrum, with peaks at various clock frequencies and their harmonics. Interfering signals usually leak out of the offending equipment by a complicated mixture of conduction and radiation. Input and output leads, particularly the mains supply, can act as transmission lines, carrying the signals a considerable distance before the energy is lost in radiation or other losses.

There is a general rule that antennas which are good for transmission will also be good for reception, and this is just as true when applied to the unwanted radiators involved in equipment which accidentally generate interference. Practically, this means that computers and similar devices which allow interference to leak out will also be susceptible to disturbances getting in. In some instances the disturbance can be due to a genuine RF signal from a legitimate transmitter such as one of the public services or amateur radio, but in most cases the source is a switching transient caused by something being switched on or off nearby – often a fridge or electric power tool. Of course the fridge or tool should be suppressed, but then so should the computer; ideally both should be suppressed to the appropriate level.

Reference

[1] National Radiological Protection Board, Chilton, Didcot, Oxon, OX11 0RQ.

3 | Good radio housekeeping

THE PHRASE *good radio housekeeping* has been coined to cover all the factors which contribute to trouble-free amateur radio operation. The phrase may be new but the ideas are a distillation of conventional wisdom which has been accumulated over decades of amateur activities. Throughout the 'fifties and 'sixties, the main problem facing amateurs was interference to VHF TV caused by harmonics from HF transmitters. This problem has diminished over the years, partly because transmitter design has improved, but mainly because of the demise of VHF TV in many countries including Britain. In recent years, interference caused by the fundamental transmission getting into all types of electronic equipment has become the major problem.

The term *breakthrough* is normally used to describe this phenomenon, emphasising the fact that it is really a shortcoming on the part of the equipment being interfered with, and not a transmitter fault. This is not to say, of course, that the avoidance of problems from faulty or inadequate transmitters is not important; on the contrary, it is too big a subject to include as part of this general housekeeping section, and is dealt with in Chapters 4 and 6.

Minimising breakthrough

The main object of good radio housekeeping is to minimise breakthrough to local domestic electronic equipment by arranging for as much of the precious RF energy as possible to go where it is wanted – in the direction of the distant station – and as little as possible into the local surroundings where, if you are lucky, it gets lost. If you're unlucky it ends up as breakthrough in your neighbour's TV or video. In many cases it can be rightly argued that the immunity of the domestic equipment is inadequate, but that does not absolve the amateur from the responsibility of keeping his RF transmissions under reasonable control. Many of the features which contribute to minimising breakthrough also help in reducing received interference so, while the virtue of good neighbourliness is undoubtedly its own reward, there is the added bonus of better all-round station performance.

The EMC regulations

Until recently the only regulations which most UK amateurs were aware of were those incorporated in their licence. So far as breakthrough is concerned, the concept of 'undue interference' was used which gave scope for wide interpretation. The official view was usually favourable to the amateur, provided it could be shown that the problem was not due to defects in his equipment.

In recent years deregulation has taken place throughout the telecommunications industry. This has had two very important effects. First, much greater use is now being made of radio and electronics in all manner of domestic devices so that the potential for EMC problems is greatly increased. Secondly, many services are now provided by competing private operators whose main concern is to provide an effective service to their customers at minimum cost. Fortunately it has been realised by governments that some form of control is required to avoid electromagnetic chaos and this control has taken the form of regulations which lay down minimum EMC performance. The UK regulations came into effect in January 1996 and, with some minor exceptions, apply to all types of equipment including radios, TVs, telephones, computers etc. The problem is that they are not stringent enough for the needs of radio amateurs.

The first factor which leaps to mind is that the levels of immunity required are often too low to prevent breakthrough from a nearby transmitter. This is recognised by a statement in the generic immunity standard EN 50082-1, which states that:

"In special cases situations will arise where the level of disturbance may exceed the levels specified in this standard, eg where a hand-held transmitter is used in proximity to an apparatus. In these instances special mitigation measures may have to be employed."

Similar statements appear in other immunity standards, including EN 55020 which deals with domestic radio and TV equipment. The example given in the standards is of a hand-held transmitter but a fixed transmitter such as an amateur station could give rise to a similar situation. Presumably, the "special mitigation measures" would include the chokes and filters which amateurs have been using for many years to increase the immunity of susceptible equipment.

A less obvious but ultimately more serious problem is that emission standards are based on the protection of broadcast signals and are much too high for amateurs who normally expect to receive very weak signals. In the future all small-signal services will have to contend with an ever-increasing amount of 'RF litter' caused by non-radio equipment and services.

As radio amateurs we need the EMC regulations; we cannot survive in the modern commercially orientated world without them. Unfortunately though, we will have to make do with regulations which are not nearly strong enough for our purposes. So what can we do? Firstly national societies are pressing for tighter regulations for domestic equipment but the practical situation is that there is a trade-off between cost and EMC performance. For instance, it would be unrealistic for manufacturers to design all domestic equipment with sufficient immunity to cover the relatively unusual situation of the set being used very close to an amateur station running high power. This leaves a shortfall between what we would like and what we have or are likely to get!

What this all comes down to is that, while the new regulations will at least define the limits which will prevent intolerable interference conditions, it is going to be good radio housekeeping which will determine whether practical amateur radio activity is possible in any particular location.

Generally speaking, the various national standards are based on recommendations from an international body known as 'Comité International Spécial des Perturbations Radioélectrique' – almost always abbreviated to 'CISPR' – so there is a a good deal of similarity between them despite differing national requirements and attitudes. In the UK, EMC standards are published by the British Standards Institute (BSI) and these are harmonised to EC standards, which are officially known as *European Norms*. Some standards, called *generic standards*, cover a whole range of equipment, while others cover specific types of equipment. Sometimes the subject of the specific standard also falls into the general scope of the generic standard. When this happens the specific standard always takes precedence. Only a small number of standards directly affect amateur radio but, because radio is such an important facet of communications, there is always a risk that amateurs may be affected accidentally by a standard which was not really intended to apply to them. This is an aspect which is being taken very seriously by the EMC Committees of the various national societies.

The immunity standards

These standards lay down the level of unwanted signal – amateur, CB, public service or other radio source – that a particular piece of equipment must be able to withstand and still function properly. Typical examples are:

(a) For radio and TV receivers and associated equipment, EN 55020. This is a fairly complicated document but the main point is that the relevant equipment must be capable of operating satisfactorily in reasonable RF field strengths. More significantly from the amateur point of view, there is also a requirement for immunity to signals on external leads such as the braid of the antenna coaxial cable, the mains input and the speaker leads.

(b) For most other types of electronic equipment not covered by a specific standard the generic standard EN 50082-1 applies. Again, the equipment is required to operate in reasonable RF fields.

(c) ITE (Information Technology Equipment) will be covered by an immunity standard based on CISPR 24. At the time of writing it is not clear whether this standard will also apply to domestic telephone equipment.

The emitted interference standards

These are the standards which lay down the limits of interference which may be emitted by any piece of equipment. Examples of these are:

(a) For ITE, EN 55022. This deals with computers and related equipment, and lays down the maximum permissible levels of interference that may be generated.

(b) For household appliances, EN 55014. This covers interference from household equipment containing motors, thermostats, and semiconductor control circuits, and includes domestic power tools.

(c) For interference from radio and TV sets, EN 55013.

Appendix 4 gives more information on some of the EMC standards which are of particular interest to radio amateurs. It must be emphasised that any levels quoted in this book are intended solely to give a flavour of what the standards are all about. Anyone wanting specific information should always consult the standards themselves. Copies of the BS standards are held in the reference sections of some of the larger public libraries and can be consulted on request.

Antennas

By far the most important factor in preventing both breakthrough and received interference problems is the antenna and its siting. It is unfortunate that most of us live in small houses with small gardens and neighbours in close proximity so that well-sited antennas are likely to be unpopular just where they are most needed. The basic requirement is to site the antenna as high as you can, and as far as possible from your own house and from neighbouring houses. If there is any choice to be made in this regard give your neighbours the benefit of the increased distance – it is usually much easier to deal with any problems in your own home. It is a sad fact that many amateurs are persuaded by social pressures into using low, poorly sited antennas, only to find that breakthrough problems sour the local relations far more than fears of obtrusive antennas would have done.

HF antennas

The question of which antenna to use is a perennial topic and the last thing that anyone would want to do is to discourage experimentation, but there is no doubt that certain types of antenna are more likely to cause breakthrough than others. It is simply a question of horses for courses; what you can get away with in a large garden or on HF Field Day may well be unsuitable for a confined city situation. In conditions where EMC is of prime importance, the antenna system should be:

(a) *Horizontally polarised.* TV down leads and other household wiring tend to look like an earthed vertical antenna so far as HF radio waves are concerned, and are more susceptible to vertically polarised radiation. This is particularly important at the higher end of the HF band. At the low end of the band, the antennas are so large and so near the ground in terms of a wavelength that the benefits of horizontal polarisation are not so evident.

(b) *Balanced.* This avoids out-of-balance currents in feeders giving rise to radiation which has a large vertically polarised component. Generally, end-fed antennas are unsatisfactory from the EMC point of view and are best kept for portable and low-power operation.

(c) *Compact.* So that neither end comes close to the house and consequently to TV down leads and mains wiring. Antennas to be careful with are the extended types such as the W3DZZ trap dipole or the G5RV because, almost inevitably, in restricted situations one end is close to the house.

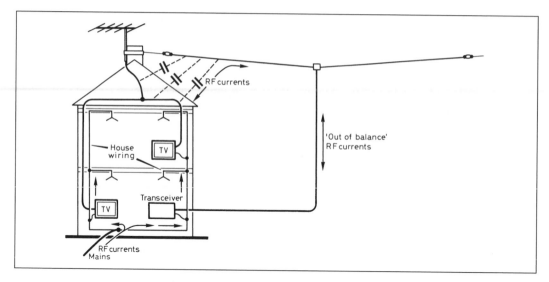

Fig 3.1. Capacitive coupling to house wiring, TV feeder etc

Fig 3.1 shows how capacitive coupling to the house wiring can occur with a dipole antenna. What the house wiring actually sees is electric charges rushing towards it and away from it in the antenna. This causes similar charges to flow in the house wiring to maintain equilibrium. These charges are, of course, RF currents which can find their way into anything connected to the wiring.

The effective capacitance between two parallel wires is greater than one might expect from application of the 'parallel plate' capacitance formula, because 'fringe' effects become dominant, and the lines of force tend to spread out as in Fig 3.2. The capacitance between two wires 1m long and 2m apart is in the order of a few picofarads. (It is perhaps worth a slight digression to point out that any wire has a capacitance in its own right, and in this case the lines of force can be considered as travelling outwards into space seeking another conductor which is infinitely far away.)

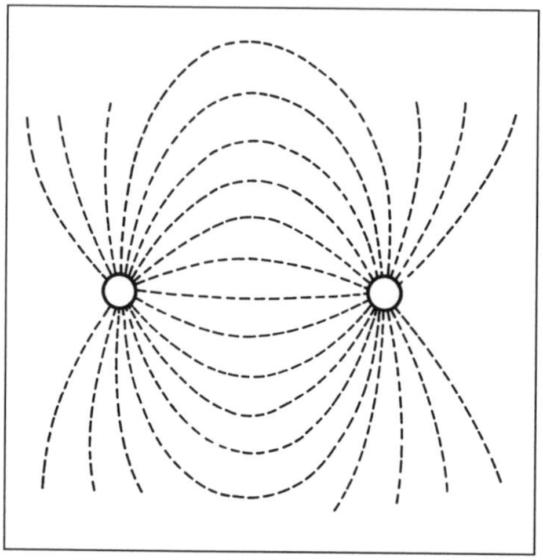

When the distance of the antenna from the house is considerably greater than the dimensions of the antenna itself, then there is not a large difference between the distance from various parts of the antenna to the house wiring, so that direct coupling from different parts of the antenna tends to cancel out. (At any given time some parts of the antenna will be at positive potential, while other parts are

Fig 3.2. Lines of force between two conductors

equally negative.) These effects can be interpreted in terms of the near and far fields of antennas of different physical size, but doing so would not really shed any light on the issue.

On frequencies of 14MHz upwards it is not too difficult to arrange an antenna fulfilling these requirements, even in quite a small garden. A half-wave dipole or small beam up as high as possible and 15m or more from the house is the sort of thing to aim for. The simple multiple dipole arrangement shown in Fig 3.3 is a popular low-cost solution. The inverted-V configuration is not ideal but, provided that the angle between any pair of elements is kept as large as possible, it makes a very practical compromise.

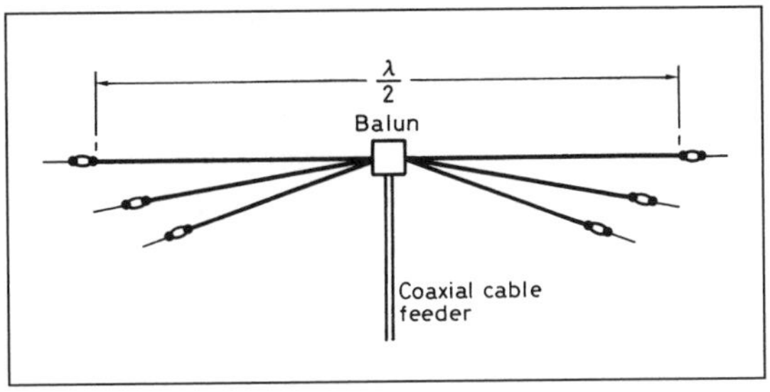

At lower frequencies compromise becomes inevitable, and most of us will have no choice but to have one end of the antenna near the house, or to go for a loaded vertical antenna which can be mounted further away. A small loop antenna is another possibility but in general any antenna which is very small compared to a wavelength will have a narrow bandwidth and a relatively low efficiency. Many stations use a G5RV or W3DZZ trap dipole for the lower frequencies but have separate dipoles (or a beam if they are lucky) for the higher frequencies, sited as far down the garden as possible.

Fig 3.3. Multiple dipoles. Each pair of elements is approximately λ/2 for the band required

VHF antennas

These follow the same general rules as for HF antennas, except that, because of the relatively high frequencies involved, it is much easier to get the antenna a few wavelengths away from the house. The big problem with VHF is that large beams can cause very high field strengths. For instance, 100W fed to an isotropic transmitting antenna in free space would give a field strength of about 3.6V/m at a distance of 15m. The same transmitter fed into a beam with a gain of 20dB would give a field strength, in the direction of the beam, of 36V/m at the same distance. Again, it comes down to the fact that if you want to run high power to a high-gain beam, the antenna must be kept as far from neighbouring houses as possible and, of course, as high as practical.

Operation in adverse situations

The obvious question arises as to what to do if your garden is small or non-existent, or domestic conditions make a simple wire tuned against ground the only possibility. First of all, and most important, don't get discouraged and go off the air altogether. Many amateurs operate very well from amazingly unpromising locations. It is really a question of cutting your coat according to your cloth. If there is no choice but to have antennas very close to the house, or even in the loft, then it will almost certainly be necessary to restrict the transmitted power, in conjunction with a consideration of the modes to be used. Not all modes are equally 'EMC friendly', and it is worth looking at some of the more frequently used modes from this point of view.

(a) *SSB*. This is the most popular mode, and most operators use it at least some of the time. Unfortunately it is also the least EMC friendly, particularly where audio breakthrough is concerned.

(b) *FM*. This is a very EMC friendly mode, mainly because in most cases the susceptible equipment sees only a constant carrier turned on and off every minute or so. This is why FM is used for CB radio in many countries. Unfortunately it is not a practical mode for HF, except for the special case of FM on the 28MHz band.

(c) *CW.* This is the old faithful for those with EMC problems, because it has two very big advantages. First, providing the keying waveform is well shaped with rise and fall times of about 10ms or so, the rectified carrier is not such a problem to audio equipment as SSB. The slow rise and fall gives relatively soft clicks which are often accepted by neighbours when SSB would not be. The second advantage is that it is possible to use lower power for a given contact. There is no doubt that CW has a big advantage over voice communication when it comes to the simple criterion of 'getting through' to the other station, ignoring the rate of information exchange (and also the social aspects of the contact). Figures up to 20dB are sometimes quoted but such high figures depend to some extent on the fact that, under poor conditions, CW messages are often very simple, with important parts repeated several times.

(d) *Data.* Generally the data modes used by amateurs are based on frequency-shift keying (FSK), and should be EMC friendly. All data systems involve the carrier being keyed on and off – when going from receive to transmit and vice versa – and consideration should be given to the carrier rise and fall times, just as in CW.

The increasing operating speeds of personal computers have made it possible the use digital signal processing to improve the 'getting through power' of relatively low-power data signals, including traditional CW. An interesting example of using data processing to enable a contact to be made under very-small-signal conditions is described in reference [1].

Earths

The provision of an adequate earth has occupied the attention of radio enthusiasts since the earliest days. When the wavelengths in use were long, as they invariably were in those days, the ground formed a vital part of the radiating system, as it does today in medium-wave and long-wave broadcasting stations. In amateur operation the antenna tuned against ground is still used for the 1.8 and 3.5MHz bands, though its use at higher frequencies has declined mainly due to its poor EMC performance. With this type of antenna the RF current actually flows in and out of the ground connection, and it is the difficulty of keeping this current out of the mains supply which is one of its most serious drawbacks. A similar situation exists with out-of-balance currents in a nominally balanced antenna system.

Fig 3.4 shows the importance of achieving the lowest possible impedance to an earth connection. In effect, the earth current splits in proportion to the impedances to earth of the two paths, the RF earth (Z_e) and the mains (Z_m). Clearly the

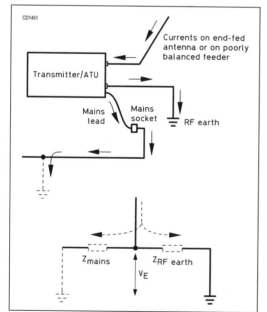

Fig 3.4. Earth current divides between RF earth and mains. The current down each path will depend on the impedances. The transmitter earth terminal will be at V_E relative to 'true' earth potential

CD1451

Currents on end-fed antenna or on poorly balanced feeder

Transmitter/ATU

Mains lead

Mains socket

RF earth

Z_{mains}

$Z_{RF\ earth}$

V_E

WARNING
Protective Multiple Earthing (PME)

Some houses in the UK, particularly those built or wired since the middle 'seventies, are wired on what is known as the *PME system*. In this system the earth conductor of the consumer's installation is bonded to the neutral close to where the supply enters the premises, and there is no separate earth conductor going back to the sub-station.

With a PME system a small voltage may exist between the consumer's earth conductor, and any metal work connected to it, and the true earth (the earth out in the garden). Under certain very rare supply system faults this voltage could rise to a dangerous level. Because of this supply companies advise certain precautions relating to the bonding of metal work inside the house, and also to the connection of external earths.

WHERE A HOUSE IS WIRED ON THE PME SYSTEM DO NOT CONNECT ANY EXTERNAL (ie radio) EARTHS TO APPARATUS INSIDE THE HOUSE unless suitable precautions are taken.

Further information on PME will be found in Appendix 1.

smaller Z_e is, the greater will be the proportion of the earth current which goes by this path in preference to the mains path.

The classic way of isolating the RF earth from the mains earth is by using an inductively coupled ATU, such as the *Z match* as shown in Fig 3.5. Configuration (a) is for end-fed antennas, and (c) is suitable for either an unbalanced antenna, such as a ground plane, or for a balanced antenna which is fed with coaxial cable with a balun at the antenna end. Configuration (b) is the usual way of feeding balanced line – either low-impedance or open-wire feeder – and requires no comment, except perhaps to remind users of the risk of static charge build-up since the antenna can be completely earth-free.

Sometimes it is suggested that the mains earth should be disconnected from the transceiver, but this is a very dangerous practice since the mains earth is there for the express purpose of preventing electric shock in the event of an equipment fault. Separation of the mains and RF earth can be achieved by using ferrite ring chokes as in Fig 3.6. If the cable is inconven-

Fig 3.5. Inductively coupled ATU (Z-match) isolates RF from mains earth

iently thick, fewer turns on a stack of several cores can be used. The object is to obtain sufficient impedance and this is best achieved by experimentation. A good place to start would be 12 turns on a stack of two cores or six turns on a stack of four cores using Fair-Rite type 43 material or equivalent (see Appendix 3).

Where the station comprises not only the transceiver but also mains-powered ancillary units, the ferrite choke should be in the common mains feed to all the units to avoid having different RF 'earth' potentials between various units. Usually the whole mains lead is wound on the cores, but it is possible to choke the mains earth lead separately. If this is done, make

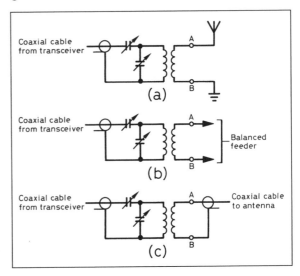

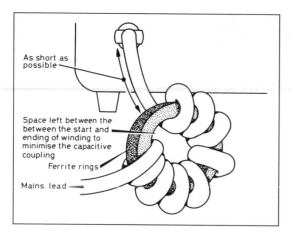

As short as possible

Space left between the
between the start and
ending of winding to
minimise the capacitive
coupling

Ferrite rings

Mains lead

Fig 3.6. Ferrite ring choke on transceiver mains lead

sure that the standard of workmanship is adequate and the conductor is of sufficient rating to comply with the safety requirements. If there is any doubt about safety aspects, the current IEE Wiring Regulations should be consulted. The best way to find these is by enquiring at your local library.

The most practical RF earth consists of several copper pipes, at least 1.5m long and preferably longer, spaced at least 1m apart, and driven into the ground so that the tops are just clear of the surface. The pipes should be joined together with the heaviest copper wire available. The connection to the ATU/transceiver should be as short and of as thick wire as possible. (This is the low impedance path though which we are hoping that the earth currents will flow in preference to the unwanted paths such as the mains). Flat copper strip or heavy-duty braid can be used to advantage. Where the shack is located in an upstairs room, the earth connection will inevitably be long and in many cases it is doubtful if an earth connection is of any benefit. Since the earth will be carrying RF currents, it will radiate and could cause problems in downstairs rooms. Where the earth lead is a resonant length, very undesirable effects can occur, making the rig much 'hotter' to RF than would otherwise be the case. With an upstairs shack, it is especially important to avoid arrangements which use the earth as part of the antenna system. In other words, go for a balanced antenna or, if an unbalanced antenna is the only possibility, use a coaxial feeder system which has the earth (or better still the counterpoise or ground plane) as far from the house as possible. Where coaxial feeder is used, the connection to the ATU/transceiver should be as in Fig 3.5(c).

One possible consequence of poor antenna/earth policy is that RF energy can enter the transceiver through its ancillaries and their connecting leads. Pick-up in the microphone cable is well known, but electronic keyers and other control equipment are also vulnerable. Where a transceiver is operated from an external power supply, it is not uncommon for RF to find its way into the stabilising circuits of the supply, causing erratic operation which is sometimes mistaken for a transceiver fault. Mild cases can be treated as cases of breakthrough, using ferrite chokes and bypass capacitors as appropriate, but the real answer is to examine the antenna/earth arrangements and the station layout to eliminate the problem at source.

Feeders

At VHF the choice of feeder is limited to the selection of a suitable coaxial cable. On HF several options are available, and each has its merits and disadvantages. These are discussed at length in references [2–4] but from the EMC point of view the simplest solution is to use coaxial cable with a suitable balun at the antenna end to achieve a balanced feed. Baluns are not difficult to make and suitable designs will be found in references [2], [4] and [5].

Where the domestic situation permits, the feeder should be buried, preferably in a protective plastic pipe (a coating of wax floor polish will help to prevent moisture from penetrating the PVC sheath). If possible, the outer of the coaxial cable should be earthed before it enters the house. Where RF currents occur on the outer of the cable, they can be eliminated, or at least reduced, by using a ferrite-ring choke, as in Fig 3.7. If twin feeders are to be used, pay particular attention to maintaining the balance of the antenna, and ensure that the individual wires of the twin feeder are always much closer to each other than they are to other conducting objects. In all cases feeders should fall away as nearly as possible at right-angles to the antenna (Fig 3.8).

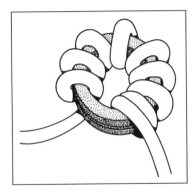

Fig 3.7. Ferrite ring choke on coaxial feeder

Lightning protection

Lightning protection is an important subject in its own right, and it is not intended here to do more than make a few comments. Locations and antennas vary widely – anyone installing an antenna system must consider the risks and decide whether full lightning protection of the installation and property is justified. Guidance can be obtained from BS 6651 *Code of Practice for the Protection of Structures against Lightning* [6]. As with the EMC standards discussed earlier, copies are available for reference at some of the larger public libraries. Your local library should be able to advise you on the nearest one. To give an appreciation of what lightning is all about, an article which appeared in *Radio Communication* in 1984 has been reproduced in Appendix 2.

While nothing but a full lightning protection installation will handle a direct strike, a limited degree of protection from static build-up on the antenna and surges due to strikes taking place some distance away can be achieved by relatively simple means. There are two options in common use by amateurs. The first is to earth the feeders outside and away from the house, using a direct connection to a substantial low-resistance earth. The second, where the feeders are earth-free, is to install a spark gap or gas-discharge tube which will break down if high voltages build up on the feeders. Again these should be mounted outside and away from the house. The earthed side should be connected to low-resistance earth by a short,

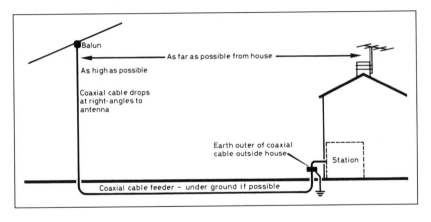

Fig 3.8. Antenna and feeder systems with EMC in mind

thick, lead. Information on making and installing suitable spark-gaps will be found in references [2–4]. Information on using gas-discharge devices will be found in reference [7].

Passive intermodulation products (PIPs)

This phenomenon has been familiar to generations of radio operators, both amateur and professional, as the *rusty bolt effect*. In recent years, the proliferation of complex public service radio systems with co-located transmitters and receivers has brought it into a new prominence, and it has now achieved not only a proper title but also the ultimate mark of technical respectability – a three-letter abbreviation.

All mixing and harmonic generating circuits use non-linear elements such as diodes to distort the current waveform, and hence to generate the required frequency components. A similar effect will be produced whenever the naturally produced semiconductor layer in a corroded metal joint forms an unwanted diode. These unwanted diodes are usually most troublesome in the antenna system itself, particularly in corroded coaxial cable connectors. In the case of a single transmitter, the effect simply causes excessive harmonic radiation but, where two or more transmitters are operating in close proximity, the result can be quite spectacular intermodulation product generation. On receive, the result is much-reduced receiver intermodulation performance, manifesting itself by rather 'watery' signals with strange, mixed-up modulation appearing where they have no right to be. In severe cases there will be a noticeably high noise floor, consisting of a mishmash of unwanted signals.

The best way to avoid problems of this sort is to keep the antenna system in good repair and to examine all connections every few months. Now and then the rusty bolt effect occurs in corroded metal gutters and similar structures not directly associated with the antenna system, but normally this will only be troublesome when high RF fields are involved.

References

[1] 'Extreme narrowband reception', P Martinez, *Radio Communication* November 1997.
[2] *Radio Communication Handbook,* 6th edn, ed D Biddulph, G8DPS, RSGB, 1994.
[3] *ARRL Antenna Handbook*, ARRL.
[4] *HF Antennas for All Locations*, Les Moxon, G6XN, RSGB.
[5] *Transmission Line Transformers*, J Sevick, ARRL.
[6] BS 6651 – *Code of Practice for Protection of Structures against Lightning.*
[7] 'Lightning and your antenna', G R Jessop, G6JP, in *HF Antenna Collection*, ed Erwin David, G4LQI, RSGB, 1991.

SUMMARY – GOOD RADIO HOUSEKEEPING CHECKLIST

HF antennas

To minimise breakthrough, antennas should be:

(a) horizontally polarised;

(b) balanced – use a balun if appropriate;

(c) sited as far from your own and neighbouring houses as practical, and as high as possible;

(d) compact, to minimise direct coupling to house wiring etc;

(e) arranged so that the feeder drops vertically down to ground level. If coaxial feeder is used, run it underground (if possible) and earth the screen outside the house.

VHF antennas

These should be mounted as far from house wiring as possible. Particularly bear in mind the very high field strengths which can occur when high power is fed to high-gain beams.

Earths

(a) If at all possible, avoid arrangements which involve the earth as part of the antenna system, eg end-fed antennas tuned against ground.

(b) Isolate the RF earth from the mains earth by using an inductively coupled ATU.

(c) Make the mains earth as high an impedance as possible to RF by using a ferrite ring choke on the transmitter mains lead.

(d) Make the RF earth of as low impedance as possible. Use several copper pipes driven well into the ground, and connect to the station using as thick wire as practical; if possible, use copper strip or heavy-duty braid.

(e) Where the station is located upstairs, an RF earth may not be of any benefit and may cause trouble due to resonance effects. If a good RF earth is impossible, the best solution is to avoid the need for one by using a well-balanced antenna system.

Passive intermodulation products (the 'rusty bolt effect')

(a) Keep all antenna metalwork in good condition, making sure that all bolts are tight and joints free of corrosion. If galvanised iron wire guys are used, make sure that they do not form rusted contacts with the mast or tower.

(b) Check all RF connectors every few months and replace any that show signs of corrosion.

(c) Avoid siting antennas close to rusted gutters or similar structures.

4 The EMC detective

O NE of the major changes in the EMC scene which has taken place
since the first edition of this book was planned is the spectacular increase in the number of reports of interference to amateur reception. Apart
from an increase in the number of cases of interference to security light
systems, there has not been a corresponding increase in transmitter interference problems. This chapter has now been split into two parts, the second part dealing with detection activities relating to received interference
– usually simply referred to as *radio frequency interference* or RFI.

It is easier to investigate cases where interference is caused by a transmitter, since the situation is more under the control of the investigator and
for this reason the majority of the discussion relates to this type of problem. In cases of RFI the investigator has to use the limited means at his
disposal and knowledge and experience are even more important than
usual. The first edition alluded to the fictional detectives of popular literature and their rather unlikely activities. A glance at the list of RFI sources
in Part 2 makes one wonder if a classical reference might be more appropriate – taking arms against a sea of troubles!

Most EMC problems are complex, involving the interplay of a number
of factors. There is nothing special about this; it is true of most accidentally
occurring situations. Familiarity with computers has given many young
electronic and radio enthusiasts the false impression that every technical
problem can be broken down to a series of simple logical steps. This is an
excellent approach where circumstances permit, but in the real world most
'non-engineered' situations involve a large number of unknown factors.
EMC problems fall into this category. It is impractical to tackle them by
reference to a simple list of cures which can be applied without further
thought. What is needed is a careful look at all the conditions involved
before coming to any decision about causes and remedies.

In this chapter remedies are mentioned only in so far as they are part of
the diagnostic process. Further information on remedies will be found in
the appropriate chapters.

PART 1 – INVESTIGATING TRANSMITTER INTERFERENCE
The preliminary investigation

Things usually start with a complaint from a neighbour about interference
to some piece of domestic equipment. In the past this would probably have
been a TV or hi-fi unit. Nowadays many breakthrough problems involve

equipment such as alarm systems or telephones, which do not involve radio as part of their normal operation. RF radiation can affect any electronically controlled device, so it pays to keep an open mind at this stage, however bizarre the complaint may seem. The first thing to find out is if it really is your station that is causing the trouble. If your neighbour has been keeping a record of dates and times – as recommended in the RSGB's leaflet *Radio Transmitters and Domestic Electronic Equipment* [1] – then reference to the station log will tell you what you need to know. Assuming it is you, the next step is to determine whether it is due to spurious emissions from your transmitter or to inadequate immunity in your neighbour's equipment. The way this is tackled depends on what test gear is available – if you have a spectrum analyser or a suitable measuring receiver the job will be greatly simplified, but for the moment let us assume that only the resources of a typical amateur station are to hand.

Ask yourself the following questions:

1. *Is the neighbour's equipment some form of radio device, such as a TV or radio receiver, which is suffering interference on specific frequencies?*
2. *If so, is similar equipment tuned to the same frequencies in your own house or at other neighbours' houses affected?*

If the answer to both questions is 'yes', then it is probable that the interference is being caused by some form of unwanted radiation from your transmitter.

If the answer to both questions is 'no', then the chances are that the problem is due to breakthrough, ie insufficient immunity in the neighbour's equipment (see Chart 4.1 on p46).

By far the commonest cause of breakthrough is pick-up by susceptible equipment of radiation from the antenna system of the amateur station, but it is worth checking that there is no RF energy leaking out of the transmitter itself. Run the transmitter into a dummy load, using the mode which normally gives the worst interference. If the interference is still evident when operating into the dummy load, then energy is leaking out of the transmitter itself, possibly directly through the case, but more likely via the mains lead. In either case the transmitter should be investigated along the lines discussed in Chapter 6. If the trouble is only present when the station is operating normally into the antenna system then a typical breakthrough problem exists.

Investigating a case of breakthrough

The first step is to try to get some idea of how severe the problem is. The easiest way to do this is to reduce the transmitter power while an assistant checks how the interference is affected. A couple of CB radios make a useful link which can be used by almost anyone, and greatly widen the field when looking for a willing assistant. If the breakthrough is significantly reduced when the transmitter power is reduced to about 50W PEP, then the problem can be classed as 'moderate'. If the interference still persists at powers down to about 10W it definitely falls into the 'severe' category. Make test transmissions on all the bands and modes available to you. It is worth trying all the modes and frequencies that you can use, even if you do not normally use them – everything is grist for the EMC detective's mill. During this preliminary phase of the investigation, find out if other neighbours are having trouble and, if so, under what circumstances. This obviously requires discretion, otherwise you will put ideas into peoples' heads and end up being blamed for every radio disturbance in the district. It is a reasonable assumption that you will already know if you have problems in your own home, but it is worth rechecking everything to see if any useful background information can be gleaned.

IF and intermodulation breakthrough

In addition to direct pick-up, radio and TV sets can suffer from more subtle forms of breakthrough. These fall into four categories:

1. *Direct intermediate-frequency (IF) breakthrough,* where the IF of some piece of radio equipment falls in or near an amateur band. The most common example is a transmission on the 10MHz band getting into the 10.7MHz IF of a VHF receiver. This is breakthrough caused by insufficient IF rejection in the receiver.

2. *IF breakthrough caused by harmonics of the amateur transmitter being picked up in the receiver IF,* for example the second harmonic of the 18MHz band entering the IF of a TV set. (The standard TV IF band includes 36MHz.) A less likely possibility is the third harmonic of 3.5MHz entering the 10.7MHz IF of a VHF receiver. Cases of this sort indicate that the transmitter is radiating too much harmonic energy – it is no excuse to say that the susceptible receiver should be better designed.

3. *Image interference.* This where a signal on the 'wrong side' of the local oscillator beats with it to give the IF. It is fairly common on the 1.8MHz band, where amateur signals give image responses on medium-wave receivers. For instance, a receiver with a 455kHz IF tuned to 990kHz (303m) would have a local oscillator of 1445kHz. This would beat with a strong amateur signal on 1.9MHz, which would be tuned in on the medium-wave band like any other signal. This is a case of breakthrough caused by poor image rejection of the susceptible receiver.

4. *Amateur signals intermodulating with the harmonics of the local oscillator or other oscillators in the susceptible equipment, causing spurious responses.* These give rise to interference which is tuneable at the receiver but which is nevertheless a case of breakthrough.

At strategic points in the story the fictional detective reviews the situation, discussing the evidence with his or her somewhat dim assistant. Presumably the main reason for this is to prevent the reader from completely losing the thread of the plot, but in the case of the EMC detective the need to look carefully at the overall picture before rushing into action is essential to avoid having to keep calling on neighbours and trying things over and over again. This inevitably leads to loss of confidence, and allows any goodwill that may have existed at first to trickle away.

Looking for the evidence

The methods employed are applicable to all types of susceptible electronic devices, from music centres to burglar alarms, the only difference being the route the RF energy takes to enter the equipment. In general, wherever external leads are connected to a unit there is a risk of RF pick-up causing trouble. As in all electrical circuits, the RF current must flow between two points of different potential; usually a crude wire antenna and a capacitance to earth. Hopefully, if the equipment designer has done a good job, these currents will have already been dealt with but, if not,

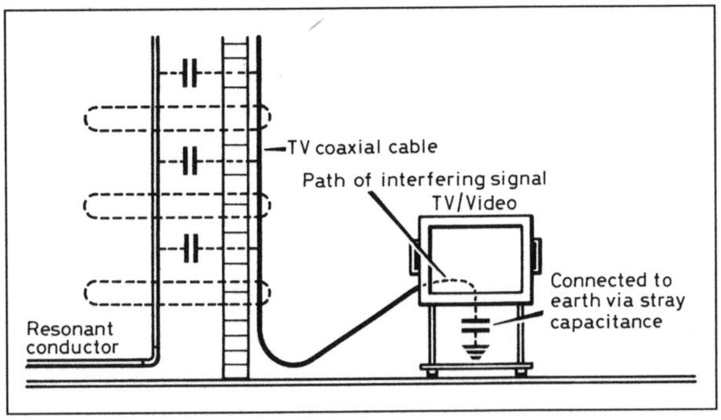

Fig 4.1. Energy coupled into TV antenna lead from resonant conductor

then breakthrough problems are likely to occur. These can only be eliminated by identifying the vulnerable leads and increasing their effective impedance to radio frequencies by suitable chokes or filters, or by improving the bypassing of RF currents to earth, as discussed in Chapter 5.

It is a reasonable assumption that a wire which is very small compared to a wavelength will not pick up significant amounts of RF. For instance, in a case of HF breakthrough to a TV/video installation a few tens of metres away from the transmitting antenna, it is unlikely that the signal will get in through the TV antenna itself. It is much more likely to be picked up on the braid of the coaxial feeder, or to be getting in through the mains or through some ancillary connection. The first thought is that the installation must have poor immunity, but before jumping to any conclusions check that there is no evidence of abnormally high signal pick-up caused by the local environment. This could be due to re-radiation from a resonant conductor in the vicinity, or to transmission-line effects causing excessive coupling into the TV antenna feeder, the mains lead or external speakers etc.

A crude transmission line can be formed between almost any conductor which is long (and roughly horizontal) and earth. In effect the fields are confined between the conductor and its image in the earth. This transmission line – if such a hotchpotch of unknowns can honestly be called a 'transmission line' – can pick up signals either directly, due to a remote section of the conductor being coupled to a source of RF energy, or by a resonance effect in the transmission line, which is bound to be mis-matched.

Fig 4.2. Interference entering TV through transmission-line coupling to the antenna lead

Figs 4.1 and 4.2 are somewhat idealised illustrations of resonance and transmission-line effects, though in reality the difference between them is

nothing like so clear cut. They are contributory factors in many cases of breakthrough, showing themselves by the fact that interference is worse on one band and is noticeably affected by moving the equipment or its leads.

The best way to confirm a resonance of this type is to move round the area with a portable receiver tuned to the transmitter frequency and to note if a marked increase in signal strength occurs anywhere. To avoid overloading

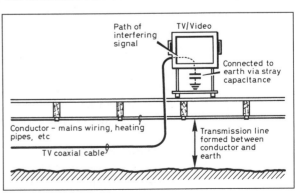

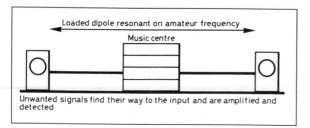

Loaded dipole resonant on amateur frequency

Music centre

Unwanted signals find their way to the input and are amplified and detected

Fig 4.3. Speaker leads act as loaded dipole

the receiver, the transmitted power should be reduced until the received signal is less than about S9.

Where a piece of equipment has ancillary items connected to it as part of the installation, eg a music centre with separate speakers, then the leads and ancillaries can form a loaded antenna which may resonate on an amateur frequency (Fig 4.3). A similar effect occurs when the TV or radio antenna coaxial feeder and all the metalwork of the antenna installation are resonant on an amateur frequency. Because of the end loading, the physical length may not give an accurate guide to the resonant frequency. The simplest way to confirm the existence of this type of problem is to disconnect the suspect lead or, where this is not possible, break up the resonance by winding the suspect lead onto a ferrite ring to form a lossy choke. If this gives a significant change in the breakthrough then you are on the right lines. Don't forget, though, that there may be more than one mode of ingress, and several breakthrough signals may be adding or subtracting, so that the effect of any diagnostic activity may not be clear cut. Any change in the interference, even an increase, is an important clue.

When you have acquired all the evidence that you are likely to get, the only course is to proceed with the appropriate remedies which will be found in Chapter 5. Inevitably there will still be an element of trial and error but, by this stage, it should have been reduced to manageable proportions.

The misguided enthusiast

Occasionally one comes up against an isolated case of severe breakthrough where the complainant is an electronic entertainment enthusiast who has piped signals from his TV, video and music centre all over the house. Very often the installer has more enthusiasm than technical knowledge, so with a bit of luck he may be having trouble from sources other than yourself and be glad of a bit of advice. Look out for badly made coaxial feeder connections, long straggling leads and coaxial cables branching off to different destinations without proper splitter units. Often such cables are left unterminated when not in use, causing unwanted resonant circuits. One of the commonest defects of such installations is the use of unsuitable TV amplifiers which have very little selectivity and poor intermodulation performance. It is worth remembering that all such devices put on the market in the UK since January 1996 should have reasonable immunity to unwanted signals. Unfortunately amplifiers purchased before then will still be around for a long time, and some have very poor immunity. When your neighbour has put his own house in order, any remaining breakthrough problems can be considered individually and the appropriate remedies applied along the lines indicated in Chapter 5.

Feeders and earths

When there are several complaints of interference from different neighbours and a variety of equipment is affected, eg TV/video, audio, control circuits etc, the immediate thought must be that there is excessive coupling from the transmitting antenna to local electrical wiring. Have a good look at your station set-up – particularly the antenna and earth system. RF on the feeders of a nominally balanced antenna is a common cause of breakthrough; not only because the feeders radiate, but also because the unbalanced currents get injected into the mains earth wiring. In severe cases unwanted RF currents in the antenna/earth system can get into power supplies and ancillary units and cause problems which are often mistaken for transmitter faults (Chapters 3 and 6). This is really an extreme example of breakthrough where the victim is the amateur himself. In most cases the presence of RF currents is difficult to detect and a simple current detector is a useful addition to the EMC detective's tool kit.

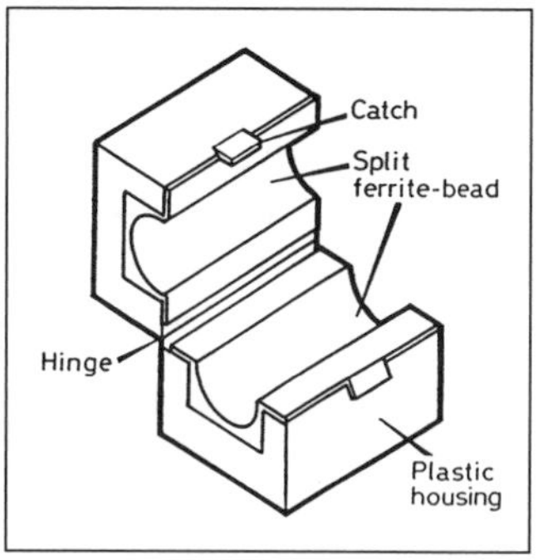

Fig 4.4. The split ferrite core

A simple RF current detector

It is possible to construct a simple ferrite current probe which will indicate RF currents on the braid of coaxial feeders or on earth leads, with an accuracy more than adequate for our purposes. The principle is to make a current transformer using a split ferrite core, which can be clipped on to the cable on which the current is to be measured.

A practical clip-on RF ammeter was designed by G0SNO and appeared in the EMC column of *Radio Communication* [2]. The following notes are taken from this article. In the original article a Maplin computer data line filter (stock number BZ34M) was used – see Fig 4.4. If this is not available then it will probably be possible to find something similar, but experimentation will be necessary since core materials vary. Devices working on the same principle but using different ferrite cores have been described in references [3] and [4].

The circuit of the probe is shown in Fig 4.5. A 10-turn secondary is wound on one half of the core. In theory 10% of the primary current flows in the secondary and through the 50Ω load formed by R1 and R2. For primary currents up to 1A the power rating of the secondary load should be 1W. In practice the core used gave a current ratio of about 8% up to 30MHz, falling to 7.5% at 50MHz. At 14MHz for example, 1A in the cable under test caused 80mA to flow through the 50Ω load, generating 4V across it. Clipping the current transformer over a cable adds a small series impedance which in an ideal transformer would be about 0.5Ω (the secondary load divided by the turns ratio squared) but in practice is about 2Ω at 14MHz and 4Ω at 21MHz. The voltage across R1 and R2 is rectified by a voltage

Fig 4.5. Circuit of RF ammeter

doubler using BAT85 Schottky diodes. R4 should be chosen so that the total of the meter resistance and R4 is 6.8kΩ. On the 100mA range the forward voltage drop of the diodes becomes significant, so that the minimum current which can be measured is 30mA.

The meter was fitted in a small plastic box with the current transformer mounted

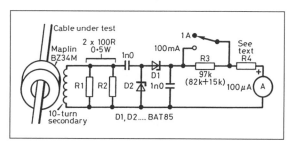

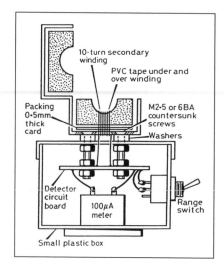

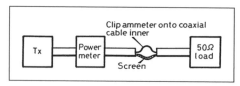

Fig 4.6. Mounting arrangement for the split ferrite core

on the lid (Fig 4.6), using the two fixing holes in the plastic housing of the core. A piece of plastic tape was used to protect the enamelled wire from damage on the edge of the ferrite, and 10 turns of 0.4mm wire were wound on to the core assembly as shown. The card was needed under the lower section of the core because it was pulled down when winding on the wire and required packing up to ensure correct mating with the upper half. Proper closure of the core is essential if accurate results are to be obtained.

The meter can be calibrated using the arrangement of Fig 4.7. With 50W into the load, the reading should be 1A, and with 0.5W the current should be 100mA.

To measure unwanted RF on the braid of a feeder coaxial cable the meter is clipped over the cable itself, since in this case it is the unwanted currents on the braid of the cable that are being measured. In a similar way the meter can be clipped on to an earth lead to see how much current is flowing in the earth path. A very revealing test is to check if there is any significant RF current on the mains cable of the transmitter. If there is, then there is a risk of breakthrough being caused by RF being carried via the mains wiring.

Estimating signal strength

This is not an easy matter, and even professionals armed with expensive equipment are wary of the practical accuracy of measurements made in environments which are cluttered by buildings and vegetation. It is most important to keep in mind the difference between the actual accuracy of a reading and the significance of the measurement in terms of the problem under investigation. In most investigations the field strength will vary markedly over quite small distances, as the main and reflected signals add and subtract, or as re-radiation from partially resonant conductors takes place. When attempting to estimate the field strength of a transmitted signal – in a case of breakthrough for instance – it is important to remember that the electric and magnetic fields are independent in the near field. This means that it is very difficult to get sensible measurements in the lower HF bands in a typical domestic situation. (See Chapter 2 for more information on near and far fields.)

Fig 4.7. Calibration set-up

In practice, the best that the amateur can hope to achieve is to get some idea of the strength of the signal as an aid to problem solving. In particular, do not be tempted to use such measurements to 'lay down the law' to third parties.

Measurements at VHF

At these frequencies it is practical to make a portable half-wave dipole and in this case both theory and practice are straightforward. The dipole can easily be constructed from two lengths of copper rod mounted on a wooden or plastic 'T', as shown in Fig 4.8. A simple choke balun can be made by winding a few turns of the coaxial feeder on a ferrite ring, in the same way as for a ferrite choke on a TV feeder. The choke should be as near to the dipole as possible.

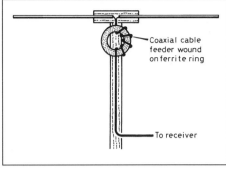

The signal across a 75Ω load at the centre of a half-wave dipole is:

$$V = E\lambda / 2\pi$$

where V is the PD in volts, E is the field strength in volts/metre, and λ is the wavelength in metres.

Fig 4.8. A portable dipole

Connecting the dipole of Fig 4.8 to a receiver with a calibrated S-meter will enable the voltage at the input to be determined. From this the field strength can be found:

$$E = 2\pi V / \lambda$$

Modern measuring receivers usually have a 50Ω input impedance, and a small correction should be made for this by adding 2dB. If the impedance is doubtful, as it will be with most communication receivers, it can be made to be 50 or 75Ω as required by using an attenuator. A 6dB attenuator would be suitable, and 75Ω devices are available from component suppliers for TV use. The receiver, with attenuator attached, should be calibrated using a signal generator.

In most cases the polarisation of the field will not be known, so the dipole should be turned around both horizontally and vertically until a maximum is found. So far as possible, the dipole should be held away from obstructions and as high up as the circumstances permit. Inevitably reflections will be present, so move around to find an average reading.

Measurements at HF

To make and calibrate an antenna other than a half-wave dipole is no easy matter, and commercial units are very expensive, underlining the difficulty of design and calibration. Fortunately, we are looking for a rough indication rather than an accurate measurement, so that use can be made of relatively simple methods of calculating the relationship between antenna voltage and field strength for electrically small antennas. It is possible to measure either the electric or the magnetic component of the field (usually called the *E-field* or the *H-field*). In a true far field it would not matter which we measured since they are mutually dependent, and the measurement of one automatically enables the value of the other to be calculated. In practice there are differences in the measured values due to the presence of objects such as buildings and various conductors, including the earth itself. Additionally, as mentioned above, in many amateur situations it will not be possible to get far enough away from the antenna to avoid the effects of the near field.

Measuring the electric field

This uses a short dipole, and is perhaps the simplest measurement to make. It is capable of satisfactory results at higher HF but it becomes difficult to obtain good readings as the frequency is reduced below about 10MHz.

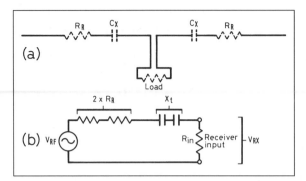

Fig 4.9. (a) The effective resistance and reactance of a short dipole. (b) The equivalent circuit. If $X_t \gg R_R$ and R_{in} then $V_{RX} = V_{RF} \times (R_{in}/X_t)$

A dipole which is shorter than a half wavelength acts as a capacitive reactance in series with the radiation resistance and the load resistance (Fig 4.9). If the antenna is less than about a quarter-wave long (from end to end – not each element) then the capacitive reactance will be so much larger than the radiation resistance that the latter can be neglected. The reactance will also be large compared to a load resistance of 50 or 75Ω, so that we can forget the complexities of resistance and reactance and assume that the effective loss of signal is simply the ratio of load resistance to antenna reactance.

The reactance can be calculated from:

$$X_c = 2 \times (-j \times 138 \, (\log l/r) \times \cot G)$$

where l is the length of each element of the antenna (half the overall dipole length); r is the radius of the elements; and G is the electrical length of each element.

In our approximate calculation we do not wish to know the phase of the currents, so that we can ignore the '$-j$'. 'cot' is the reciprocal of the tangent (1/tan).

Take, for example, a short dipole with element lengths of 50cm and element diameter of 2mm. The frequency will be assumed to be 14MHz (λ = 21.4m).

$l = 0.5$m; $r = 1$mm, so l/r is 500 and log 500 is 2.7.
G is the ratio of l to λ (in this case expressed in degrees).
$(0.5/21.4) \times 360 = 8.4°$ and tan 8.4° = 0.148.
cot 8.4 degrees is 1/tan = 6.77.

In round figures, for both elements, we get a total $X_c = 2500 \times 2 = 5000\Omega$. For a receiver with a 50Ω input the loss of signal will be approximately 50/5000 or 40dB.

The electric field intercepted by a short dipole is about half its physical length, so that a dipole 1m from end to end and aligned parallel to an electric field of 1V/m will pick up an EMF of 0.5V. This adds another 6dB to our calculation. The total loss from field strength to receiver input would be 46dB. For the 1V/m field, this would give about 5mV at the receiver input.

The effect is as if there were a capacitor in each element of the dipole – about 4.5pF in the above example. This capacitance is really a basic property of the antenna, staying constant with frequency and depending only on the length and thickness of the elements. There are other ways of calculating this capacitance and these give roughly the same value [5].

The general construction of the short dipole can be as for the half-wave dipole of Fig 4.8 but for HF the choke balun will require more turns. Information on making a suitable choke will be found in Appendix 3 – 'TV antenna cables'.

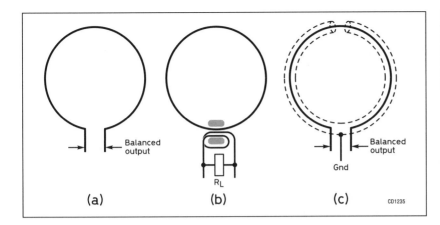

Fig 4.10. Loops for HF field strength measurement. (a) Voltage or current loop. (b) Short-circuit current loop with current transformer. (c) Shielded loop

(a)   (b)   (c)   CD1235

Measuring the magnetic field

In practice the proximity of ground, brick walls etc has much less effect on H-field measurements than on E-field measurements. This is because these objects usually have the same magnetic permeability as free space. An H-field loop can be used for frequencies down to 2MHz and below and generally gives more consistent readings close to a building, or even inside, provided it is kept away from wiring or pipes which may re-radiate signals. When professional organisations such as the Radiocommunications Agency make field strength measurements at HF, a loop antenna is usually used.

The units of H-field strength are amperes per metre (A/m) or decibels relative to 1μA/m. In the far field, the E-fields and H-fields are related by $E/H = 120\pi = 377\Omega$ so an E-field strength of 1V/m is equivalent to an H-field strength of 2.652mA/m. When H-field strength measurements are made, it is common practice to quote the result in terms of the equivalent E-field strength in V/m or in dB(μV/m). This can sometimes cause confusion if it is not clear whether the actual measurement is an E-field or H-field measurement.

Fig 4.10 shows three types of H-field measuring loop. (a) is an unshielded voltage loop. If the load impedance is sufficiently high, the measured output is equal to the induced EMF. The voltage v_i induced in a loop is given by the following formula:

$$v_i = 2\pi f \, \mu \, H_i \, N \, S$$

where f is the frequency in hertz; μ is the permeability of the loop core (for an air-cored loop, this is equal to μ_0, the permeability of free space, ie $4\pi \times 10^{-7}$ henrys per metre); H_i is the component of the magnetic field at right-angles to the plane of the loop; N is the number of turns; and S is the area of the loop in square metres.

This assumes that the circumference of the loop is small compared to a wavelength (less than about 0.08λ), that it is untuned and well below self-resonance.

For example, a one-turn air-cored loop with an area of 1m² gives an output of 20.9mV at 1MHz in an H-field of 2.652mA/m (equivalent to 1V/m). For a more compact loop, eg 200mm diameter, the area would be 0.0314m², giving an induced voltage of 0.656mV in 2.652mA/m at 1MHz.

For an open-circuit voltage loop, the induced voltage is proportional to frequency which is clearly a disadvantage. This can be overcome by loading the output with a resistor whose value is significantly lower than the inductive reactance X_L of the loop at the lowest frequency of interest. As X_L and v_i both increase with frequency, the output remains constant with frequency (above a certain frequency). The loop now approximates to a short-circuit current loop. It is necessary to know the inductance L which can be calculated approximately from the following formula for a single-turn loop:

$$L = \mu\, b\, \ln(b/a)$$

where μ is the permeability of the core ($4\pi \times 10^{-7}$ H/m for an air-cored loop); a is the radius of the wire in metres; b is the radius of the loop in metres; and ln is log to the base e.

For example, if a 200mm diameter loop is made with a length of inner from RG213 coaxial cable, $a = 1.46$mm, $b = 100$mm, $\ln(b/a) = 4.23$ and $L = 0.53\mu$H. Hence, $X_L = 33\Omega$ at 10MHz. A load resistance of 3.7Ω gives an output of $v_i/10$ at 10MHz and $v_i/30$ at 30MHz. The sensitivity is relatively constant from 30MHz down to 3.5MHz and is about 10% low at 1.8MHz. Nevertheless, the output is only 0.66mV in the equivalent of a 1V/m field.

The sensitivity can be increased by using a current transformer as shown in Fig 4.10(b). The core can be a large ferrite bead or a clip-on ferrite core such as Maplin BZ34M. Using one-turn primary and a four-turn secondary with $R_L = 50\Omega$, the primary impedance is $50\Omega/16$ or 3.125Ω (neglecting leakage inductance) so the primary voltage is 0.57mV in the equivalent of a 1V/m field. This is stepped up by 4:1 to give 2.28mV into 50Ω. The ratio of 1V to 2.28mV is 52.8dB so the loop is said to have an antenna factor of 52.8dB.

Ideally, an H-field loop should respond only to the H-field, being little affected by the E-field. The E-field response can be minimised by adding a split electrostatic screen as shown in Fig 4.10(c). A length of RG213 coaxial cable can be used with the screen split at the centre. The capacitance of the screen lowers the self-resonant frequency (SRF) and, if this is to be kept above 30MHz, the maximum cable length is about 600mm. Screened loops may be tuned to resonance. This has the advantage of making the output higher for a given field strength, but makes calibration more difficult because of the Q has to be defined and the bandwidth taken into consideration.

Investigating the suspect transmitter

If the answer to the original two questions:

1. *Is the neighbour's equipment some form of radio device, such as a TV or radio receiver, which is suffering interference on specific frequencies?*
2. *If so, is similar equipment tuned to the same frequencies in your own house or at other neighbours' houses affected?*

was 'yes', it is likely that the amateur station is radiating an unwanted signal which is interfering with anything using that frequency (see Chart 4.2 on p47). By its very nature, this type of interference almost always involves some form of radio receiver, though it will not necessarily be a broadcast radio, TV or video; it could be some form of radio control where the radio function is not immediately obvious.

The general name for unwanted signals radiated by a transmitter is *spurious emissions* and there are two broad categories:

1. *Harmonically related* spurious emissions, which are usually called simply *harmonics*.
2. *Non-harmonically related* spurious emissions, usually just called *spurious* or *spurs*.

Harmonics will always be present in any transmission. The harmonic content of a signal is simply an indication of the distortion of the sine wave which constitutes that signal. An absolutely pure sine wave would have no harmonics in its make-up, but this would be an ideal situation which does not occur in practice (Fig 4.11).

In practical radio work the aim is to reduce the harmonics to a level where they are insignificant compared to any legitimate signals which may be using the frequencies on which the harmonics fall. Many amateurs will remember the days of VHF TV, when the harmonic output of HF transmitters had to be reduced to a level where they were small compared to fringe-area TV signals. Since the decline of VHF TV, the incidence of harmonic interference from HF transmitters has greatly lessened but it can still occur, and may raise its head again if other vulnerable services start to use old VHF TV bands.

Non-harmonically related spurious emissions are usually unwanted mixer products generated by the heterodyning processes which are used to generate the output frequency in modern transceivers. In adverse circumstances these leak through the various filters, and end up being radiated (Fig 4.12). Transverters are particularly prone because of the additional mixing process involved.

There is another type of spurious emission which used to be very common; this is the unwanted products of multiplier stages. In this technique the operating frequency is achieved by multiplying up from a relatively low frequency oscillator, and the unwanted products arrive at the output by a process of harmonic generation and mixing. This oscillator/multiplier process is still occasionally used, particularly in simple CW or FM transmitters, and is worth keeping in mind when investigating problems in vintage or homebrew equipment (Fig 4.13).

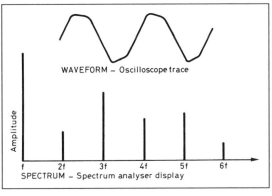

Fig 4.11. Typical harmonic content of a distorted sine wave

Fig 4.12. Spurious mixer products. Spectrum of a poorly adjusted QRP transmitter

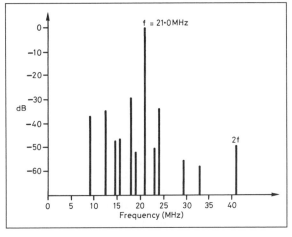

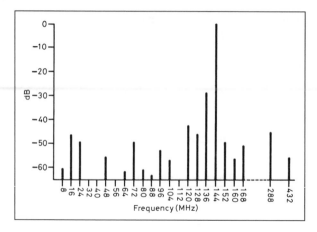

Frequency (MHz)

Fig 4.13. Multiplier products. Spectrum of a 144MHz transmitter in which an 8MHz oscillator is multiplied up to 144MHz. Harmonics of the 8MHz oscillator mix with one another to produce spurious outputs

The above-mentioned emissions are usually relatively small in amplitude – unless the transceiver has been grossly misaligned – but there is a totally different class of spurious emissions which can give rise to large unwanted signals being radiated. This is oscillation due to instability, caused by some stage of the transmitter oscillating at a frequency which may be quite unrelated to the normal operating frequency.

Spurious emissions are discussed in greater detail in Chapter 6, where for convenience the two categories have been labelled *predictable spurious emissions* and *instability*.

Evidence of spurious emissions

Before spending time on more-detailed investigations, confirm that the interference disappears when the transmitter is operated into a dummy load – if it is still there, the spurious emission is leaking out of the transmitter by some means other than the antenna, and this should be dealt with directly as a transmitter problem (see Chapter 6).

If a spurious emission from your station is causing interference in a neighbour's house, then it is likely that similar equipment, tuned to the same frequency and located nearer to your station, will also be affected. If the interference is to radio or TV, there will be no problem in finding a receiver for checking purposes. It may be necessary to rearrange antenna conditions on the test receiver to achieve a comparable pick-up of the spurious signal. Most households have battery-operated radio receivers and many can muster a portable TV. This makes the situation very straightforward. Where the interference is to something not operating on the normal broadcast bands, the problem is first to find out on which frequency the affected equipment is operating, and then to listen round that frequency on a suitable receiver. There is an added complication in the case of non-broadcast radio equipment where there may be only one example in the locality, making the question "Is similar equipment tuned to the same frequency affected?" meaningless, and we have no means of knowing whether the problem is breakthrough or spurious emissions. Nowadays, breakthrough is a much more common cause of interference than transmitter spurious emissions. In cases where there is no clear evidence to the contrary, it is reasonable to start by assuming that breakthrough is the likely culprit.

In general, where a spurious emission problem is suspected, the first step is to get hold of a receiver which covers the frequency of the affected equipment and use this to listen for any spurious signals. If you are lucky enough to have access to a proper measuring receiver or, better still, a spectrum analyser, checking for spurious emissions will be a positive pleasure. (Contrary to popular belief the construction of a spectrum analyser quite adequate for this type of diagnosis is not beyond the average home constructor, and is a very worthwhile project [6].) Most of us, however, will have to fall back on a receiver with a more doubtful performance. It is most important to make sure that the test receiver is set up a reasonable distance from the suspect transmitter and its antennas, otherwise it will be overloaded and create all sorts of internally generated spurious signals. Even in favourable situations where there is no overloading problem, it is always necessary to bear in mind that all receivers have spurious responses of their own and these can easily be misinterpreted.

Recognising the dangerous trouble maker

It is generally true to say that spurious emissions caused by harmonics and mixer products, once detected, are fairly straightforward to deal with, either by realigning or perhaps modifying the transmitter, or by fitting the appropriate filter to the transmitter output. The really serious problem arises when instabilities in the transmitter give rise to oscillations which can be of very large amplitude – in very bad cases comparable to the nominal transmitter power. Older amateurs will remember when most transmitters were homebrew and one of the main design features was achieving stability in the power amplifier and driver stages.

Similar problems can still occur in modern equipment if sufficiently misused, and the result can be very large unstable signals being radiated which can cause widespread interference. On the HF bands 'widespread' could mean hundreds or even thousands of miles. Needless to say, the authorities in all countries take a very dim view of this sort of thing.

Fortunately, with modern, well-designed transceivers, instability is rare unless the equipment has been tampered with or has been inexpertly repaired. Be particularly wary if power transistors have been replaced with 'near equivalents'. When instability does occur it often (but by no means always) reveals itself by bad signal reports, particularly on CW, and by erratic output power as the drive power is increased or as the load is changed – for instance by small adjustments of the antenna tuning unit (ATU). In valve amplifiers erratic anode tuning is a common symptom of instability and should always be investigated (see Chart 4.3 on p48).

If you have any reason to think you may have an instability problem of any sort, go off the air until you are sure that all is well. Again, the best way to check is to use a spectrum analyser but, failing this, carefully tune a receiver over as much of the RF spectrum as possible – at least from the medium-wave broadcast band up to several times the transmitter frequency – to see if there are any large spurious signals. Oscillations due to instability usually sound very rough and are easily identified.

Start by checking the transmitter into a dummy load but don't forget that changes of loading can cause instability to come and go. As before, make sure that the test receiver is not overloaded – in these circumstances you have enough problems without confusing yourself with false receiver responses! If you haven't got the facilities to carry out the sort of check single handed, the alternative is to arrange an 'organised signal test' as described in Chapter 6.

Needless to say, the most dangerous oscillations are those near enough to the wanted frequency to be radiated efficiently by the antenna. This can occur either through direct instability at the signal frequency or by a relatively low-frequency parasitic oscillation which beats with the output frequency to give a 'comb' of spurious outputs surrounding the carrier at multiples of the parasitic frequency. This type of parasitic oscillation can occur in transistor amplifiers where the gain of transistors increases as the frequency decreases. The high gain at low frequency can lead to oscillation unless care is taken in the circuit design and adjustment.

Under certain conditions, bipolar VHF power transistors can also generate an output at half the frequency at which they are being driven. This is usually called *frequency halving*. Again, care should be exercised when tuning up a transistor PA. Frequency halving should be easy to detect using a receiver which can be tuned around the frequency of the expected spurious emission (half the transmitter operating frequency). Further information on frequency halving will be found in Chapter 6.

It is worth reminding ourselves that the UK licence requires the amateur to check his station from time to time to ensure that its performance is technically adequate, with particular reference to the "suppression of unwanted emissions".

The direct approach

In many instances the very facts of the case point directly to the culprit. If radio or TV interference is occurring only on frequencies which are harmonically related to the transmitter frequency, there is not much doubt that the problem is harmonic radiation. Examples are the fourth or fifth harmonic from the 144MHz band, causing interference to UHF TV, or the second harmonic of the 50MHz band, giving trouble at the higher end of the VHF radio band. In such cases it is quite legitimate to go straight to the fitting of the appropriate filter to the output of the transmitter – though the prudent operator, however confident, will confirm the diagnosis with a borrowed filter before rushing off to buy one.

There are two important things to remember about fitting filters to transmitters. First make sure that the filter is suitable for the power in use, preferably with a bit in hand, and second make sure that the filter is correctly loaded: in most cases this means that it must 'look' into 50Ω. On VHF and UHF this is usually provided directly by the antenna system, but on HF an ATU may be needed. The filter is fitted between the transmitter and the ATU, as in Fig 4.14.

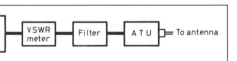

Fig 4.14. Position of the filter. The ATU ensures that the filter sees a 50Ω load

In modern HF transceivers, the VSWR meter is often incorporated into the transmitter itself. Its function is to facilitate tuning the ATU to ensure that the transmitter sees a 50Ω load. It is possible for a VSWR meter to generate harmonics – though usually at a low level – and for this reason it should always be connected between the transmitter and any filter which may be fitted.

Types of filter

There are three basic types of filter: band pass, high pass and low pass. The characteristics of these are shown in Fig 4.15.

The band-pass filter

Where a transmitter/antenna system serves only one band, as is common on VHF and UHF, a band-pass filter is practical. This has very little loss for wanted signals in the relevant band, but severely attenuates any signals which are outside it. There are a number of good designs for home-constructed VHF and UHF band-pass filters; more information can be found in references [7] and [8].

On HF the ATU is a form of band-pass filter, and it is well worth considering using one as part of normal good practice. Usually the filtering effect is limited but in many cases it will be sufficient to clear up harmonics and spurious mixer products – provided that the latter are not too close to the carrier.

The low-pass filter

This is the commonest type of filter, and at one time was considered essential in any HF set-up – again, this goes back to the days of VHF TV. A low-pass filter, as its name implies, will severely attenuate all frequencies above the cut-off frequency. On HF, for instance, this would be about 30MHz. It is still good practice to include a low-pass filter in an HF station, particularly if you have any reason to be doubtful of the transmitter harmonic performance [9].

On VHF a low-pass filter is an alternative to a band-pass filter if the spurious emissions are harmonics, and therefore above the carrier, rather than mixer products which may be either above or below the carrier.

The high-pass filter

This type of filter is the reverse of the low-pass filter in that it attenuates all frequencies below the cut-off frequency. It is not normally used in the output of a transmitter, since any filtering action it might perform would be better done by a band-pass filter. High-pass filters are often used in conjunction with braid-breaker filters to separate UHF signals from relatively low-frequency amateur signals in cases of breakthrough, as discussed in Chapter 5.

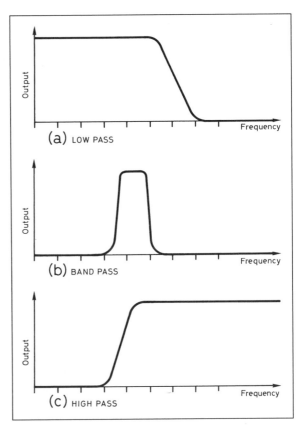

Fig 4.15. The three types of filter

PART 2 – INVESTIGATING INTERFERENCE TO RECEPTION

The two most important questions in investigating interference to reception (RFI) are "What is causing the problem?" and "Where is it?"

The first of these questions can often be answered by piecing together the evidence gleaned from listening to the signal and considering the time and frequency characteristics. The answer to the second question may follow directly from the first but, if it does not, then further measures will be needed to track down the source.

Looking for clues

First make sure that the interference does not come from anything in your own house. The best way to do this is to switch off the mains supply. If the interference disappears completely then finding the source should be a matter of elimination. If it is impractical to switch off the mains supply, then switch off everything individually. It is most important to ensure that everything in the house is checked. It is not unusual for the source to be something which was either not known about or was assumed to be above suspicion.

If the problem is definitely not in your own house, note down the times that the interference is present. Does this give any clues? Interference which comes on at certain times of the day might indicate lights, central heating or similar time-dependent or seasonal sources. A bit of polite observation of what is happening locally may show that the interference is related to certain activities. If it is fairly certain that the interference is coming from a specific house, the best course is to approach the householder and ask them to assist – if possible by tuning off the mains. It must be emphasised that a friendly approach is most important. In many cases there will be no obligation on the part of the householder to do anything about the problem, so getting off on the wrong foot could be disastrous. Once the source has been identified there are a number of actions which can be taken. These are discussed in Chapter 7.

Receiver defects

Where the interfering signal sounds very like a real radio signal, either speech or some form of data, then it is possible that it is in fact an intentional radio signal. The most likely possibility is that it is a spurious response to a relatively large out-of-band signal. Such responses can be caused either by strong signals *intermodulating* or by unwanted receiver responses such as *image reception*. On HF intermodulation effects exist all the time to some extent because there are so many strong signals around. They are usually known as *intermods* and minimising them is a fundamental part of good receiver design. The effect is not so well known at VHF but occurs sometimes when an amateur is located close to a powerful transmitter. Hand-held transceivers connected to an outdoor antenna can be particularly susceptible. (See 'Radio paging' below.)

There are two ways to check a spurious response. The simplest is to fit an attenuator of about 10dB in the antenna lead. If the apparent interference drops by more than one would expect, then it is probably an intermod. (Most HF receivers have a switchable attenuator for use when intermods are a problem – on 7MHz at night for instance.) This check will not work for all spurious responses, and a better way is to improve the front-end selectivity by fitting a narrow filter in the receiver antenna input. With the filter in place the interference should reduce significantly. There is also the possibility that the apparent interference is a a real radio signal in the amateur band. It may be an illegal signal but don't forget that many bands are shared so that the unidentifiable signal may be legitimate.

Tracking down interference

Where the source of interference cannot be found by observation, assisted by a little judicious questioning, it will be necessary to resort to more subtle methods.

First check to see how much of the spectrum is affected by the interference and particularly see if it can be received on a medium-wave receiver which is tuned away from any strong broadcast signals. If it can, then you are in luck since almost every household possesses a portable MF receiver with a ferrite-rod antenna. This can be used as a direction finder, using the null to indicate the direction of the interference. There are two nulls, one for each condition where the rod antenna is in line with the signal. The easiest way to resolve the ambiguity is to check the null from several different places. If several helpers with their own receivers are available the task can be made much simpler and has the merit of providing innocent entertainment – particularly to passers-by!

If the interference is limited to the HF bands the simplest approach is to use a portable receiver with a short whip antenna, and try to find where the signal is strongest. In difficult cases it may be necessary to resort to direction finding, but this would involve constructing a loop antenna with adequate sensitivity and satisfactory directional properties [10].

Above about 100MHz a portable dipole can be used, constructed as in Fig 4.8. Minimum signal will be received when the ends of the dipole are pointing towards the source of the interference. Usually incidental interference is a mixture of horizontal and vertical polarisation but, in cases where there is little or no horizontally polarised component, direction indications will be confusing and it is better just to move about with the antenna to find where the signal is maximum, holding the dipole in whichever position gives best results. It is easier to detect changes of signal strength if the receiver is switched to AM or SSB rather than FM, and an S-meter is a great help. Where the source is a radio transmitter some distance away, rather than a local incidental interference source, it may be necessary to turn to proper direction finding techniques such as are used for VHF DF activities.

The strength of received interference

It is very difficult to get any sort of reasonable estimate of the strength of interference by simply looking at the S-meter of an amateur receiver. Apart from the fact that most S-meters are inaccurate, particularly at small signal levels, the reading will depend very much on the type of antenna used. A better indication of signal strength can be obtained by using the techniques described in Part 1. Such an arrangement can be very useful in making comparative measurements though, as already pointed out, it is unwise to place too much reliance on the absolute accuracy of any readings.

Some sources of RFI

The following notes on RFI sources which might be found in a typical residential location are taken from the RSGB's leaflet *Interference to Amateur*

Radio Reception, edition 1 [11]. These leaflets are regularly updated, and later editions may have additional sources listed. One could hope that in the long term the list might get shorter but there does not seem to be much chance of this in the foreseeable future!

Television line timebase harmonics

The line timebase frequency of 625-line television systems is 15.625kHz. Harmonics may be heard as narrow-band signals on multiples of this frequency, for example, 3500kHz, 3515.625kHz, 3531.25kHz etc. As the line frequency is 1MHz divided by 64, harmonics are found on multiples of 125kHz. If the TV is receiving an off-air programme, the harmonic will usually have a sound which changes with picture content when heard on an SSB or CW receiver.

To prove that a TV set is the source, try watching another TV set (with low RFI!) and select different channels until you find one where changes in the picture coincide with changes in the sound heard on the radio. If the TV set causing the interference is being used for video playback, the line timebase harmonics will normally have narrow-band 50Hz frequency modulation which is not locked to the mains.

Switch-mode power supplies

A switch-mode power supply (SMPS) generates a square wave at a frequency of about 30–90kHz or more. On the LF, MF and lower HF bands, harmonics from an SMPS can produce broad-band RFI with broad peaks and 100Hz modulation. The peaks are spaced at multiples of the switching frequency. On the higher HF bands and at VHF, the peaks may merge together.

TV power supplies

Most modern television receivers have a switch-mode power supply. When heard on an AM or SSB receiver, the sound usually changes with picture content (see also TV line timebase harmonics above) but is broad-band and may peak at a certain frequency such as 14–18MHz. With some TV sets, the switch-mode power supply also runs when in standby mode. On some models the switching frequency changes to around 1.75–2MHz on standby.

Lighting

If the RFI occurs mainly after dark, does it appear when a light is on in a room nearby?

For lighting which uses 12V halogen spotlights, the transformers may either be a conventional type or an *electronic transformer* which is a switch-mode power supply with AC output.

There are two types of low-energy fluorescent lamps which fit into a normal lamp holder. Most types are electronic and contain a switching regulator which produces similar emissions to a switch-mode power supply but some types are conventional fluorescent lamps in a compact form with a relatively heavy iron-cored choke.

Video recorder power supplies

Video recorder power supplies normally operate continuously and, although most use linear power supplies, some models use switch-mode supplies. A few video recorders, not intended for the UK market, may have been 'personally imported' and these may have little or no mains filtering. They are likely to be multi-standard models with PAL and MESECAM and can be very noisy on the 1.8MHz and 3.5MHz bands.

Computer power supplies

In a desktop computer, the switch-mode power supply is normally in a screened box with a mains filter and may therefore produce much less RFI than a computer monitor where the SMPS may be unscreened. Laptop computers have an external mains power supply unit/charger which is normally an SMPS without screening.

Fax machines

The power supply in a fax machine runs 24 hours a day and is almost always a switch-mode type. It may be built-in or an external unit and some types are not screened.

Electric motors

RFI from an AC or DC electric motor with brushes and a commutator is broad-band without peaks. Its pitch varies as the motor speed varies. The variations in speed and the pattern of use can give clues about the source. For example, this might be a washing machine or dryer, sewing machine, electric lawn mower, food mixer, electric drill, hair dryer or even a model railway. It is not likely to be a refrigerator as these normally use induction motors which do not produce RFI.

Thermostats

Faulty thermostats can arc for one to 30 seconds or more, producing broad-band RFI with no peaks and 100Hz modulation. This may be heard on a number of HF and/or VHF bands. If it occurs 24 hours a day all year round, it could be a refrigerator thermostat. If it does not occur at night or during the summer, it could be a central heating thermostat such as a room thermostat or, more likely, a boiler thermostat. The arcing may occur at intervals of about five to 20 minutes although in some cases it could be as often as two or three times per minute.

Conventional fluorescent lights

RFI from fluorescent lights is broad-band with no peaks and is modulated with a 100Hz buzz, mainly on the LF, MF and lower HF bands. Fluorescent lights have been required to include RFI suppression since 1978, although most met the relevant standard long before this date. If the tube is worn out and flickering at 50Hz, this can increase the level of RFI.

Dimmer switches

RFI from dimmer switches is similar to that produced by fluorescent lights and is stronger when the lamp is dimmed than when on full brightness. Dimmer switches sold in the UK have been required to include RFI suppression since 1978 although most met the relevant standard long before this date. They seldom cause problems to amateur reception unless they are faulty or are a type not designed for the European market.

Computers

Various oscillators in a computer and its associated components such as the keyboard and mouse can produce narrow-band radiated emissions. Some are crystal controlled and generally have no drift or modulation, while others use a ceramic resonator which drifts and may have slight frequency modulation which can be heard as a 'warbling' noise on an SSB or CW receiver. Such modulation may sound like someone typing on a keyboard or playing a game.

Almost all PCs have a crystal oscillator at or near 14.318MHz although this signal may not be particularly strong. Nevertheless, if it is present at the same time as other signals, it shows that the other signals are likely to come from a computer. In many cases, a computer monitor radiates more RFI than the computer itself. In addition to broad-band emissions from the SMPS in a computer monitor, there may be line timebase harmonics which are similar to TV line timebase harmonics except that the spacing is larger. For example, harmonics from VGA or SVGA computer monitors may be spaced at 31.5, 35.2, 35.5kHz or more. Computer line timebase harmonics normally give a very pure crystal-controlled note and are likely to be strongest on the 1.8 and 3.5MHz bands. More information on computer RFI will be found in Appendix 6.

Intruder alarm systems

Intruder alarm systems normally contain a microprocessor and can radiate signals from the wiring to the sensors on the HF and/or VHF bands. As they normally use a ceramic resonator, the harmonics drift slightly and may have slight modulation which can be heard on an SSB receiver. This modulation may change if the alarm ever goes off and may also change when the user presses keys on the control panel.

Other digital electronic devices

Digital electronic circuitry can radiate narrow-band signals on certain frequencies such as harmonics of the clock frequency and may also produce broad-band signals. Such sources include NICAM decoders and other digital electronics in TV sets, video recorders and satellite receivers/decoders. Many of these devices are connected to long cables which can radiate RFI on HF bands as well as VHF.

Cable TV

Many modern cable television systems use vision carriers from 56MHz upwards on multiples of 8MHz. The street cabinets normally contain a switch-mode power supply which may produce detectable emissions on the HF bands due to common-mode signals conducted along the coaxial cables.

Telephone equipment

Fax machines contain a microprocessor which runs continuously. If a computer is connected to a modem, this can allow RFI from the computer to be radiated via the telephone line. If the modem can receive fax or voice calls, the owner may leave the computer running all the time.

If a telephone subscriber has an ISDN (Integrated Services Digital Network) line, the line carries 90V DC which powers a switch-mode power supply in the customer's premises.

Businesses and even some homes may have their own internal telephone exchange or PABX. Some types can produce RFI on the HF and VHF bands.

If the RFI is strongest under telephone lines or close to a telephone pole, the source could be one of the items mentioned above but in many cases it is something completely unrelated to the telephone system. If anything feeds RFI onto the mains in a house, this can be coupled onto telephone wires via the mains transformer of any mains-powered telephone equipment such as an answering machine or a cordless phone.

Vehicle ignition systems

Although there have been regulations controlling ignition interference since 1952, this can be a problem for weak-signal reception near a busy road. Many transceivers contain a noise blanker which is effective against the short impulses from vehicle ignition systems.

Vehicle remote keyless entry receivers

Some cars made since mid-1994 use radio keys operating on 433.92MHz. Radio key receivers in some cars contain a local oscillator which runs continuously somewhere in the range 433.275–433.475MHz.

Other types use a super-regenerative receiver and some after-market alarms sold in 1994 and 1995 can emit broad-band noise across the 430–440MHz band.

Radio teleswitches

These are a type of electricity meter which may be used to control off-peak electricity. One type, manufactured before 1992, radiates harmonics of 1.52MHz including 50.116, 144.400 and 145.920MHz. These frequencies are highly accurate as they are phase-locked to the carrier of BBC Radio 4 Long Wave on 198kHz. On an SSB receiver, it is possible to hear low rate data which sounds like continuous but very slow packet radio.

'Touch lamps'

These are table lamps with a touch-operated switch which turns the lamp on and off and selects several levels of brightness. They contain a saw-tooth oscillator which operates continuously and produce emissions which are similar to an SMPS but with a fundamental frequency of around 190kHz. Some models sold before 1996 contain no RFI suppression.

Garage door openers

The super-regenerative receivers for some 173MHz remote-controlled garage door openers manufactured in the late 'eighties radiate broad-band noise on 430–440MHz. They can also receive VHF radio paging and rebroadcast it at a number of frequencies on the 430–440MHz band!

Water conditioners

Electronic water conditioners are claimed to reduce deposition of lime scale. Some types use a sequence of audio frequency tones which can have harmonics up to 28MHz in some cases. When received in the CW (or SSB) mode the harmonics of the audio tones beat with the beat frequency oscillator so that the listener hears audio tones which change every second or so in a sequence which repeats every few minutes.

Electric fences

RFI from an electric fence is a regular clicking noise. The source is likely to be sparking at a faulty insulator rather than the electric fence unit itself. Try looking for flashovers in the dark (with the landowner's permission).

Overhead power cables

Overhead power cables can radiate broad-band noise with 100Hz modulation. High-voltage cables always produce a certain amount of RFI due to corona discharge from the cable itself but RFI can be greatly increased due to arcing at a faulty insulator. In this case the level of RFI may reduce in dry weather.

Radio paging

This is in a different category of interference from those listed above, being a genuine radio frequency signal rather than RFI. It sounds rather like packet radio but usually starts with a tone. Strong signals from nearby radio paging transmitters may be heard on the 2m band or other bands but, in most cases, such breakthrough is caused by shortcomings in the amateur receiver. Transceivers with extended receiver coverage are more likely to be affected than those which only cover amateur bands. Hand-held transceivers connected to an outdoor antenna can be particularly susceptible.

REFERENCES

[1] *Radio Transmitters and Domestic Electronic Equipment*. Leaflet EMC 01, available from the RSGB.

[2] 'EMC' column in *Radio Communication* April 1993.

[3] 'Technical Topics' column in *Radio Communication* October 1992.

[4] 'JS snap-on RF current probe', J B Smith, *Radio Communication* June 1995.

[5] 'EMC Matters' column in *Radio Communication* April 1991.

[6] 'Simple Spectrum Analyser', R Blackwell, *Radio Communication* November 1989.

[7] *VHF/UHF Manual*, 3rd edn, G R Jessop, RSGB, Chapter 6.

[8] 'A simple way to design narrow-band interdigital filters', I White, *Radio Communication* February 1984.

[9] 'A low-pass filter for high power', G Eddowes, *Radio Communication* August 1989.

[10] *Radio Frequency Interference*, ARRL, Chapter 4.

[11] *Interference to Amateur Radio Reception*. Leaflet EMC 04, available from the RSGB.

SUMMARY

Transmitter interference
The three charts (see pp46–48)
Charts 4.1 and 4.2 start with the two questions:

1. Is the equipment some form of radio device suffering interference on specific frequencies?
2. If so, is other similar radio equipment tuned to the same frequencies also affected?

From this point further questions are asked which, with luck, will direct the investigator in the right direction.

Cases which do not give simple answers
Where the answer to both questions is not a clear-cut 'yes' or 'no', it means that the problem probably falls into the 'IF and intermodulation' category.

IF and intermodulation problems

1. Direct breakthrough into the IF of a receiver.
   (a) The fundamental of a 10.1MHz transmitter getting into the 10.7MHz IF of a VHF receiver.
   (b) IF breakthrough into satellite TV receivers (Chapter 9).
   Treat these as cases of breakthrough.

2. Harmonics of an amateur transmitter being picked up in the IF of a receiver.
   (a) The second harmonic of 18MHz, breaking through into the IF of a susceptible TV receiver.
   (b) The third harmonic of 3.5MHz breaking through into the 10.7MHz IF of a VHF radio receiver.
   Treat these as cases of excessive transmitter harmonics.

3. Image interference. The common example of this is signals from amateur transmitters operating on the 1.8MHz band causing image interference to medium-wave broadcast receivers.

4. Amateur signals beating with harmonics of the local oscillator or other oscillators in the susceptible equipment to give spurious responses.

Conditions 3 and 4 will give interference which is tuneable at the receiver, but are really cases of breakthrough and should be treated as such.

Breakthrough is a much more common cause of interference than transmitter spurious emissions, so in cases of doubt it is reasonable to start by assuming that the problem is breakthrough, and to proceed down Chart 4.1.

Interference to reception
1. Make sure that the source of interference is not in your own house. The best way to do this is to switch off the main supply. If items are switched off individually it is easy to miss equipment which is permanently wired to the supply.
2. Make sure that the apparent interference is not due to a receiver defect. Very large signals outside the amateur bands can overload the receiver front-end, causing spurious signals to appear inside the band. This is becoming fairly common on the 144MHz band as more high-power transmitters for paging and similar services are operated on nearby frequencies. In such cases the solution is not to complain about the transmitter, but to improve the receiver selectivity. A narrow band-pass filter in front of the receiver is the usual solution, but don't forget that in a transceiver it will have to handle the transmitted power.
3. Try to establish the source of the interference by considering the characteristics of the received signal and the times it is present.
4. Locate the source using portable receiver with a directional antenna.

Chart 4.1

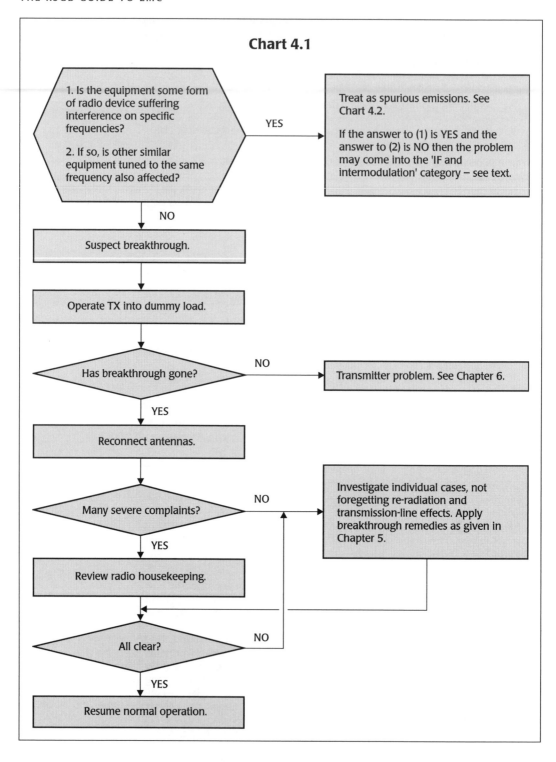

1. Is the equipment some form of radio device suffering interference on specific frequencies?

2. If so, is other similar equipment tuned to the same frequency also affected?

YES →

Treat as spurious emissions. See Chart 4.2.

If the answer to (1) is YES and the answer to (2) is NO then the problem may come into the 'IF and intermodulation' category – see text.

NO ↓

Suspect breakthrough.

Operate TX into dummy load.

Has breakthrough gone? — NO → Transmitter problem. See Chapter 6.

YES ↓

Reconnect antennas.

Many severe complaints? — NO → Investigate individual cases, not foregetting re-radiation and transmission-line effects. Apply breakthrough remedies as given in Chapter 5.

YES ↓

Review radio housekeeping.

All clear? — NO →

YES ↓

Resume normal operation.

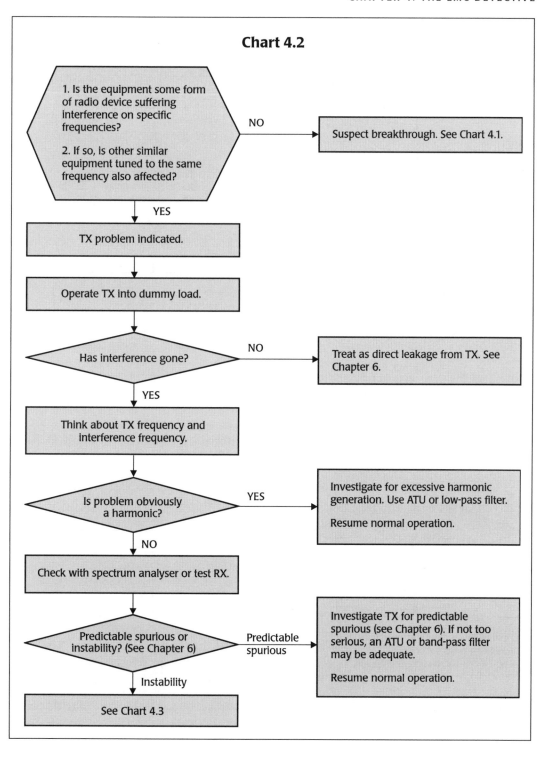

Chart 4.3

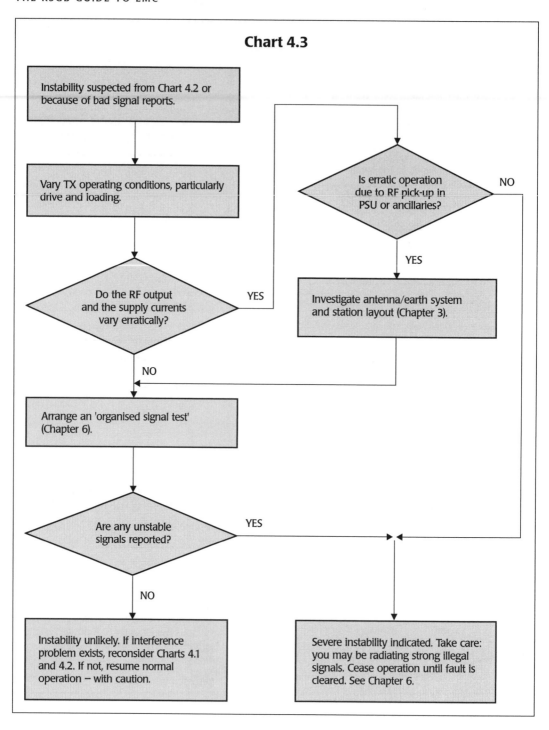

Instability suspected from Chart 4.2 or because of bad signal reports.

Vary TX operating conditions, particularly drive and loading.

Do the RF output and the supply currents vary erratically?

Is erratic operation due to RF pick-up in PSU or ancillaries? — NO

YES

Investigate antenna/earth system and station layout (Chapter 3).

YES

NO

Arrange an 'organised signal test' (Chapter 6).

Are any unstable signals reported? — YES

NO

Instability unlikely. If interference problem exists, reconsider Charts 4.1 and 4.2. If not, resume normal operation – with caution.

Severe instability indicated. Take care: you may be radiating strong illegal signals. Cease operation until fault is cleared. See Chapter 6.

5 Breakthrough

PART 1 – THE BACKGROUND

Breakthrough is the most prominent EMC problem in amateur radio because it involves other people, and the way it is tackled directly affects public attitudes to our activities. In the UK the number of EMC cases involving breakthrough has declined somewhat in the last few years. There are probably two reasons for this. First, the new EMC regulations have made manufacturers aware of the necessity of designing with EMC in mind, and secondly the acceptance by radio amateurs that good 'radio housekeeping' is a vital factor in establishing and operating a station.

In this chapter we assume that the basic detective work has been done and that we are reasonably confident that breakthrough is the problem. In the real EMC world it is not possible to be more than reasonably confident about the mechanism of any case of interference – absolute certainty is a thing which rarely comes the EMC detective's way. The personal problems which arise from breakthrough are often greater than the technical ones, and this very tricky subject is discussed in Chapter 8.

What causes breakthrough?

Practical radio communication always involves both transmission and reception. Breakthrough is simply unwanted reception. The underlying principles governing the reception of signals are the same whether they are welcome or not, and it is worthwhile spending a little time looking at the mechanism of signal pick-up before proceeding to specific remedies.

Imagine that we have a piece of electronic equipment – it could be a TV, a hi-fi or a controller of some kind, but for simplicity let's call it a 'black box'. RF energy can get into the box by two basic routes, either by direct pick-up of signals by the circuitry inside the box or through external leads acting as an antenna. Direct pick-up can only take place if the box is made of plastic or wood, or other non-conducting material. Even then the energy involved is likely to be small, unless the frequency is high enough for the wiring inside the box to make an 'antenna' which is a significant fraction of a wavelength. Generally this means frequencies above 50MHz. On the HF bands, where the wavelength is relatively long, ingress through external leads is much more common.

Leads acting as antennas

In considering the mechanism of pick-up via external leads, it should be remembered that RF energy does not just leak into the black box, like water filling a tank. As with any other electrical circuit, the energy must be going to somewhere from somewhere. In other words, electric charges are passing in and out of the box, giving up some of their energy to the internal circuits as they do so. In some instances, the leads form a crude dipole in which the charges oscillate backwards and forwards, inducing RF currents into the circuits inside the box, but it is more common for the currents to flow into the box from leads acting as an unbalanced antenna. In this case the circuit is completed by some sort of earth connection – usually via the mains or by direct capacitance to earth. This capacitance will be between the conductors and metalwork comprising the box and any external earthed objects, including the earth itself. The capacitance to earth cannot be calculated using the standard 'parallel-plate' formula often quoted in connection with capacitors used as circuit components. Due to fringe effects, the true capacitance will be considerably larger – as is mentioned in Chapter 3 in relation to antenna capacitance.

Any wire suspended in an electromagnetic field will act as an antenna, and electric charges will oscillate backwards and forwards in the wire in sympathy with the electric field. The amount of energy which can be extracted depends on two factors:

(a) How the wire is lined up in relation to the electric field (see Chapter 2). However, in many breakthrough situations the polarisation of the field is so confused by reflections and re-radiation that for all intents and purposes it can be considered randomly polarised. In this case there will always be quite a lot of signal pick-up whichever way the wire is aligned.

(b) How well the load is matched to the antenna.

The tuned antenna

When the intention is to make an efficient receiving antenna, the loading is arranged to cancel out any reactance and to provide a resistive termination which matches the source resistance. In ordinary radio parlance the antenna is *tuned to resonance* and *matched to the load*. In this condition the antenna will extract energy from its *capture area* (see Chapter 2).

The high-impedance load

At the other extreme from the ideally matched antenna, we have the situation where the dipole is terminated in a load which is of such a high impedance that it is effectively an open-circuit. If we take the simple case of a short dipole parallel to the electric field, the voltage (V) at the terminals is half the antenna length multiplied by the field strength (E).

$$V = E \times L/2 \text{ volts}$$

where L is in metres and E is in volts/metre.

Modern active antennas exploit this principle, usually using field-effect transistors to give a very high input impedance. The signal voltage is converted down to 50Ω using active devices.

Pick-up in practical breakthrough cases

In real breakthrough situations, pick-up occurs through a combination of the above effects, almost always made more complicated by local re-radiation and transmission-line effects from the mains wiring and other conductors which form an integral part of the modern house. In fact the EM field pattern in such cases is so confused that any attempt to quantify breakthrough signals would be doomed to failure. Fortunately it is only necessary to identify where the unwanted signals are coming from, and then to prevent them entering the susceptible equipment.

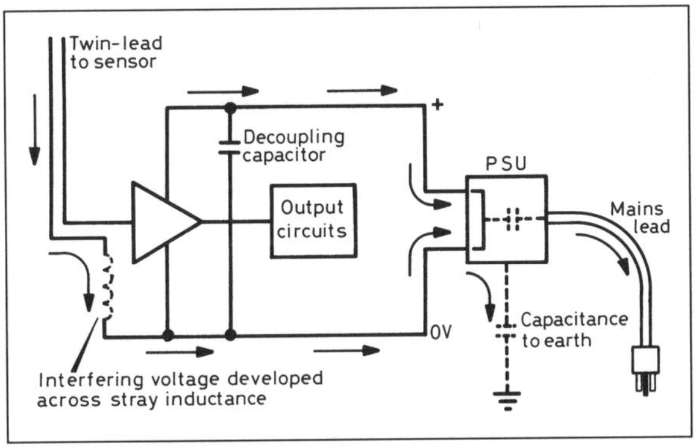

Fig 5.1. Path of RF signal in a typical sensor/alarm device

Fig 5.1 gives some idea of the path that an interfering signal might take if our black box were an alarm of some kind, operated from the mains supply, having a sensor connected to it by (unscreened) twin cable several metres long. The conductors of the twin cable will act as a single antenna connected both to the input to the amplifier and to the 0V rail. RF voltages will be injected into the amplifier by the RF current passing through the impedance of the 0V connection on its way to the power supply (PSU), and thence to earth via the mains lead or through stray capacitance. It does not matter whether the power supply has a mains earth connection or not – there will be an adequate path through various capacitances.

In some instances the amplification may take place at RF, particularly where modern audio transistors are used, since these often have gain up to tens or even hundreds of megahertz. In other cases the RF is detected at the first semiconductor and then amplified as an audio signal. As usual in EMC problems, neither of these effects are likely to be clear-cut.

Keeping the RF out

There are two basic ways to keep RF energy from getting into sensitive circuits. The first is by choking the lead or leads which are acting as antennas outside the box, and the second is by bypassing the signals at the sensitive points on the circuit inside the box. The second technique will be dealt with first, and is included mainly as food for thought for anyone building or modifying their own equipment. It is not recommended as a general EMC troubleshooting procedure, except for qualified technicians. As a general rule, it is most unwise to do any work inside equipment which is not your own. You could be letting yourself in for a lot of trouble; in particular you could be held responsible in the case of accident – with disastrous consequences.

Bypassing techniques

Bypassing of unwanted RF is only applicable where leads are carrying DC or low-frequency AC. It is really just a special case of *decoupling* and, as with all decoupling, there are two factors to consider:

1. To use a capacitor which gives the lowest possible impedance to the unwanted signal.
2. To find the correct place to connect the 'earthy' end of the capacitor.

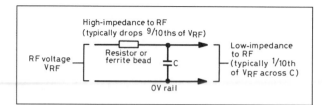

Fig 5.2. The principle of bypassing or decoupling

For most requirements a ceramic capacitor between 1nF and 10nF will be satisfactory, and it should be connected with the shortest possible leads – remember that a typical lead 2.5cm long has an inductance in the region of 20nH (0.02μH), so that any significant length of lead will increase the effective impedance of the bypass path. It is also possible for the lead inductance to resonate with the capacitor, causing unpredictable effects at high frequencies.

The second point is more problematic because it is not always easy to decide where the correct 0V point actually is – particularly if the requirement for short capacitor leads is to be realised. Generally speaking, the 'earthy' end of the capacitor should go to the point to which the amplifier 0V connection is made, and to which its inputs are returned.

In some instances it may be possible to use a small ferrite bead, such as the FX1115, threaded on the lead to give an impedance for the capacitor to 'work against' – as in Fig 5.2. This is the classic decoupling circuit, where a potential divider is formed so that the majority of the unwanted voltage is dropped across the series impedance and very little appears across the bypass capacitor. If circuit conditions permit, it may be possible to use a low-value resistor in place of the ferrite bead. A standard RF choke – as opposed to a ferrite bead – could be used but this is not recommended as high-Q inductors can give rise to resonance effects. In practice, there is always some source impedance due to lead inductance etc, so that bypassing can often be quite effective without any added series element.

Fig 5.3 illustrates good bypassing and decoupling practice: leads are kept as short as possible, and the 0V rail should be of very broad track or, if practical, a ground plane should be used.

Choking-off the unwanted antennas

Fig 5.3. Good bypassing or decoupling practice. FB: ferrite bead. Cb: bypass capacitor = 1nF (short leads). Cd: decoupling capacitor (short leads). Rd: decoupling resistor. E: common 0V point – all connections to E to be as short as possible

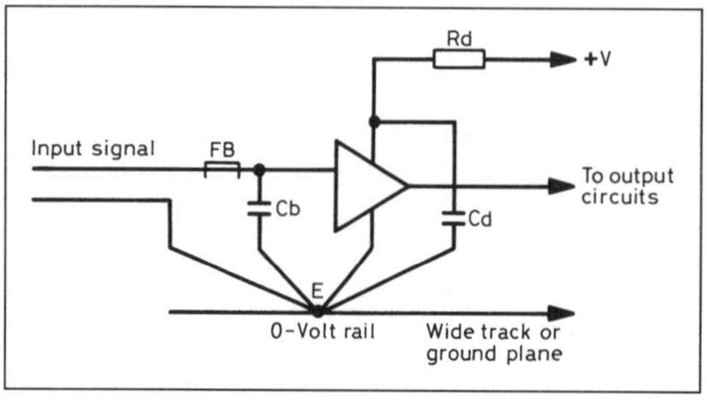

As has already been said, the fitting of internal bypassing components is not practical as a general EMC troubleshooting procedure, but fortunately it is possible to achieve the same results in a much more acceptable way. If a high impedance is connected in series with the lead acting as an unwanted antenna outside the black box, then the internal shunt capacitance and resistance – either intentional or accidental, we don't care which – will cause the majority of the unwanted RF energy to be dropped across the series impedance, and hence only a small residue finds its way into the box. Fig 5.4 gives an idea of the situation which could occur in our black box. The advantage of this technique, which makes it so practical, is that the series impedance can be provided by a suitable home-made ferrite choke, thus avoiding any modifications to the equipment itself.

Ferrites

Ferrites turn up all over the place in modern circuits, but despite their popularity they are not well understood. This is most likely because they do not fall easily into any simple category of everyday materials.

Many solids have a crystalline structure but magnetic materials are special in that the crystals are divided into *domains* in which the atoms themselves are aligned so that their magnetic fields reinforce one another, giving the domain an overall magnetic polarity. A disadvantage of most magnetic materials is that they are good conductors of electricity, so that eddy currents make them unusable at frequencies above a few kilohertz. Ferrites are manufactured from magnetic materials, chemically combined so that they are effectively non-conductive but still possess the required crystal structure for domain formation, and hence they have a relatively high permeability.

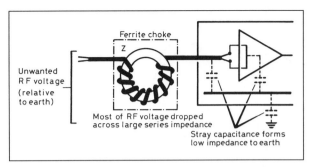

Fig 5.4. The series choke. The impedance of Z forms a potential divider with stray capacitance

When a ferrite is not in a magnetic field, the polarities of the various domains tend to cancel one another and the overall effect is zero. When a field is applied, the atoms of each domain try to align themselves with the field, mutually interacting so that domains which are more favourably aligned grow at the expense of their neighbours until a dynamic balance is reached. All this takes time, and the net result is that ferrite materials are relatively slow to respond to a changing magnetic field.

Just how slow depends on the chemistry of the particular material. Generally, ferrites which have large domains have a high permeability but are slow to respond. In electrical terms this slowness is a loss; energy is used to align the domain, but before the action is complete the next half-cycle comes along and the domain tries to align the other way. The losses increase markedly as the alignment time become a significant part of a half-cycle.

The trade-off between permeability and loss enables manufacturers to produce ferrites with a wide range of properties. In the present case we require a material which gives us adequate permeability and also sufficient loss to dampen any resonances. In effect the choking impedance will be a mixture of inductive reactance and resistance due to losses.

Ferrite chokes

So far as EMC is concerned, the most popular form of ferrite device is the *toroid* or ring. A choke is formed by winding a number of turns of the lead in question on to the ring. If no other information is available, a satisfactory choke can be made by winding as many turns as can be accommodated in a single layer, until winding covers about three-quarters of the ring. This enables the ends of the winding to be kept apart to minimise stray capacitance across the winding. One of the advantages of a ferrite toroid is that a relatively high inductance can be formed with a small number of turns. This is partly due to the toroidal shape forming a good magnetic path, and partly to the fact that ferrite materials can be made with high permeability.

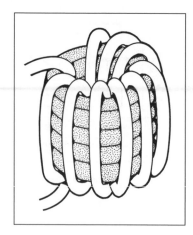

Fig 5.5. A stack of four rings. Thin cable is shown so that the core stack can be clearly seen

How many turns?

The inductance of a coil is proportional to the square of the number of turns – that is, twice as many turns will give four times the inductance – and a turn on a toroidal core means every time the wire goes through the hole in the ring. Since in practice there is a limit to the number of turns that can be accommodated on one ring, it is often convenient to use two or more cores to increase the inductance, as in Fig 5.5. (The inductance of a toroidal choke is proportional to the thickness of the ring and a stack acts as one thick ring.) Appendix 3 gives the characteristics of several types of ferrite choke along with background information on the test methods used.

Typical of suitable ferrite cores are Fair-Rite Corporation type 2643802702 which, at the time of writing, are the ones supplied by the RSGB. They have an inside diameter of 22.85mm (0.9in), and are made from Fair-Rite type 43 material. These rings are 12.7mm thick, about twice the thickness of most of the rings which have traditionally been used for EMC purposes.

For the higher HF bands (7 to 28MHz) 12 turns on a single core are recommended. If it is not possible to get 12 turns on the ring then eight or nine turns on a stack of two rings will give very similar results. For 1.8 to 14MHz, 12 turns on a two-ring stack are satisfactory. At VHF stray capacitance across the winding becomes a major factor, and at 144MHz six or seven turns on a single core should be used. To minimise stray capacitance the turns can be wound in two parts so that the input and output are kept separate, as shown in Fig A3.30 (Appendix 3).

For frequencies above about 15MHz, a fairly effective choke can be made by winding 20 or more turns on a length of ferrite rod salvaged from the antenna of an old medium-wave radio. For thick leads, a convenient arrangement is to use three lengths of rod taped to form a core of roughly triangular cross-section, as in Fig 5.6. (Somewhat fewer turns are needed if three rods are used.) The rod (or rods) should extend at least a centimetre or two beyond the windings.

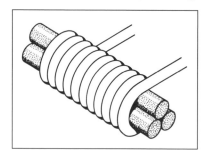

Fig 5.6. Cable wound on three ferrite rods

It is possible to purchase clip-on ferrite cores, but generally these are not so satisfactory as ferrite rings. For leads which are too thick to wind on to ferrite rings, it may be possible to use the ferrite yokes from the deflection assembly of the cathode ray tube of a TV receiver or monitor. More about both of these will be found in Appendix 3. (*Heed the warning in Appendix 3 about taking care when removing the yokes – an imploding CRT can cause serious injury. In addition the EHT connection can be at high potential (due to stored charge) long after the power has been switched off.*)

Types of ferrite

It is important to use the correct type of ferrite core, otherwise results will be unpredictable. The last thing that the investigator wants is to end up trying different chokes in front of an audience who may be all too ready to be unimpressed. Many rings do not have any identification marks, and the best way to ensure that you get the right type is to purchase them from a reliable supplier who is selling cores specifically for EMC purposes.

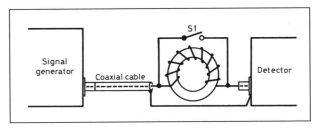

Fig 5.7. Ferrite choke test circuit

Checking ferrite cores

Ferrites are complicated materials and not easy to characterise but, as a quick check of whether an unknown core is likely to make a practical choke or not, the 'series-loss' test will be found useful. This circuit is also quite a good illustration of how the choke operates in practice.

Wind 10 turns of insulated wire on to the core and connect the ends of the winding between a signal generator and some form of RF detector as in Fig 5.7.

The signal generator and the detector should have 50Ω output and input respectively. If there is any doubt about this, a 6dB attenuator should be inserted either side of the test circuit to define the source and load resistance. (Further information on attenuators will be found in Chapter 6 and Appendix 7.) The switch and the terminals for the choke (and the attenuators, if required) can be mounted on a plastic box. Tune the signal generator to a frequency of about 3.8MHz and switch S1 from closed to open – the difference indicated on the detector between the two conditions should be at least 10dB. Repeat the test at 28MHz – the difference should be greater than 23dB. Measurements at 28MHz may be unduly optimistic due to resonance effects so it is worthwhile checking at other frequencies.

If a core with a known good EMC performance, such as a Fair-rite 2643802702 (see above), is available it can be used as a basis for comparison. If the test box is working correctly, results from a core of this type will be considerably better than the figures quoted above. Any of the RF detectors discussed in Chapter 6 could be used. If the detector is uncalibrated, the difference can be measured by re-adjusting the signal generator output so that the detector output returns to some pre-determined level.

Common-mode and differential signals

In many cases the cable wound onto the toroid will have more than one conductor: it may be a mains lead, or perhaps a length of flat twin or twisted pair carrying audio or the output of a sensor. It is sometimes asked how the choke can act on the unwanted RF while not affecting the normal use of the conductors in the cable.

Where two or more conductors are very close together compared to the wavelength of an RF field, then they are effectively one conductor – or in our case one unwanted antenna. The unwanted RF currents flow up and down them together, creating a magnetic field which is the same as would exist round a single conductor. Currents of this type are known as *common-mode* currents, and are dealt with by the normal action of the ferrite choke. Where a signal (in our case the wanted signal) is between the wires, as in Fig 5.8, currents which are equal in magnitude, but opposite in direction, flow in the wires. Because the wires are close together, or in electrical

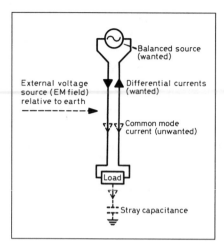

Fig 5.8. Differential-mode and common-mode currents

terms *closely coupled*, the magnetic fields at any point except in the space between the wires tend to cancel – effectively confining the field between the two wires. Since there is no significant external magnetic field from these *differential* signals there is no inductive action, and the signals pass through the ferrite choke unaffected.

In a coaxial cable, the wanted signals are carried by the fields confined between the inner conductor and the inside of the braid, and are completely isolated from the effect of the ferrite ring. The unwanted currents effectively flow on the outside of the braid and see the high impedance of the choke.

Screened cables

Where a pair of wires is screened, the common-mode currents will flow on the screen and the differential signals will travel on the inner conductors. It is important that the screen should be connected to the correct point on the circuit, otherwise it might do more harm than good. The screen should be connected to the 0V rail at the point to which the inputs are referred (point E in Fig 5.3). Ideally this should be a thick piece of track or, better still, a ground plane. Where the case of the equipment is made of metal (or possibly plastic with a conductive coating) it should be bonded to the same point. In EMC investigations conditions are often far from ideal, and it may be found that trouble is caused by interference entering the equipment via the screen. Where this is the case, a ferrite choke should be fitted as near to the susceptible equipment as possible to provide a high impedance to currents on the screen. The situation is very similar to that which exists with TV and radio coaxial feeders, and this is dealt with in some detail later in this chapter.

PART 2 – BREAKTHROUGH TO SPECIFIC EQUIPMENT

So far we have looked at factors which are common to all breakthrough situations, and it is now time to 'get down to brass tacks' and consider specific problems. Traditionally, the major EMC problem in amateur radio is breakthrough to TV and radio and, though nowadays the radio includes audio gear of various types, this is probably still true. It is not surprising that this should be so when it is considered that this type of equipment involves high-gain amplifiers, coaxial feeders crying out to act as unwanted antennas and, most important of all, that it is to be found in almost every home.

A complication with all types of radio-based equipment is the likelihood of intermodulation and cross-modulation, added to the classical breakthrough modes of direct amplification and rectification. Apart from the confusion that might arise in distinguishing breakthrough from transmitter problems – as discussed in Chapter 4 – these effects do not alter the anti-breakthrough procedures. Whatever the mechanism of the interference generation inside the susceptible equipment, our object is to keep the unwanted signal out.

Things should change for the better as the new EC standards become effective. One of the requirements is the ability to withstand reasonably large (unwanted) signals applied to all the external leads, including the braid of the coaxial feeder and the mains lead. As mentioned in Chapter 3 and Appendix 4, the regulations are quite complicated but, if we assume immunity to signals at levels of 2V or 3V, we will be in the right region for most practical purposes. It is important to note that the regulations do not require every item of equipment be tested to prove compliance – this would be quite impractical – so that it is always possible (though unlikely) for any particular set to have a manufacturing fault which makes it unusually susceptible.

Be prepared

The complexity of practical EMC investigations is legendary, but the situation can be made much less formidable by a well-organised approach, and this will have the added bonus of impressing third parties that you know what you are doing – even if it isn't completely true. Where an installation is complicated, make a sketch along the lines of Fig 5.12, leaving room to make comments on the effectiveness (or otherwise) of the different chokes. Make sure that you have all that you are likely to need before starting – a list of suitable items is given in the summary at the end of this chapter. Try to arrange any visits to allow plenty of time so the job does not have to be rushed. The other vital preparation is to make arrangements for test transmissions from your own station. If at all possible, enlist the help of another amateur and set up a reliable means of communication – a couple of 144MHz or CB hand-held transceivers are ideal. When using the hand-held transceiver, keep a reasonable distance away from the equipment being investigated, thus avoiding any spectacular breakthrough or possibly damage (real or imaginary) from this source.

TV and video cassette recorders (VCRs)

In a TV installation the most vulnerable point is the antenna input and, in the majority of cases, eliminating unwanted signals at this point will clear up the problem. The most common route for the unwanted signals to get in to the set is via the braid of the coaxial feeder. The small size of UHF TV antennas makes it unlikely that large signals will be picked up directly by the antenna and be propagated down the coaxial feeder as a normal received signal, unless the frequency of the interfering signal is relatively high – above about 100MHz or so. When interfering signals are picked up on the braid of a TV or radio feeder, it is usual to assume that the currents flow only on the braid and that the inner conductor is unaffected. This is not really true: the actual flow of common-mode current will depend on the conditions at each end of the feeder (as seen by the interference), complicated by the skin effect. Fortunately, for practical purposes it is quite adequate to take the simple view that the currents flow on the braid and that the object is to reduce or eliminate them.

First have a look at the general installation. Are the coaxial connectors correctly fitted with the braid firmly gripped and making good electrical contact with the outer connection of the plug? Figs 5.9(a) and 5.9(b) show

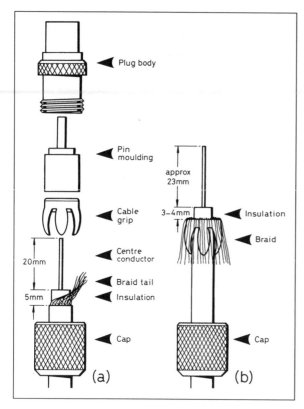

Plug body

Pin
moulding

approx
23mm

Cable
grip

3–4mm

Insulation

Braid

Centre
conductor

20mm

Braid tail

5mm

Insulation

Cap

Cap

(a)

(b)

Fig 5.9. Two methods of fitting domestic TV co-axial connectors. (a) Wrap the braid tail round the 5mm of inner insulator and push cable grip down on to it, ensuring that whiskers of braid do not short to the centre conductor. (b) Braid is 'teased' out, bent back over cable grip and cut off

the two methods of fitting TV coaxial connectors. Where the cable and cable grip are the right size, as they usually will be for the low-loss cable normally used with UHF TV, then the method shown in (b) is to be preferred. Method (a) may be useful where the cable is considerably thinner than the cable grip, making the braid difficulty to secure any other way. Make sure that the centre pin is properly soldered – this is a point often missed by busy installers, but it is well worth doing. Apart from a potential intermittent contact, subsequent oxidation can form a rectifying junction, giving rise to unexpected interference effects.

Corrosion of the connector at the end of the cable coming down from the antenna may mean that water has got into the cable and worked its way down into the connector. The commonest cause is chaffing or splitting of the sheath, allowing water to enter, though it could be a failure of the seal at the antenna itself. Whatever the cause, a cable which is corroded will show a marked increase in loss at the TV frequencies but, more important from the EMC point of view, the individual wires of the braid make poor contact with one another, reducing the overall screening performance. A corroded or disconnected screen will have effects similar to those discussed in Chapter 9 (Fig 9.2). The solution is to replace the cable and possibly the antenna, though it may be difficult to persuade a neighbour – who probably has not noticed the deterioration in TV performance – that the expenditure is justified. The best way of proving that the antenna system is at fault is to connect the TV to a different antenna, located in more or less the same place. This may not be as difficult as it might seem at first sight; there may be an independent TV antenna feeding another set in the same house – in the children's room or a 'granny flat' for instance, and connecting across would only require a reasonable length of coaxial cable.

It is important to remember to fit a ferrite-ring choke if a long extension lead is used for test purposes – otherwise pick-up on the braid could confuse the issue. If it is necessary to move the TV or VCR to another room, make sure that the owner is in charge of the operation and that the question of insurance has been considered – just in case the worst should happen.

Antenna amplifiers

In recent years, the fitting of various types of signal booster amplifiers has become increasingly popular, and these have their own EMC problems. Amplifiers are usually fitted for two reasons: either because the signal is very weak or because the feeder losses are excessive. In many cases these two reasons amount to the same thing – the antenna is mounted as high as possible because the signal is weak, and this results in a long coaxial feeder with consequent losses. In either case, the only sensible place to locate the amplifier is right at the antenna. Amplifiers of this type usually have a good noise figure – many of the more modern ones use a GaAs FET (gallium arsenide field-effect transistor) as the active device.

A well-designed masthead amplifier, which is correctly installed close to the antenna, is unlikely to give problems at HF because the length of unwanted antenna will be limited, but at VHF and UHF conditions could be very different. Problems arise if the unwanted signal reaching the input to the amplifier device is large enough to drive it into non-linearity and cause cross-modulation. Once this has taken place, there is nothing that can be done at ground level to correct it. An amplifier fitted to a UHF TV antenna should not amplify signals below the UHF band, though some general-purpose amplifiers have significant gain at frequencies down to 30MHz and below. If a masthead amplifier is suspected, the only practical way to prove it is by substituting antennas as discussed above. Masthead amplifiers get their DC power supplies through the coaxial feeder, so that any filters or braid-breakers must pass (and not short-circuit) the required DC current. Unless specific information is available, it is best to use only ferrite ring chokes in the down leads from such amplifiers.

Indoor amplifiers installed near the TV set are much more likely to cause problems, especially where HF is concerned, but fortunately they can easily be removed from the circuit for test purposes. An amplifier in this position, of course, does nothing to overcome cable losses but, because of the good noise figure of the amplifier, it may improve the performance of a TV receiver that has poor sensitivity.

Distribution amplifiers

Some amplifiers have several outputs, allowing more than one set to be operated from the same TV antenna without the losses involved in passive splitters. These can be purchased as UHF amplifiers, sometimes optimised for a specific channel group, or as UHF/VHF amplifiers covering a wider bandwidth down to about 40MHz. In the UK (where there is no VHF TV) the UHF-only amplifier, preferably one designed for a specific channel group, is an obvious choice. An amplifier should be considered as part of the TV set (or sets), and the standard techniques using chokes and filters on the antenna side of the amplifier will still apply. Typical arrangements are shown in Fig 5.10. Further information on amplifiers can be found in Appendix 5 and also in reference [1].

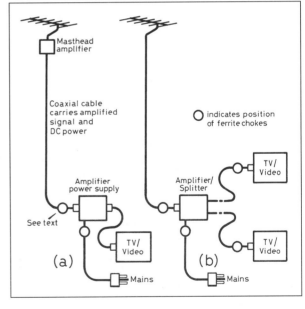

Fig 5.10. Fitting chokes to an antenna amplifier. (a) Masthead amplifier. (b) Indoor amplifier feeding two TV sets

Chokes and filters for TV installations

The simplest way of choking-off signals travelling down the braid is to use our old friend the ferrite ring choke; used in this way it is often called a ferrite ring *braid-breaker*. There is a practical problem making them, in that the coaxial cable most commonly used for UHF TV is too thick to be wound conveniently onto the core. Added to this, low-loss TV coaxial feeder uses cellular polythene dielectric, which can allow the inner conductor to short-circuit to the braid if the cable is forced into a tight winding. It is best to make the choke separately, using a length of smaller-diameter coaxial feeder with suitable TV connectors at each end – usually a plug at one end and a socket at the other, as in Photo 5.1.

For HF breakthrough, about 12 to 14 turns on a stack of two cores gives a practical choke, and seven turns on a single core should be satisfactory for 144MHz. If a thicker core such as the FairRite 2643802702 (nominal thickness 12.7mm) is used, one core will be sufficient except at the lower HF bands. (More information on ferrite chokes will be found in Part 1 of this chapter and also in Appendix 3.) The coaxial cable used for the choke should, of course, be 75Ω, but there is no need to use low-loss cable since the length involved is quite short. Don't forget to test the choke for continuity and freedom from short-circuits before you use it in earnest – it can be embarrassing to find these things out when you are performing before an audience!

Photo 5.1. A ferrite ring choke suitable for TV coaxial downlead

A well-known, home-made braid-breaker is shown in Fig A3.19 in Appendix 3. It has the advantage of incorporating a high-pass filter which will attenuate HF and VHF signals which may be passing down the coaxial cable in the normal way (between inner conductor and the inside of the braid). The small capacitors C1 and C2 are part of the high-pass filter, so far as the TV signals are concerned, and are a high series reactance at HF, giving the filter its braid-breaker action. R1 provides a leakage path to prevent the build-up of static electricity. This filter is less popular than it once was because it causes a discontinuity in the coaxial feeder and has been known to cause unexpected problems, particularly on teletext. For obvious reasons, this type of braid-breaker cannot be used where the coaxial cable is also supplying DC power to a masthead amplifier.

The five-element UHF TV high-pass filter shown in Fig 5.11 appeared in the EMC column of *Radio Communication* [1], accompanied by the following notes.

"A small offcut of Veroboard can be used if the layout is followed exactly. When cutting the board, it is important to remove all traces of any copper strip to minimise coupling between the input and output. The capacitors are the miniature ceramic plate type. L1 and L2 are self-supporting coils mounted flush with the board. They consist of one and a half turns of 0.8 to 1mm diameter copper wire as shown. The solid inner core of a piece of TV aerial coaxial cable is ideal and the insulation from the inner can be used as a coil former. URM70 cable is preferable for the flying leads as normal TV aerial cable is rather thick and inflexible. The

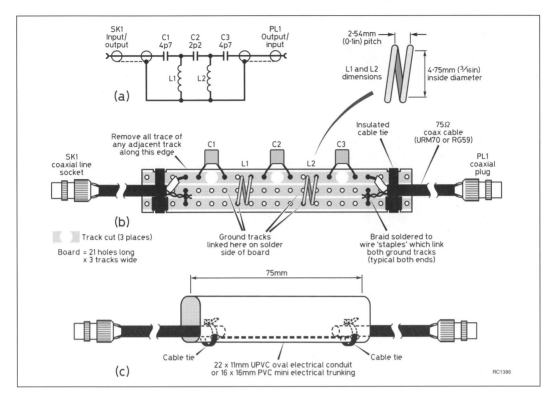

(a)

SK1 Input/output — C1 4p7 — C2 2p2 — C3 4p7 — PL1 Output/input

L1 L2

L1 and L2 dimensions

2·54mm (0·1in) pitch

4·75mm (³⁄₁₆in) inside diameter

(b)

Remove all trace of any adjacent track along this edge

SK1 coaxial line socket

C1 — C2 — C3

L1 — L2

Insulated cable tie

75Ω coax cable (URM70 or RG59)

PL1 coaxial plug

Track cut (3 places)

Board = 21 holes long x 3 tracks wide

Ground tracks linked here on solder side of board

Braid soldered to wire 'staples' which link both ground tracks (typical both ends)

(c)

75mm

Cable tie

22 x 11mm UPVC oval electrical conduit or 16 x 16mm PVC mini electrical trunking

Cable tie

RC1386

filter can be housed in a piece of plastic tubing about 75mm long with cable ties to secure the flying leads to the holes drilled in the sides of the tube."

Further information about the performance of the filter and its use in conjunction with a ferrite ring braid-breaker will be found in Appendix 3 and also in reference [2].

Try the chokes and filters in order, starting with the antenna choke (F1 in Fig 5.12). Do not remove a device if it does not seem to work – in many cases of breakthrough, the unwanted signals enter the installation by more than one route and the observed interference is the result of the signals adding or subtracting. If a ferrite choke is only partially successful, another should be tried in series to increase the rejection but it is usually not worthwhile to go beyond two. When the sources have been identified, chokes which are not needed can be removed. Actually the order of trying chokes does not matter too much, so long as things are done in an organised way – but it is important to start with the antenna.

The chokes fitted to the mains leads (F2 and F3 in Fig 5.12) are made by winding the cable onto ferrite rings in the same way as a ferrite-ring braid-breaker. It goes without saying that in this case it is essential to avoid damaging the cable in any way. If the cable is unusually thick it may be necessary to use fewer turns and more rings. The rules are similar to those for braid breakers. For HF use about 12 to 14 turns on a stack of two cores, or the

Fig 5.11. Construction of a five-element UHF TV high-pass filter. (a) Circuit. (b) Veroboard layout seen from component side. (c) Housing

Fig 5.12. Typical domestic TV installation, showing positions of ferrite chokes. F1: antenna coaxial feeder choke (or filter). F2/F3: mains chokes. F4/F5: coaxial chokes on RF lead (VCR to TV). F6: choke on additional leads to controls or external speakers or displays

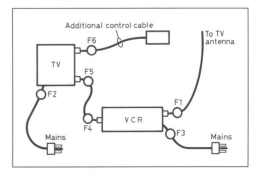

Additional control cable

F6

To TV antenna

TV

F5

F2

F4

VCR

F1

F3

Mains

Mains

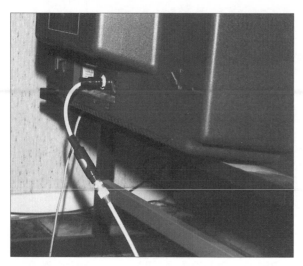

Photo 5.2. A commercial filter fitted to the antenna feeder lead of a TV set

same number of turns on one thicker (12.7mm) core. For VHF fewer turns on a single core should be used. Because of the closed magnetic circuit in a toroidal core, it is not necessary to pull the cable tight onto the ferrite material; all that is required is for the winding to be secure and the ends not too close together. If it is not possible to use ferrite rings – because the plug cannot be removed, for instance – then a ferrite rod choke can be used, though the choking effect will not be so great, particularly on the lower HF bands. (Appendix 3 has information on split ferrite cores and also on using ferrite yokes from the deflection assemblies of scrap TV sets and computer monitors.) Where possible, a well-screened SCART lead should be used between the VCR and the TV set, rather than the coaxial RF connection. If a coaxial cable has to be used, it may be necessary to fit a ferrite ring at either end, depending on which unit is susceptible. If you are unlucky and the lead is abnormally long, they may be required at both ends.

Some modern TV installations have additional control and audio cables connected to either the TV or the VCR, and these should be dealt with in the same way as the mains leads. It is reasonable to expect the owner of the equipment to disconnect non-essential ancillaries during the diagnostic process and, where ancillaries are gimmicky and poorly engineered, it may have to be accepted that it is not practical to expect such a system to operate without interference.

Specific problems associated with satellite and cable TV installations are dealt with in Chapter 9.

Commercial braid-breakers and filters

Braid-breakers and filters are available from a number of commercial manufacturers, and these are usually very effective provided that the correct type is used. Some devices are simply high-pass or band-stop filters optimised for specific bands, while others include a braid-breaker. Sometimes it may be necessary to use two devices – for instance a braid-breaker in series with a high-pass filter – to achieve the desired rejection.

At the time of going to press, the RSGB keeps a stock of suitable filters supplied by a reputable manufacturer. Details of current devices and prices can be found in *Radio Communication*. These filters have the advantage of being unobtrusive, as shown in Photo 5.2. Detailed information on these filters will be found in Appendix 3.

There are many types of commercially manufactured mains filters on the market but not all are effective in dealing with breakthrough. Generally, filters which do not provide a high impedance on all the mains input wires – live, neutral, and earth (if used) – will not give much protection, since the unwanted RF currents usually flow in and out of the equipment as a common-mode signal, and not differentially between the wires. The best thing is to start by trying a ferrite-ring choke, and not to use a commercial mains filter unless a special need arises. In any case, examine the specification of the filter carefully before committing yourself. More information on mains filters will be found in Chapter 7.

Radio and audio equipment

In general, the approach to radio and audio problems is the same as that for TV, though there are differences of emphasis. Interference caused by the braid of the antenna coaxial cable acting as an unwanted antenna is still a serious problem, but the larger elements on VHF broadcast antennas makes direct pick-up of interference (which is then passed down the co-axial cable in the normal way) more likely.

The speaker leads of a stereo system frequently pick up interference which is transferred to the input of the amplifier, either through stray capacitance or through negative-feedback networks. The leads should be choked by winding them on to ferrite rings or alternatively, if this is not possible, on to lengths of ferrite rod or split ferrite cores.

One way of simplifying on-site operations is to have chokes already made up. These consist of a length of lead wound onto a ferrite ring with connectors fitted at both ends. With this technique it is possible to make a very neat arrangement, and since the wire diameter can be chosen to suit the application, it may be possible to use a smaller ferrite ring than would otherwise be possible.

A small ceramic capacitor of about 1nF (1000pF) can also be included at the end which is going to plug into the main equipment, as shown in Fig 5.13. This should be done with caution: too large a value could lead to instability and possible damage to the equipment. If you are not familiar with the audio equipment in question, it is safer to leave the capacitor out. Make sure the connectors are correctly wired and that there are no short-circuits; some hi-fi units can be damaged if operated into open-circuit or short-circuit loads. This technique can be used on other leads, such as those going to a tape deck or a record deck, but in this case the capacitors should be smaller – about 100pF is typical. Again, do not include the capacitor if there is any doubt about its effect on the performance of the equipment – in most cases the choke will be adequate on its own. As with a TV, the remaining control and mains leads should be fitted with whichever type of ferrite choke is practical.

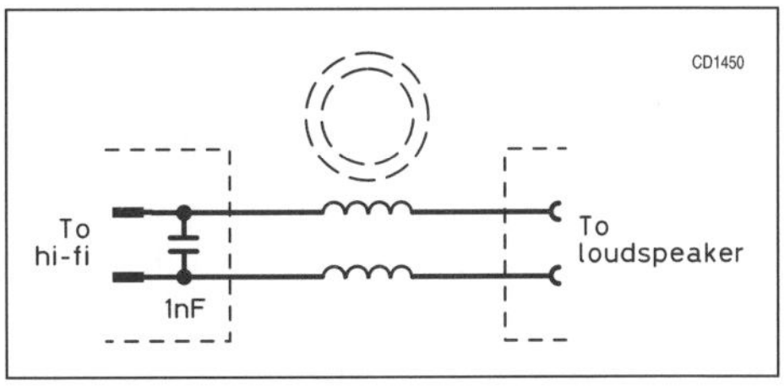

Where breakthrough to a portable radio is experienced, there is not very much that can be done from the outside of the set since there are no external leads to choke, but fortunately it is usually possible to find a location where the interference is negligible. Frequently portables only give trouble when operated from the mains, and this is a clear indication that a ferrite choke is required on the mains lead.

Fig 5.13. Twin speaker lead wound on ferrite core to make plug-in choke unit

The human factor

The annoyance caused by radio interference to audio equipment depends very much on the mode in use. AM or SSB is worst in this respect since, once the RF is detected, it will be amplified and delivered to the speakers as a distinctly audible signal. FM is much less troublesome, and usually manifests itself only by a click as the transmitter is switched on and off. Likewise, the data modes based on frequency-shift keying (FSK) should also only give clicks, though in some techniques they occur fairly frequently. In annoyance rating CW comes somewhere between SSB and FM since, though the clicks occur at the keying rate (which is fairly high), there is no other amplitude modulation. The audible effects can be minimised by ensuring that the keying waveform of the transmitter has long enough rise and fall times – about 5 to 10ms is reasonable.

Interference to security systems

If you are installing the equipment yourself make sure you buy it from a reputable supplier and that it carries the CE mark. Even in equipment which has already been installed, it may be possible to improve matters by looking for sources of local re-radiation or transmission-line coupling – see Chapter 3. Information on dealing with breakthrough to security systems can be found in Chapter 9.

Telephones and associated equipment

The first thing to check is whether the equipment is rented from a company or authority which undertakes to correct breakthrough, free of charge, as part of normal service. If this is so, make sure that you deal with the appropriate department – breakthrough is not all that common, and the receptionist at the service or complaints department may be unaware of the company's policy. More information on dealing with breakthrough to telephones will be found in Chapter 9.

Intractable cases

It is inevitable that some cases of breakthrough will prove too difficult to solve. In some instances the problem will be social rather than technical, and it is difficult to advise on such a situation. We all know from everyday experience that people can vary from extremely helpful to almost insanely awkward. Chapter 8 looks at the various problems and makes some suggestions on lines of approach.

Where a case fails to yield to the procedures we have been discussing in this chapter, it is time to call for some help, and in most cases this means contacting your national society. In the UK, the RSGB's EMC Committee has set up a country-wide network of EMC co-ordinators. Their addresses and telephone numbers are published at frequent intervals in *Radio Communication* and also in the *RSGB Yearbook* [3]. The idea is that a member with an EMC problem should first try the standard remedies and, if these are unsuccessful, the co-ordinator should be contacted. If the co-ordinator cannot advise on a suitable solution, the problem will be passed on to one of the EMC Committee's specialists who deals with that particular aspect of EMC. Needless to say, this procedure does not guarantee a successful outcome in every case but at least the technical advice given will be the best available and, most important of all, it will be impartial.

If a piece of equipment is clearly very susceptible to breakthrough, the manufacturer should be consulted, though how one should go about this varies from country to country. In the UK it is best to take the matter up with the retailer first, and it is the owner of the equipment who should make the approach – not the amateur. If this does not lead to a satisfactory outcome, the nearest co-ordinator should be contacted and the general situation discussed. It may well be that the equipment in question is a well-known source of trouble and there is a precedent for dealing with the manufacturer.

REFERENCES

[1] 'EMC' column in *Radio Communication* June 1997.
[2] 'EMC' column in *Radio Communication* February 1998.
[3] *RSGB Yearbook*, RSGB.

SUMMARY

The causes of breakthrough

(a) *Direct pick-up by circuits inside the 'black box'.* This will only take place if the box is made of non-conductive material – usually plastic – and if the interfering frequencies are high enough for the internal circuitry to form an antenna which is an appreciable fraction of a wavelength.

(b) *Pick-up by external leads acting as crude dipoles.* The best example of this is speaker leads on a stereo hi-fi system.

(c) *Pick-up by external leads acting as antennas relative to earth.* This is a very common situation, the earth path being either through the mains lead or via capacitance to ground.

Keeping the RF out

There are two ways to keep RF energy out of sensitive circuits:

(a) *By providing a path that has a low impedance to RF energy, effectively bypassing the input of the sensitive circuit.* This approach is appropriate when building equipment, but is usually not practical as a general EMC troubleshooting technique.

(b) *By greatly increasing the source impedance by using a ferrite choke on the input lead and relying on internal shunt resistance and capacitance to act as the lower half of a potential-divider circuit.* This technique has the great advantage that it does not require any modifications to the equipment itself, and it is the only practical procedure in most cases.

Types of ferrite choke

There are three types of ferrite chokes commonly made by amateurs. These are:

(a) *The ferrite ring choke.* This is made by winding a number of turns on to the ring until it is about two thirds full. The actual number of turns required depends on the core material and the number of rings in the stack. For further details see Part 1 above and Appendix 3.

(b) *The split-core or 'clip-on' choke.* The core is made in two parts which can be clamped together after the winding is completed. See Appendix 3.

(c) *The rod choke.* Where requirements are not too exacting, a useful choke can be made by winding the lead onto a piece of ferrite antenna rod from an old AM radio. For thicker cables, three lengths of rod can be taped together to form a core of roughly triangular cross-section. As many turns as possible (20

SUMMARY *(continued)*

or more) should be used and the core should be longer than the coil so that it sticks out at least 15mm at each end. A choke of this type will have less impedance than either a ring or a split-core choke, but can be useful especially at frequencies above about 15MHz.

Things to check In a domestic installation

(a) *Badly made coaxial connections.* Make sure that all coaxial connectors are correctly fitted and that the centre pin is soldered.

(b) *Corroded connectors on antenna down leads.* This probably indicates that water has entered the cable and worked its way down under the insulation.

(c) *Antenna amplifiers.* A large signal arriving at an amplifier can cause cross-modulation, and give rise to interference which cannot be removed at a later stage in the system. This is much more likely in the case of an indoor amplifier located near the TV because the braid of the coaxial feeder acts as an unwanted antenna. In general, any of the chokes or filters prescribed for TV antenna down leads can be used in front of an indoor amplifier (though reference should be made to Appendix 3 where reservations are expressed regarding the use of notch filters in front of TV amplifiers). With a masthead amplifier, remember that the coaxial lead between the amplifier and the power unit carries the DC power up the cable as well as bringing the signal down, so in this lead only chokes which pass the required DC current can be used. A simple ferrite-ring choke is the best choice if there is any doubt, since to DC this is really no different from the coaxial cable itself.

A typical breakthrough kit

(a) One combined braid-breaker and high-pass filter for TV frequencies – either a home-made item or a suitable commercial device. Where operation is confined to specific bands, it may be worth having a special filter for those bands.

(b) One ferrite-ring choke braid-breaker with a TV coaxial connector at each end.

(c) Two back-to-back TV coaxial cable connectors for joining lengths of coaxial cable together.

(d) Two ferrite rings for making chokes.

(e) A length of TV coaxial cable with connectors at each end.

(f) Two lengths of ferrite rod from old medium-wave broadcast radios for making rod chokes. Two suitable split ferrite cores would be a good alternative.

(g) Audio connectors and other items to make up plug-in chokes as in Fig 5.13.

(h) Odd useful items such as a spare TV coaxial plug, 'phono' plug, insulating tape, small cable ties, lacing cord etc.

Procedure

(a) In radio and TV installations, always start with a braid-breaker (and possibly a filter) in the antenna coaxial cable – more often than not this will cure the problem straight away.

(b) Do not remove a choke or filter if it does not immediately cure the problem. Leave it in place until chokes in other leads have been tried and results assessed.

(c) Be calm and business-like, and try to keep your temper, however aggravating the audience may be!

6

Transmitter problems

PART 1 – SPURIOUS EMISSIONS

During the first quarter of the last century, a French civil servant retired from public life to devote his time to what had always been his main pre-occupation – scientific investigation. In the course of this work he discovered a theorem which made his name famous ever after throughout the world of science and engineering. The gentleman in question was Jean Baptiste Joseph Fourier, and his theorem concerned the analysis of periodic functions into component parts. The application which is familiar to all radio enthusiasts is that every wave can be broken down into a sine wave plus harmonics. When Fourier propounded his theorem he was actually investigating the nature of heat, but the idea that the sine wave is the simplest entity in any waveform comes into all branches of science. In more complicated situations, such as a modulated radio frequency signal, the output will be a combination of several waveforms, but these can always be broken down into the component sine waves and their associated harmonics.

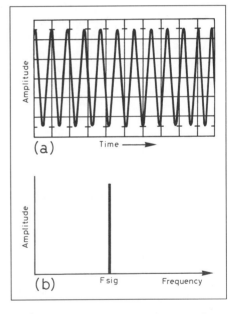

The time and frequency domains

These expressions frequently appear in radio text-books, and are a prime example of something which sounds very impressive but is really quite a simple concept. We are so used to thinking of waves in the form shown in Fig 6.1(a) that we tend to forget that this is only a graphical representation of a variable – usually voltage or current – which is changing in amplitude as we move along the 'x' axis. If x is time, as it usually is, then the representation is said to be in the *time domain*. The typical oscilloscope trace of an RF voltage is in the time domain.

Fig 6.1. (a) A sine wave displayed on an oscilloscope – the time domain. (b) A sine wave displayed on a spectrum analyser – the frequency domain

There is another way of representing waveforms where the x axis is not time, but frequency, as in Fig 6.1(b). This is the *frequency domain*. As we go from left to right, the amplitude of the signal is plotted against increasing frequency. This principle is exploited in the spectrum analyser.

When the subject of composite waves is discussed, newcomers occasionally question the reality of the components. For instance, in an AM signal, it might be asked whether the varying carrier actually exists or whether only the constant carrier and sidebands really exist. All too often the answer given is that the constant carrier and sidebands can be proved to exist mathematically, and the impression is left that, in some way, the carrier varying in amplitude is something of a fiction. The fact is that all the manifestations have equal reality; it all depends on whether you are looking at the time domain or the frequency domain. It is rather like someone being both daughter and wife – the situations are not incompatible, they are just the answer to different questions. The lady is a daughter in the 'parent domain' and a wife in the 'marriage domain'.

The quest for a pure signal

In amateur radio a high priority has always been given to signal quality. In the early days this was probably due simply to pride in producing the best possible signal but as years went by the emphasis on signal purity as a way of minimising interference, both to fellow amateurs and also to other services, became increasingly important. In today's crowded radio environment it is without doubt the most important feature of transmitter design. The aim of any design must be to produce the desired RF output, occupying only just enough bandwidth to encompass the required modulation, with no energy radiated on any other frequency. This is, of course, an ideal situation which can never be achieved in practice, but a really well-designed transmitter can come surprisingly close to it.

The two major considerations in approaching the ideal are, first, the basic technique chosen to generate the final radio frequency and, second, how much time and money is to be spent on good practice in implementing the chosen technique.

In addition to spurious emissions caused by the frequency generation process, which are predictable (at least in principle), there are others which are not. These fall into the general category of instability, and are due to unintentional feedback causing oscillation in some stage of the transmitter. Fortunately such instabilities are fairly rare in modern transceivers but, because of their unpredictability in both frequency and magnitude, when they do occur, they can cause very serious problems. In this chapter, the two categories have been labelled *predictable spurious emissions* and *instability*.

Predictable spurious emissions

As has already been said, these depend on the technique used to generate the final frequency. There are three basic techniques used in amateur transmitters.

1. Mixing the output of two oscillators together to produce a third frequency. A practical transmitter may employ several mixer stages in order to achieve the required output frequency.
2. Starting with a relatively low-frequency oscillator and multiplying the frequency by factors of two or three in successive stages until the required frequency is reached.
3. Direct generation at the final frequency, using a low-level oscillator, and amplifying the signal up to the required output power.

The mixer or heterodyne method

This has gradually taken over as the standard technique of signal generation in amateur transmitters. There are several reasons for this but the most cogent is that there is really no other practical way of achieving SSB output on the different HF bands.

A glance at the block diagram of any modern commercially built amateur transceiver shows that the mixing processes used are quite complex, usually involving several mixer stages. To some extent, the complexity is due to the combining of the transmit and receive functions, particularly where the modern trend of making the receiver tuneable over the whole HF band is followed. It is unlikely that anyone would embark on the design and construction of a complex transceiver without a thorough study of the engineering problems or, more probably, a design taken from a reputable journal or handbook. However, a brief look at a simple example of the use of a mixer in frequency generation will help indicate where troubles can arise.

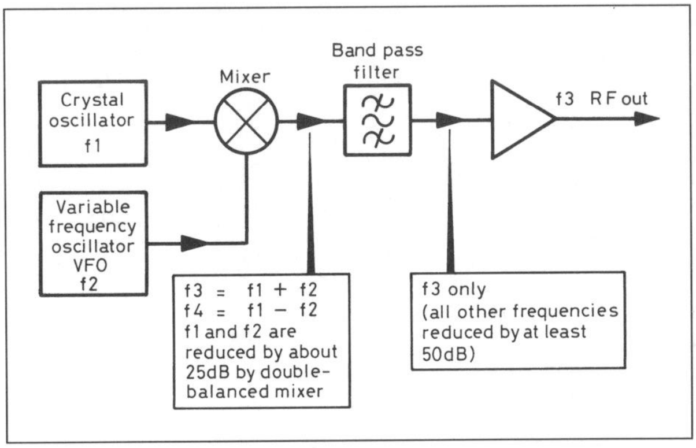

Fig 6.2 shows the outline of the simplest possible mixer transmitter. The principle is that the fixed oscillator is mixed with the output of the variable frequency oscillator (VFO) to produce the sum or difference of f_1 and f_2, giving a third frequency f_3. In a practical mixer, f_1 would be the heterodyne oscillator and would be of larger amplitude than f_2. Let's suppose that we want to cover the 14MHz band, and we have to choose suitable frequencies for f_1 and f_2. As well as the sum and difference of f_1 and f_2, all the intermodulation products will be present at the output of the mixer, and the design task is to arrange the two frequencies and the selectivity of the band-pass filter to ensure that only the wanted frequency is present in the output. Anything other than the wanted RF output will be a spurious signal, and if radiated could cause interference.

Table 6.1 lists the intermodulation products generated by two frequencies; of course the list goes on *ad infinitum*, but the significance of the product becomes less as the order increases. If for the fixed oscillator (f_1) we choose a frequency of 9.000MHz, and for the variable oscillator (f_2) a frequency range of 5.000MHz to 5.500MHz, the sum of these would cover 14.000 to 14.500MHz, but we need to check all the intermodulation products from Table 6.1. For instance, taking the third-order product $2f_1 - f_2$, we see that it will fall into the band 13 to 12.5MHz, and we must now ask ourselves whether the filter will have sufficient selectivity to eliminate this. Certainly a simple tuned circuit would not be good enough, as can be seen from Fig 6.3. This case emphasises the benefit of using a double-balanced mixer such as the diode ring in Fig 6.4(a), as opposed to an unbalanced type such as the dual-gate FET mixer shown in Fig 6.4(b). A double-balanced mixer tends to cancel many of the unwanted outputs, including $2f_1 - f_2$, allowing some relaxation on the filtering requirements.

Fig 6.2. A simple mixer frequency generator

Table 6.1. Intermodulation products produced by two frequencies

Fundamental	Second order	Third order	Fourth order	Fifth order
f_1	$f_1 + f_2$	$2f_1 + f_2$	$3f_1 + f_2$	$4f_1 + f_2$
f_2	$f_1 - f_2$	$2f_1 - f_2$	$3f_1 - f_2$	$4f_1 - f_2$
	$2f_1$	$2f_2 + f_1$	$3f_2 + f_1$	$4f_2 + f_1$
		$2f_2 - f_1$	$3f_2 - f_1$	$4f_2 - f_1$
	$2f_2$	$3f_1$	$2f_1 + 2f_2$	$3f_1 + 2f_2$
			$2f_1 - 2f_2$	$3f_1 - 2f_2$
		$3f_2$	$4f_1$	$3f_2 + 2f_1$
				$3f_2 - 2f_1$
			$4f_2$	$5f_1$
				$5f_2$

Example: Frequencies if $f_1 = 9.0$MHz and $f_2 = 5.0$MHz

9.0	14.0	23.0	32.0	41.0
5.0	4.0	13.0	22.0	31.0
	18.0	19.0	24.0	29.0
	1.0	6.0	11.0	
	10.0	27.0	28.0	37.0
			8.0	17.0
		15.0	36.0	33.0
				3.0
			20.0	45.0
				25.0

If a circuit of this type gives unexpectedly high spurious outputs, check the level and waveform of the signals feeding the mixer – where frequencies are relatively low quite a modest oscilloscope will be adequate for the purpose. If these seem to be in order, look for faults in the mixer or the filter. In a brief discussion it is impossible to do justice to the fascinating subject of mixers and their intermodulation products, and further information will be found in reference [1].

The multiplier method

This was the traditional technique for both amateur and commercial HF transmitters, and was almost universal until the coming of SSB in the late 'fifties and early 'sixties. It was very well suited to the valve technology of the time, but suffered the fatal disadvantage that it did not lend itself to SSB. In general, this technique will not be encountered today except in vintage equipment or in simple homebrew equipment such as a CW HF transmitter, or possibly in a VHF FM transmitter. Fig 6.5 shows the outline of a transmitter for the 21MHz band. The variable frequency oscillator (VFO) covers 3.5 to 3.575MHz, and this is multiplied by two in the first multiplier to give 7.0 to 7.15MHz. The 7MHz signal is filtered and then multiplied again, this time by three to give an output at 21 to 21.45MHz. This is filtered and passed on to the power amplifier (PA) and hence to the antenna. In traditional designs the multiplier and filter was simply a valve with a tuned circuit in the anode. The valve was biased well beyond cut-off, so the relationship between anode current and grid drive was very non-linear. This is a good example of how a non-linear circuit generates harmonics, and is worth studying for this reason alone, even if one has no particular interest in old techniques.

When this technique was used, it was common to bias the (valve) PA beyond cut-off (Class C), and to tune and match the anode using a tuned circuit. This points up another fact – that a Class C stage, because of its non-linearity, is a prolific generator of harmonics and, if it must be used, good filtering is essential.

Fig 6.3. Response of single tuned circuit $2f_1 - f_2$ **(16 – 5MHz = 13MHz) attenuated by only 14dB**

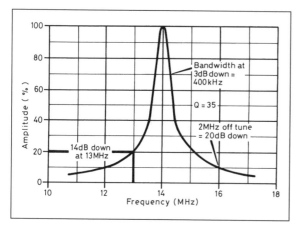

It is quite possible to select the wrong multiple when tuning up a transmitter of this kind. For instance, if in Fig 6.5 the first multiplier were mistakenly tuned to the third harmonic instead of the second, and then this was again tripled in the second multiplier, the result would be a transmitter covering 31.5 to 32.175MHz! It was to combat this sort of mistake that the requirement for an amateur station to have an absorption wavemeter was originally laid down. Even using modern techniques, it is still possible to accidentally end up on entirely the wrong frequency, and an absorption wavemeter, particularly if it is combined (as it often is) with a dip oscillator, is a very useful piece of test equipment. It should not be looked upon as just another legal requirement. Information on constructing an absorption wavemeter and dip oscillator (often called *GDOs* – grid dip oscillators – though they nowadays use transistors) will be found in reference [2].

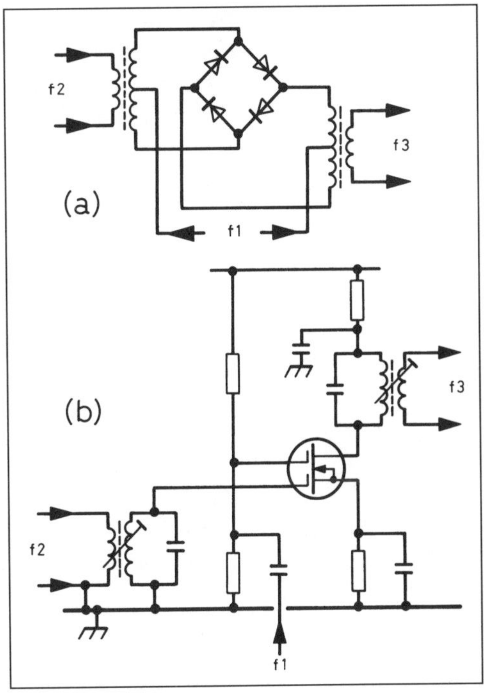

Frequency multiplication is often used in modern transmitters and receivers to provide a heterodyning frequency (usually from a crystal oscillator) and it is important to avoid unwanted harmonics from getting past the output filter. The lower the original frequency and the higher the required multiple, then the greater is the filtering problem. Where possible, it is better to use an overtone crystal, rather than the high harmonic of a fundamental crystal. A good example of this is in a 144MHz band transverter where a fifth-overtone crystal oscillator operating at 116MHz might be used to mix with 28MHz to give 144MHz [3]. If a low-frequency oscillator and harmonic generator were used, a large number of out-of-band spurious signals would be created which could well cause interference to essential services, understandably bringing the wrath of the authorities down on the head of the amateur.

Fig 6.4. (a) Ring mixer. (b) A dual-gate FET mixer

Direct generation at the final frequency

This is rarely encountered in amateur practice, except for single-band transmitters operating at 7MHz or below. For this purpose, it is a favourite of QRP home constructors, and in the hands of an experienced constructor/operator is capable of very satisfactory results. The only points to look out for in this case are oscillator drift and general stability of the design and layout.

With the advent of synthesisers the direct generation of much higher

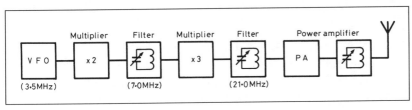

Fig 6.5. An oscillator/multiplier transmitter

frequencies has become quite practical, and in commercial and military designs which require the coverage of much wider bands than in amateur equipment it is sometimes used to good effect. Generating the carrier in this way means that there are no mixing or multiplying operations and consequently no spurious products. The only spurious outputs are those due to the synthesiser itself, and in equipment of this type the design of the synthesiser is a major consideration. It should perhaps be said that when the term 'synthesiser' is used in modern amateur radio discussions it always means a *digital* synthesiser; other types using banks of crystals and mixers etc are of only historical interest. At the present time, most digital synthesisers use either the phase-lock or frequency-lock principle. There is another type becoming more practical as devices get faster in operation, and this is *direct digital synthesis*. In this method the required frequency is generated directly in the synthesiser chip [4].

In modern amateur equipment, synthesisers are usually used in combination with the mixing technique, giving a very neat and practical way of generating the carrier. The main benefit of the synthesiser is not really improved basic radio performance, but rather ease of control – with digital frequency selection, memories and all the extras which feature so prominently in the advertisements.

How small should predictable spurious emissions be?

All transmitters generate harmonics (or, to be more formal, harmonically related spurious emissions), and all except the very simplest single-band, low-frequency equipment will generate spurious mixer or multiplier products. In a practical transmitting installation not all spurious emissions will be radiated well because the antenna may not be resonant at that particular frequency. However, since the antenna characteristics are unknown at the transmitter design stage, spurious levels are always quoted for operation into a resistive dummy load. Modern transceivers almost always require a 50Ω dummy load, though some older transmitters were designed for a nominal 75Ω load.

Emissions are usually quoted in 'decibels with respect to the carrier' (dBc), though sometimes an absolute power or voltage is used. In this case the level will be stated in 'decibels relative to 1mW' (dBm) or as so many microvolts. In amateur radio the use of 'dBc' is almost universal. For HF transmitters, all spurious outputs should be at least 60dB below the carrier (–60dBc), but this may not be good enough where a harmonic falls on to a VHF broadcast frequency, and greater harmonic attenuation will be required in these specific cases. For low-power equipment, coming into the QRP category, some relaxation is permissible, and –40dBc would probably be adequate. With transmitters for frequencies above 30MHz, the aim should be to have spurious levels at least –80dBc, and where a harmonic falls on a UHF TV channel even lower levels may be required.

Reducing predictable spurious emissions

Assuming that the design has been well thought out and suitable heterodyne frequencies have been chosen, then excessive spurious emissions will be due to inadequate filtering or to signals somehow leaking past the filters.

Leakage can take place on equipment which originally had a good specification if it has been repaired or modified – particularly if screens have been tampered with. Check that all wires entering a screened compartment are decoupled; in some instances it may be worthwhile to use *feedthrough* capacitors.

These capacitors have one plate connected to the body, which is soldered or bolted to the wall of the screened compartment, while the other is connected to the feed wire which passes through the capacitor (Fig 6.6). More information on this topic will be found in reference [5]. Generally, there is no point in going to elaborate decoupling techniques unless they are applied to all the leads entering the screened compartment (except RF leads). Screening is like a colander – it is no use carefully blocking up one hole and expecting it not to leak. The important thing is to make sure that the screening is as comprehensive as possible and that good RF decoupling techniques are used on all leads.

A frequent cause of leakage past filters is the existence of a common ground return impedance. Where high-performance filters are used, quite a small common impedance will cause significant leakage (Fig 6.7).

The solution is to ensure a low impedance by using printed circuit boards (PCBs) with a substantial ground plane or, where this is not possible, to achieve a similar effect in some other way.

Where simple tuned-circuit filters are used, ensure that taps and link windings are correctly designed to minimise unwanted coupling, and don't forget that the loaded Q of the circuit is considerably less than that of the circuit on its own [1].

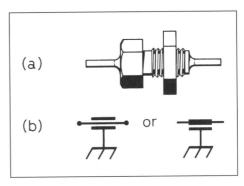

Fig 6.6. (a) Feedthrough capacitor with thread and nut fixing (solder flange versions are available). (b) Circuit diagram

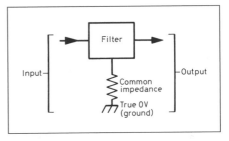

Fig 6.7. Common impedance to ground couples input to output

Incorrect transmitter operation

A special class of predictable spurious emissions are those caused by incorrect setting up of the transmitter. The most obvious example is the generation of distortion products by misuse of power amplifiers in SSB transmitters. The frequency components in the voice spectrum of an SSB transmission are really separate RF signals which are individually amplified by the power amplifier. Where several RF signals are handled by an amplifier, there will be some intermodulation between them caused by non-linearity in the amplifier. Practical amplifiers are always non-linear to some degree, and the effect is worsened by overdriving; in extreme cases the amplifier will simply 'run out of steam', and increasing the input results in no increase of output.

The odd-order intermodulation products (ie third-order, fifth-order etc) appear around the carrier as in Fig 6.8, causing interference to users of adjacent frequencies [1]. A generally acceptable figure for these products is about –35dBc or lower. The way to achieve this is to ensure that your amplifier is as linear as possible, and to avoid the temptation to increase the microphone input too much.

Modern transceivers have ALC (automatic level control) to maintain the

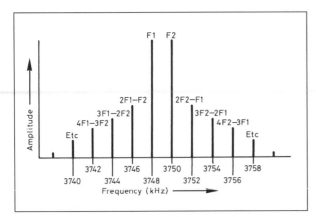

F1 F2

2F1–F2   2F2–F1
3F1–2F2   3F2–2F1
4F1–3F2   4F2–3F1
Etc   Etc

Amplitude

3740   3742   3744   3746   3748   3750   3752   3754   3756   3758

Frequency (kHz) ⟶

Fig 6.8. Odd-order 'intermods' from a two-tone SSB signal on the 3.5MHz band

drive at a more or less constant level, and hence avoid overdriving the power amplifier. Most also have signal processing to increase the effective speech power. While it is possible for faults in these circuits to cause unacceptable intermodulation performance (usually called *splatter*), it is much more likely for such effects to be caused by incorrect operation of the equipment. Study manufacturers' instructions carefully, and check any experimental adjustments by obtaining a reliable signal report. If there is any real doubt about performance, set up an 'organised signal test' as described in Part 2 of this chapter.

So far as CW transmissions are concerned, it is important to use a keying waveform which permits the RF energy to build up and decay over a period of a few milliseconds, so that key clicks are avoided. A similar consideration applies to data modes, where the transmitter is quickly switched from transmit to receive, though in this case there is the added complication of complying with the requirements of the data system in use.

Spurious emissions due to instability

In the present context, instability means something oscillating when it should not. There are two main types of instability which affect transmitters.

(a) Direct instability, where an RF amplifying stage oscillates at or near its normal operating frequency.
(b) Parasitic oscillations *(parasitics)* where a circuit oscillates at some frequency which may be quite remote from the operating frequency.

Not everyone would agree about these definitions but they are a convenient way of identifying the different effects.

Direct instability

This was a common problem in valve transmitters, and one of the prime design features was avoiding feedback from the anode circuits to the grid. This type of problem may still be encountered in vintage equipment, and also in modern valve power amplifiers, but it is not restricted to valves. It can occur with transistors, though the techniques used in semiconductor designs make it less common.

This type of instability is perhaps the most dangerous spurious condition, since it is possible to radiate a very large unstable signal on or near the normal operating frequency where the antenna can be expected to radiate efficiently.

Fortunately, direct instability is relatively easy to detect, particularly if one has already been alerted to a possible problem by bad signal reports. Sometimes a stage will oscillate when it is not being driven, and this can cause an unstable transmission to take place when the carrier control is turned to minimum, or on SSB when there is no audio input from the microphone. Any unexpected readings on the RF power meter or on the power supply current meter should be investigated immediately. With home-built equipment, look out for erratic changes in the operating conditions while tuning up the various stages.

When investigating a suspect transceiver, vary the operating conditions, especially the drive and loading. Erratic changes of output or supply current are an indication of instability. However, this does not necessarily mean that the transceiver is faulty. Erratic operation is quite often caused by RF entering the power supply or ancillary control circuits due to poor station lay-out and unsuitable antenna/earth arrangements (see Chapter 3). In fact, if the transceiver is a commercially manufactured unit of well-proven design, this is a far more likely possibility than instability due to a transceiver fault. It is also important to remember that varying the loading to a semiconductor power amplifier stage can cause protective circuits to come into action and severely reduce the output power.

Parasitic oscillations

These cover a wide range of effects and vary from severe oscillations, which will have similar symptoms to direct instability, to low-level oscillations which are difficult to detect. Frequently, a low-frequency parasitic makes itself known by beating with the carrier to give sidebands. This sometimes happens in transistor RF amplifiers, where the gain of the device is much greater at low frequencies than it is at HF or VHF, so that any unintentional feedback causes oscillation at frequencies of a few megahertz upwards. This oscillation and its harmonics beat with the signal that the stage is intended to amplify, causing a comb of spurious outputs. To avoid this, circuits should be designed with due regard to the low-frequency conditions as well as optimising the RF performance. Pay special attention to decoupling and consider using two capacitors: a small one suitable for HF or VHF as required, and a larger one for low frequencies. VHF parasitics can occur in HF transmitters, and these beat with harmonics of the carrier to give outputs in the HF band. This tendency to beat and form a large number of spurious signals means that it is usually fairly easy to detect the presence of parasitics, particularly as they almost always have a very rough, unstable-sounding note [6].

In valve amplifiers it is common practice to include parasitic stoppers in grid and anode circuits [1]. In some applications an anti-parasitic choke is formed by mounting a carbon composition resistor inside a coil. When investigating problems in a vintage transmitter, it is worth checking that these resistors have not become open-circuit or suffered a radical change of value through age or misuse. (Suitable carbon-composition resistors are becoming hard to find, so it is worth acquiring any which may turn up at rallies or junk sales.)

Parasitic oscillations sometimes occur in the most unexpected places such as audio amplifiers and power supplies. Modern designs frequently use devices which have a high open-loop gain in circuits where the overall gain is controlled by external feedback components. Incorrect choice of feedback conditions or poor decoupling can lead to oscillation. In effect, there is some frequency at which the gain and phase conditions are such that parasitic oscillation can take place. It is most important to look at the manufacturer's data and recommendations when using integrated amplifiers and similar devices, and arrange the circuit so that the device is always operated in the recommended gain range. Good layout and decoupling are also essential; don't be fooled into thinking that because the circuit is dealing with DC or audio frequency that layout does not matter. The parasitics don't know that it is a low-frequency circuit!

Frequency halving

A spurious emission which doesn't come into either of the above categories is *frequency halving*. This occurs in bipolar transistor power amplifiers, when the input and output conditions are such that the parameters of the device are modified between one cycle and the next. The result is a significant output at half the input frequency. The practical effect is that an output at half-frequency appears at certain tuning conditions. Divisions other than two are possible but less common. Harmonics are also present in the output and often the most obvious symptom of this effect is a 'harmonic' at one and a half times the nominal frequency. When tuning a VHF power amplifier into a dummy load, it is advisable to make sure that it is tuned well away from any frequency-halving condition, otherwise a change of load, such as connecting an antenna, may cause it to change to the halving condition.

Direct leakage of the RF from the transmitter

At one time this was a fairly common problem but is now rarely encountered, probably because of an increasing awareness of the importance of good EMC techniques in both commercial and amateur designs.

The way to minimise leakage is to use good screening and decoupling throughout the whole equipment and then to enclose it in a metal case which forms as near a complete screen as possible. Holes in the case for controls, indicators or for ventilation should be as small as possible, and where practical covered with a conductive mesh (from the EMC point of view, many small holes are better than one big one). It is most important to avoid gaps or slots in the case. A long narrow slot will 'leak' as much as quite a large circular hole. Leads which pass out through the case should be filtered to prevent RF getting out [5]. The mains lead is particularly important but in this case it is essential to ensure that any components used are suitable for operation at mains voltages.

Mild cases of leakage can be cured by the use of ferrite chokes on the leads which are giving trouble. This will usually be the mains lead, and the techniques are similar to those discussed in connection with breakthrough in Chapter 5. Severe leakage indicates a fault condition. Check for defective decoupling and filtering, and that internal screens have not been damaged or possibly left out altogether.

Before concluding that an interference problem is due to direct leakage, check by running the transmitter into a dummy load (if the interference persists then the problem is leakage). Nowadays it is much more likely that effects which appear to be due to direct leakage are in fact due to general poor radio housekeeping, causing the transmitter to be 'hot' to RF

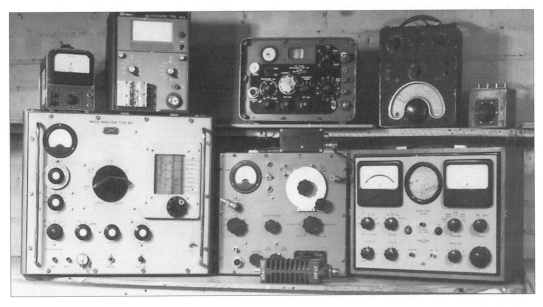

and giving the superficial impression of transmitter leakage. This is dealt with in more detail in Chapter 3.

PART 2 – TESTING AND TEST EQUIPMENT
Detecting and measuring spurious emissions

This depends very much on the test equipment at the amateur's disposal, which can vary from almost nothing through to a fully equipped radio workshop. For many amateurs the main interest is operating, with engineering activities confined to masts and antennas. In such cases it is possible to get by with a minimum of test equipment. This means that reliance must be placed on using a transmitter of known good specification and operating it with due care. If there is any doubt about the levels of harmonics (or other spurious emissions) then a suitable filter should be used (Chapter 4). In particular, take note of any bad signal reports which could indicate that all is not well.

Before looking at test equipment for the amateur whose interest is experimenting and homebrewing, it is appropriate to consider a test procedure which is available to all amateurs, and which is no more than a formalised version of a typical signal report. To distinguish it from a casual report which can often leave much to be desired, this procedure has been called an *organised signal test*.

The organised signal test

The best approach is to call on the services of an experienced local amateur who can receive your signals at the S9 + 10dB level or greater. If there is no one living close enough, it is possible to set up a receiver a reasonable distance away (a few hundred metres would do) but this is obviously not so convenient. Where practical, it is better to set up a communication channel separate from the receiver or transceiver being used for the test. Two

Photo 6.1. Some vintage test equipment in an amateur workshop. Top left to right: LF millivoltmeter (from a few hertz up to about 4MHz, 'sixties'); RF millivoltmeter (up to hundreds of megahertz, 'sixties'); signal generator (95kHz to 80MHz, early 'fifties'); switched attenuator (75Ω). Lower left to right: Wave analyser (30kHz to 30MHz, direct conversion with pre-mixer selectivity, late 'fifties, weight 23kg!); signal generator (100kHz to 80MHz, modified for digital readout, 'fifties); heterodyne voltmeter (superhet with 10.7MHz IF and no pre-mixer selectivity, late 'sixties). Centre front: power attenuator (nominal rating 50W). Beware – collecting old gear can be habit-forming!

VHF portable transceivers might be suitable for the link. The receiver used for the test must cover the frequencies of interest and must have good selectivity. In effect this means a good IF filter, and where VHF is concerned better results may be obtained by using an HF receiver and a converter. (The congested state of the HF bands dictates that a high-quality IF filter is a 'must' on a modern HF receiver.) The test should be arranged at a time of minimum band activity; on HF, find a time when the bands of main interest are closed for long-distance traffic. In general, this sort of test will not check harmonics or similar predictable spurious emissions which are a long way from the carrier; however, if a wide enough frequency range is available on the receiver (and a wide-band antenna is used), spurious emissions of this type can be revealed. This type of test is really intended to cover three important transmitter faults:

(a) serious instability, direct or parasitic, giving outputs on or near the operating frequency;
(b) transmitter faults and maladjustment, giving rise to splatter in SSB transmissions;
(c) key clicks on CW transmissions.

Carrying out the test

Arrange for the signal level at the receiving end to be as large as possible (at least S9 + 10dB) and then reduce it by adding attenuation at the receiver input, so that the final signal is no greater than about S9. This will ensure a noise-free signal but one which is not large enough to cause overloading. This latter point is most important: almost all the difficulties with this test come from excessive received signal so that receiver defects are mistaken for transmitter problems. The actual test procedure will depend on the experience of the receiving operator. The following notes are intended only as a guide for those who are unfamiliar with the technique.

When looking for instability, the suspect station should transmit on the appropriate mode while the receiving station tunes around as far as practical on both sides of the frequency. Problems will be revealed by odd, unstable-sounding signals coming and going in sympathy with the signal being tested.

When the problem is a (supposed) poor-quality SSB signal, the receiving station should tune very carefully about 100kHz on either side of the wanted signal. The signal should fall off sharply outside the normal SSB bandwidth and the intermodulation products which appear above and below the wanted signal should be much smaller than the signal itself. To get a feel for the situation, it may help to visualise the IF pass band as a 'box' being moved up and down the band as the receiver is tuned. The object is to see how much signal is in the box as it is moved to different frequencies either side of the wanted signal, as compared to the signal in the box when it is tuned right on the wanted signal. Where the finer points of signal quality are in question, experience is important; it is easy to confuse defects at the receiving end for problems at the transmitter. Fortunately, where a serious transmitter problem exists, it should not be difficult to identify. When AGC is in use the actual audible level is not very meaningful, and the S-meter should be used to give an indication of relative level, though it should be calibrated against a signal generator for accurate results. To get a subjective assessment the AGC should be switched off but, since the unwanted signals will be unintelligible, it may be difficult to compare levels by ear. Before being dogmatic about the quality of a signal, check signals from different sources to get the feel of what a good signal should be like.

Detecting key clicks is relatively unambiguous. Tune around the wanted signal to see if any clicks are audible at frequencies a few kilohertz away. There should be no significant clicks once the wanted signal is outside the pass band of the receiver's IF filter.

Acquiring and using test gear

Where equipment is to be designed and built at home, then the acquisition of test gear is a more important consideration and can become an interest in its own right. The wide diversity of activities is one of the great strengths of amateur radio but it makes it difficult to generalise as to what is desirable (from the EMC point of view) in the typical amateur workshop. The coming of computerised testing has released a large quantity of older test gear on to the market. Generally this requires more human involvement in setting up and making measurements but has the big advantage that it is likely to be easier to maintain. Modern processor-controlled equipment could be very difficult for the amateur to maintain, partly because of its complexity but also because special programmed devices may be very difficult to replace. If you intend to buy such equipment second-hand, make sure that it operates correctly on all its functions and avoid items offered as 'requiring attention' unless you are confident of your ability and have access to the necessary servicing information.

The following list and discussion is intended to generate ideas and to give a few hints to anyone who is intending to become involved in experimental homebrewing.

The spectrum analyser

This is the aristocrat of the radio test gear world. Anyone who has access to one will find it invaluable in all sorts of alignment work and, more importantly, it makes the detection and measurement of spurious emissions a relatively simple matter. Unfortunately commercial spectrum analysers are extremely expensive – way out of reach of the typical radio amateur – and it is unlikely that a cheap second-hand one will be discovered unless it is in very poor condition. Modern analysers are impressive instruments, enabling accurate measurements to be made with the minimum of human intervention, but for most amateur purposes such a level of sophistication is unnecessary.

It is quite practical to make a spectrum analyser which will give good service in the amateur workshop, with a reasonable expenditure of time and money. An article in *Radio Communication* by Roger Blackwell, G4PMK, describes the construction of a unit which converts an oscilloscope to a spectrum analyser [7]. This was reprinted as Appendix 2 in the previous edition of this book (*The Radio Amateur's Guide to EMC*), but has been

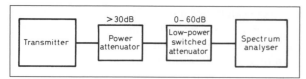

Fig 6.9. Connecting a spectrum analyser to a transmitter

removed from this edition as information is readily available in other RSGB publications including references [1] and [9]. There is certainly no better way of learning about radio measurements than by tackling such a project and finding out how to get the best out of the resulting instrument.

When making measurements on a transmitter output, the analyser is connected to the antenna socket via a suitable attenuator, as in Fig 6.9. It is most important that the correct attenuator is used – this is not just an academic point, as it is easy to do very expensive damage to the input circuit if too much RF power is fed into the analyser. Make it a rule always to use more attenuation than necessary to start with, and to remove it when the required level is established. The attenuator must of course be able to dissipate the full power of the transmitter. It is usual to use a high-power attenuator adjacent to the transmitter to absorb the power, and to use a low-power switched attenuator at the input to the analyser to give flexibility for different measurements.

A good rule to remember in connection with attenuators is that 30dB divides the power by 1000, so that you get 1mW out for every watt in, and a further 10dB divides by 10 so that 40dB would give 0.1mW and so on. Another rule to remember is to connect high-power attenuators the right way round – if you connect the output end to the transmitter, the low-power output resistors will almost certainly be burnt out. With low-power attenuators, either end will handle the small dissipation and it does not matter which way round they are connected.

The measuring receiver

Before the days of spectrum analysers, the standard method of measuring spurious emissions was to use some type of measuring receiver. This is simply a receiver (usually fairly insensitive by communication receiver standards) which can be tuned across the frequencies under investigation. The overall gain is adjusted by switched attenuators and the signal level displayed on a calibrated S-meter so that the strength of signals can be accurately measured. Receivers of this type are still used in field-strength investigations and, like all modern professional radio test equipment, are very expensive by amateur standards.

Vintage measuring receivers are sometimes to be seen on sale at rallies and surplus equipment sales and can be a good buy, but great care is needed because many instruments look as if they might be useful but may in fact be quite unsuitable. Ideally, a receiver should have plenty of selectivity before the mixer and switched attenuation in the front-end and in the IF stages. Some designs use direct conversion to audio frequency, and these can be very satisfactory – again provided there is adequate pre-mixer selectivity. The technical practice in the era when these old instruments were in vogue dictated sound construction and relatively simple circuits, so they are usually easy to repair and maintain. The sound construction also means that they are large and heavy. This is no problem if the instrument is purchased at a rally – there will almost certainly be a fellow enthusiast to give

a hand to carry it to the car park. Whether the same enthusiasm will be displayed when you arrive home with it is a different matter.

Generally a measuring receiver is used in the same way as a spectrum analyser, and in experienced hands is capable of very good results. The big difference is in the time it takes to look for spurious signals, which on a spectrum analyser are presented directly on a screen.

Sometimes one comes across instruments on the surplus market going under the name of *selective voltmeters* or *heterodyne voltmeters*. Generally these were designed with the intention of measuring (with a fair degree of accuracy) signals of known frequency, and often there is no selectivity in front of the mixer. This means that there will be a number of significant spurious responses generated in the instrument itself. These instruments are quite satisfactory for checking harmonics and known spurious emissions, but can be confusing if used to search for unexpected spurious signals.

In any situation where it is not clear whether a signal is coming from the transmitter or is a spurious response in the test receiver, the following check will help to resolve the doubt.

Tune in the spurious signal, and connect a tuneable band-pass filter between the attenuator and the input to the test receiver (where the notch filter is in Fig 6.11 – see later). If the spurious signal can be peaked up when the band-pass filter is tuned to the same frequency as the test receiver, the spurious signal is coming from the transmitter.

Where nothing else is available, an ordinary communications receiver can be pressed into service, provided the shortcomings are appreciated. The most important is that unless the receiver is very well screened and has a means of reducing RF and IF gain it may be impractical to connect it in the transmitter/attenuator arrangement of Fig 6.9. It is very difficult to reduce the leakage of RF energy from a high-power transmitter to a level where sensible measurements are possible. Things are much easier when dealing with QRP designs or where the low-power stages of a transmitter are being checked.

Photo 6.2. A measuring receiver from the late 'seventies, intended for measuring radio interference. The design follows traditional communications receiver practice, and has a calibration facility, a switchable attenuator and an output meter. The 1.75kHz IF is 9kHz wide and is available at a socket at the rear. The IF output from a receiver of this type was fed to a spectrum analyser to give the plot of Fig 7.14

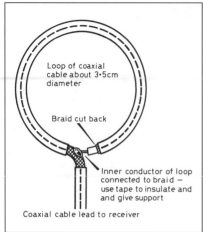

Loop of coaxial
cable about 3·5cm
diameter

Braid cut back

Inner conductor of loop
connected to braid –
use tape to insulate and
and give support

Coaxial cable lead to receiver

Fig 6.10. The screened loop

All receivers have spurious responses, and in general these become more troublesome as the signal level increases. The golden rule is to keep the level of the fundamental signal as low as possible, consistent with being able to detect the spurious signals that you are looking for. When a communication receiver is being used, the fundamental should not be greater than about –40dBm; on a typical HF receiver this will be in the region of S9 + 30dB. S-meters are notoriously inaccurate and should be calibrated against a signal generator (near the frequency of interest) before any credence can be given to the indications. (If no generator is available relative readings can be checked by using a fixed, steady signal, and switching in attenuators at the receiver input.)

Sometimes the only practical possibility is to operate the transmitter being tested into a dummy load and to arrange the receiver as far away as possible, with a metre or so of wire connected to the antenna input. Needless to say, this will only give the roughest indication of spurious emissions but, carried out carefully, is considerably better than nothing.

When looking for the source of unwanted oscillations, a screened loop formed out of a length of coaxial cable, as in Fig 6.10, will be found very useful. It is used with a suitable receiver (or a spectrum analyser if one is available) to find the region where the signal is strongest.

The tuned detector

This is really an improved version of the absorption wavemeter, and depends on a simple tuned circuit to give the required selectivity. Circuits have been devised to reduce the loading on the tuned circuit, and hence to increase the effective Q [8]. Even with such refinements, a simple tuned detector cannot distinguish between signals which are close together, especially if the one being detected is far smaller than an adjacent one, as is usually the case in transmitter tests.

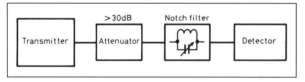

> 30dB   Notch filter

Transmitter — Attenuator — — Detector

Fig 6.11. Using a notch filter

The situation would be considerably improved if the level of the carrier could be reduced without affecting the signals we are trying to measure. This can be achieved, with certain limitations, by introducing a notch filter after the attenuator and before the detector. The general arrangements for using a notch filter are shown in Fig 6.11.

Tuneable notch and band-pass filters

Commercial tuneable filters can be quite complicated (and expensive) but the devices suggested here are about as simple as anything can be in the radio world.

The two types of filter shown in Figs 6.12(a) and 6.12(b) can be built in a few hours, and the cost will be negligible if a well-stocked junk box is available. The filters should be housed in metal boxes, large enough to allow the coil to be mounted at least one coil diameter away from the sides.

The components should be mounted so that the leads are as short as possible – particularly those to the coaxial connectors. The position and number of turns on the link windings of the band-pass filter is best found by experiment; a good number to start with is between one-fifth to one-tenth of the number on the main winding.

The notch filter is rather more of a design problem. It is easy to achieve a fairly deep notch but the important point is to avoid affecting harmonics or other frequencies of interest so far as possible. A good compromise is to arrange for the frequency of interest to tune with a value of capacitance which has a reactance of about 100Ω or so. That would be about 450pF at 3.5MHz or 225pF at 7MHz, and so on up to 56pF at 28MHz. It may seem surprising that a relatively low L to C ratio is used, with the consequent loss of circuit Q, but in this case it is necessary to ensure that away from resonance the reactance of the filter circuit is not too great.

A notch filter can be used with a spectrum analyser or a measuring receiver, and will effectively improve the dynamic range by 30dB or more. This will be particularly welcome in the case of a home-made analyser where the signal handling cannot be expected to match that of the expensive commercial units. It is important to remember that the notch filter will also reduce the level of signals which are fairly close to the carrier, and its use could give a false impression in such cases (Fig 6.13).

The band-pass filter can be used to select a signal for observation in the reverse process to the notch filter but because of the different configurations the selectivity is much less. If both filters are to be used together, then it may be convenient to use a 3dB attenuator pad between them to reduce interaction.

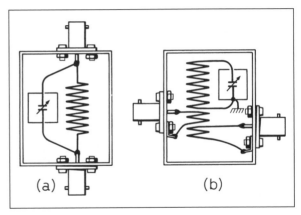

Fig 6.12. Two simple filters. (a) The notch filter. (b) The band-pass filter

Fig 6.13. (a) Frequency f_1 plus spurious. The analyser will be overloaded by f_1 if gain is increased. (b) Notch tuned to f_1. This reduces f_1 by about 40dB and also adjacent spurious signals to some extent. More remote spurious signals are very little affected. Analyser gain could now be increased without fear of overload to reveal spurious signals which would otherwise be undetected

A sensitive detector

Where signals are large, a simple diode detector and meter will suffice (Fig 6.14). In many instances, a much more sensitive instrument is required, and again the best source is second-hand test gear on sale at rallies and surplus equipment sales. Look out for 'RF millivoltmeters' or 'RF milliwattmeters' – not to be confused with the AF or LF equivalents which are unsuitable for radio frequencies. Sensitive RF millivoltmeters go down to about 1mV full scale, and many of the designs are based on the use of a balanced pair of germanium diodes, followed by a very

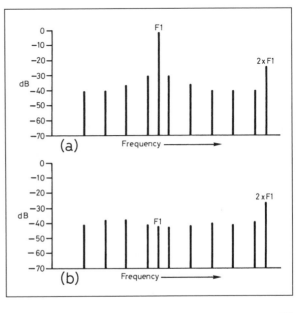

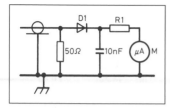

Fig 6.14. A simple detector. R1: select to suit meter. D1: silicon diode, eg 1N4148. M: sensitive meter, 50 or 100µA FSD

high-impedance amplifier. The detector/amplifier circuit incorporates range switching and linearising circuits to simplify the scaling of the meter, making quite a sophisticated instrument.

For the amateur who is prepared to use an external switched attenuator and a highly non-linear calibration curve, it is possible to make a sensitive detector using a pair of low-cost germanium diodes, such as OA47s, in a circuit like that of Fig 6.15(a). The operational amplifier must be a high-impedance, FET input type. The only other point to watch is the layout of the diode input circuit. The arrangement of Fig 6.15(b) is recommended. The detector and high-impedance amplifier circuit must be mounted in a metal box with supply leads and output leads (if an external meter is used) suitably decoupled. The attenuator may be a separate unit in its own screened housing, connected to the detector by coaxial cable.

It is important to note that the operation of the detector depends on the particular properties of germanium diodes, and modern silicon diodes are not suitable. A home-made detector of this type can be made to give sensitivities of about 10mV (about 2mW in 50Ω) full-scale deflection with reasonable repeatability, though the zero may need to be re-adjusted occasionally to allow for thermal drift.

A sensitive, untuned detector can be used to make a rough check on harmonics by seeing how much the detector reading is reduced when the notch filter is tuned to the carrier. If the reduction is not over 30dB then something is seriously wrong (Fig 6.11).

Attenuators

Fig 6.15. (a) A sensitive detector with range selection by switched attenuator. For component values, see Table 6.2. (b) Input circuit – use double-sided board

Low-power fixed attenuators are simple to construct, providing good RF practice is followed. Resistor values for attenuators will be found in Appendix 7. It is also quite practical to construct switched attenuators, and information will be found in several amateur publications [9]. In addition, surplus units are fairly common, though many of these will be 75Ω.

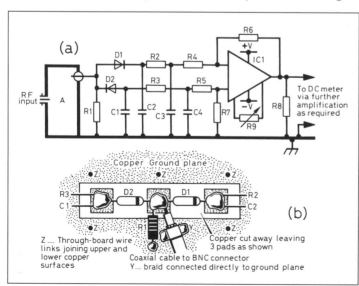

Table 6.2. Typical component values for Fig 6.15(a)	
R1	50R
R2, 3, 8	4k7
R4, 5	4M7
R6, 7	10M
R9	To suit IC1
C1–4	10n ceramic
D1, 2	Germanium diodes (eg OA47)
IC1	FET op-amp (eg TL071)
A	Switchable attenuator (may be separate unit connected by coaxial cable)

High-power attenuators are more of a problem, and it may be difficult to find a suitable one at a reasonable price.

One way round this is to make use of the dummy load which is (or should be) part of every amateur station – Fig 6.16 shows the general arrangement.

The dummy load forms the first resistor in a pi-attenuator, and R1 and R2 form the other two. Of course, it is impossible to achieve a perfect match because the input impedance will always be less than 50Ω, but in practice, if R1 is made fairly large, the effect is small. A

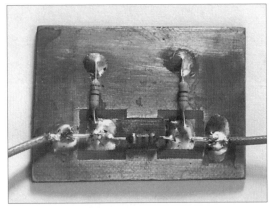

Photo 6.3. A home-made low-power attenuator. Two 'islands' are cut in the copper cladding to make pads. If PTFE-insulated coaxial cable is available, soldering to the copper is easy

typical value for R1 might be 470Ω, with 56Ω for R2. The two resistors can conveniently be mounted in a small metal box with coaxial connectors at either end. Suitable boxes can be found in electronic component suppliers' catalogues.

R1 must be high wattage (roughly one-tenth of the transmitter power in the present example), and it may be convenient to use several resistors in series/parallel. R2 need only be about one-tenth of the wattage of R1, so a

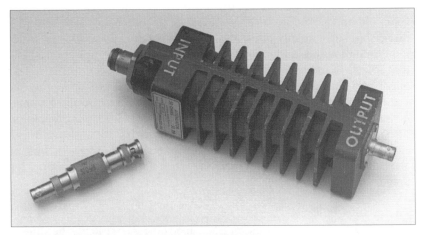

Photo 6.4. High-power attenuator (50W, more for short periods) and low-power attenuator (less than 1W). Note the input/output markings on the high-power unit

Photo 6.5. Using a dummy load as an attenuator (cover removed to show attenuation resistors). Series resistors are each 220Ω, 2.5W. Shunt resistors are 100Ω and 130Ω in parallel (¼W). Attenuation is 25dB (approx). Will handle up to about 30W and more for short periods. Note that the series resistors will get very hot if the unit is used continuously at powers of more than 10W

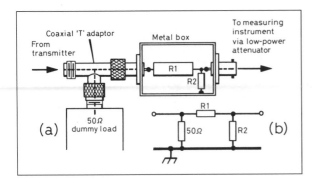

(a)

(b)

Fig 6.16. (a) The dummy load attenuator. (b) Circuit

1W resistor will cover most requirements. Both R1 and R2 must be suitable for RF use, which in effect means that they must not be wire-wound and the leads must be kept as short as possible.

If high powers are involved, pay particular attention to the construction to ensure that there is adequate clearance to avoid flash-over etc.

The attenuation of the unit shown in the figure will be about 25dB, and in most cases it would be followed by a low-power attenuator connected to the output side.

The signal generator

This is not specifically an instrument for EMC investigations but is essential for calibration and comparison purposes. Signal generators can be home built, and are a very good project for anyone who enjoys the challenge of careful construction. Alternatively there are a large number of generators on the surplus market, ranging from older units dating back to the 'fifties and 'sixties at very reasonable prices, to equipment which is only a few years old and priced accordingly. Most of the older units are of simple design but substantially built, and still capable of good service provided their limitations are understood. In many cases the RF output will be 75Ω (not 50Ω as in modern generators) but in practice this is unlikely to be a major problem in amateur use. It is uncommon to find FM on very old signal generators, though most of them suffer to some extent from incidental FM when the AM facility is in use. Most vintage signal generators use simple valve oscillators which tend to drift as the unit heats up. This is true of a lot of valve equipment, and can be counteracted by switching on about half an hour or so before starting work so that the temperature has time to stabilise.

The oscilloscope

Again this is not specifically an EMC instrument, but it has become so much a part of the electronics scene that no workshop should be without one. The popularity of the oscilloscope has the advantage that reasonably priced models intended for the non-professional user are available in the electronic suppliers' catalogues. On the other hand, it also means that the chance of picking up a bargain on the surplus market is limited. There are some quite good old oscilloscopes from the valve era to be found on the second-hand market at very low prices but, generally speaking, they are large and heavy. They are only likely to recommend themselves to the amateur who has plenty of space – not to mention some strong friends and a tolerant spouse!

When considering an oscilloscope, look for the maximum frequency which can be displayed. Expensive modern instruments go up to hundreds of megahertz, but a few tens of megahertz is more likely for one in range of the amateur pocket. Some oscilloscopes have a direct input to the 'y' plates and this is a useful feature which permits operation up to much higher frequencies than would be possible through the amplifier, provided a signal of large enough amplitude is available.

An oscilloscope is invaluable for checking the modulation and keying waveform of transmitters [10], and for fault finding on audio and digital circuits.

Precautions in the amateur workshop

Apart from the usual application of common sense required in any do-it-yourself workshop activity, there are a few safety points which are specific to the overhaul of test equipment.

(a) When working on an equipment using valves, remember the high-voltage supplies. If you are not used to valves don't be put off, but DO be very careful. Be very wary indeed of anything with a cathode ray tube – all CRT supplies are dangerous, but some old designs with mains-derived EHT (extra high tension) supplies are positively lethal!

(b) Make sure you always stand on a good insulating surface – not directly on a concrete floor. Avoid shocks between your hands: there is an old saying about keeping one hand in your pocket when working on live equipment [11].

(c) Don't do anything on live equipment except essential measurements, and always use well-insulated probes.

(d) Before plugging a new acquisition into the mains, check the mains plug and power supply wiring, and fit a low-rated mains fuse. Have a look at the condition of any electrolytic capacitors in the power supply. If they are obviously past their best, it may be worth replacing them before going any further. (It is not unknown for electrolytic capacitors to explode, shooting out unpleasant debris with considerable force that could cause injury – particularly to eyes.)

(e) Some older pieces of test gear have the mains supply connected by detachable metal cased connectors which could become live if the wiring is faulty; ideally these should be replaced with a modern connector or a fixed mains lead.

(f) Check and double check that equipment is disconnected from the mains before carrying out any repairs – this may sound trivial, but it is all too easy to make a mistake in the heat of the faultfinding battle.

(g) Beware of toxic substances. Many of the substances previously used in transformers and capacitors are now known to be highly toxic. Avoid contact with any leaking oils and waxes (use disposable gloves) and dispose of the components and cleaning materials sensibly [12]. A more modern hazard is beryllia (beryllium oxide). This is used in RF power transistors and occasionally in high-power RF attenuators because it is an insulator with an excellent thermal conductivity. Beryllia is a ceramic material which is safe in normal use but very toxic indeed in powder form. Be very wary of anything that looks like broken ceramic and on no account try to saw or file it.

REFERENCES

[1] *Radio Communication Handbook,* ed D Biddulph, G8DPS, 6th edn, RSGB, 1994.

[2] 'FET dip oscillator for 1.6 to 215MHz', A L Bailey, *Radio Communication* November 1981.

[3] *VHF/UHF Manual,* 4th edn, ed G R Jessop, G6JP, RSGB, 1983, Chapter 5.

[4] 'Direct digital synthesis', P H Saul, *Radio Communication* December 1990.

[5] 'Technical Topics', *Radio Communication* April 1983.

[6] 'Combination RF wattmeter and parasitic detector', F Brown, *Radio Communication* April 1983.

[7] 'Simple Spectrum Analyser', R Blackwell, *Radio Communication* November 1989.

[8] 'A simple and sensitive field strength meter', J M Noeding, *Radio Communication* September 1981.

[9] *Test Equipment for the Radio Amateur,* Clive Smith, G4FZH, 3rd edn, RSGB.

[10] 'In Practice', *Radio Communication* December 1994.

[11] 'Technical Topics', *Radio Communication* January 1985.

[12] 'Technical Topics', *Radio Communication* October 1984.

SUMMARY

Predictable spurious emissions
Harmonics
These are multiples of the carrier frequency and are generated by non-linear amplification in the power amplifier or driver stages. Where harmonic generation is causing a problem and the transmitter seems to be operating correctly otherwise, a low-pass filter should be fitted at the output (Fig 4.14).

Spurious emissions caused by the process of carrier generation
If a transmitter suddenly starts to produce excessive spurious emissions, try to find out the frequency or frequencies, and then work out which stage is likely to be producing them. When the stage has been identified, check for:

(a) faults in the filtering, particularly for common ground (0V) impedance, linking input and output;

(b) faults in decoupling circuits;

(c) loose or damaged screening;

(d) faults causing distorted inputs to a mixer;

(e) faults in a mixer circuit itself, particularly where a double-balanced mixer may be operating incorrectly;

(f) tuned circuit filters not tuning correctly.

When aligning a vintage transmitter using the oscillator multiplier technique, be careful not to tune any of the stages to the wrong multiple. This could lead to the transmitter operating on entirely the wrong frequency.

Spurious emissions caused by incorrect transmitter operation
Over-driving an SSB transmitter
This is usually called *splatter* and is caused by non-linear amplification of the SSB RF signal. The most likely stage to be affected is the power amplifier, particularly if an external linear amplifier is used.

The effect is that the transmission seems to be broad with unintelligible signals on either side. In the absence of a spectrum analyser, the best way to check is to arrange an organised signal test. The general procedure at the receiving end is as follows.

(a) Arrange receiving antenna conditions so that the signal reaching the receiver is no greater than about S9 – so that there is no chance of receiver overload confusing the report.

(b) Listen carefully to the transmission, tuning on either side of the nominal signal frequency. The signal should fall off very sharply outside the normal speech frequency band. If in doubt as to what to expect, listen to other SSB signals to get the feel of what can be expected from a good transmission.

Avoid splatter by:

(a) ensuring that the automatic level control (ALC) circuits in the transceiver are operating correctly, and that the meter readings are all normal;

(b) keeping the 'mic gain' to a reasonable level, especially if a new microphone is being tried;

(c) checking carefully after making any modifications to signal-processing circuits;

(d) when a linear amplifier is in use, making sure that it is driven at the correct level. This is particularly important on field days and similar activities where operators may be unfamiliar with the equipment.

Key clicks
These are caused by switching the transmitter on and off too sharply, generating clicks that can be heard many kilohertz away from the nominal frequency. As

SUMMARY *(continued)*

with splatter, the best test is to get a report from an experienced amateur. The procedure is pretty much the same, except that the object now is to search for key clicks either side of the nominal frequency.

Unpredictable spurious emissions
Direct instability

This is when an amplifying stage in a transmitter oscillates at, or near, its normal operating frequency. This type of instability shows itself by the presence of RF output when the carrier control is turned to minimum, or more likely by erratic rise of output as the carrier control is advanced. Often the output does not fall as the carrier control is reduced from a high to a low level.

Sometimes a stage will go unstable as the load is changed. For instance, a power amplifier may go unstable when the ATU is adjusted. In general, any erratic behaviour of the RF output should be considered as a possible symptom of instability.

If instability is suspected, check by using a spectrum analyser or a suitable receiver. If an ordinary communications receiver is used, locate it as far away as practical to avoid overloading, and search as widely as possible on either side of the nominal frequency.

Avoid instability by:

(a) following good RF practice when constructing transmitters;

(b) paying particular attention to decoupling and earth return paths;

(c) making sure that screens are really effective. In second-hand equipment check that screens have not been left out or replaced with half the screws missing.

Parasitic oscillations ('parasitics')

These are oscillations which can take place in any part of a transmitter, and can be on any frequency from audio to VHF. Parasitics are due to unintentional feedback causing an amplifier to oscillate at some frequency which is determined by accidental resonances. Low-frequency parasitics (and their harmonics) beat with the carrier to give spurious outputs either side of the transmitted signal. High-frequency ones beat with the carrier and its harmonics to give a large number of spurious outputs.

Parasitics can be detected using an analyser or a receiver in the same way as for direct instability.

Parasitic oscillations can occur in any circuit which has gain; modern integrated circuits are particularly prone to unexpected RF oscillation if not correctly used.

Avoid parasitics by:

(a) using good RF technique with proper attention to ground planes etc;

(b) decoupling amplifiers for all frequencies – not just the range the circuit is intended to operate on;

(c) taking care when replacing RF power transistors, particularly if 'near equivalents' are being used;

(d) fitting 'parasitic stoppers' as called for in manufacturers' data and in the design information in amateur radio handbooks.

7 Interference to amateur reception

PART 1 – DEALING WITH INTERFERENCE AT SOURCE

There is not much doubt that interference to reception will become the most important problem in amateur radio in the coming years. In fact it is probably not too much of an exaggeration to say that it is going to be the major factor in the survival of amateur radio as an activity that can be pursued in a normal residential environment. The new emission regulations will give some protection but, as discussed in Chapter 3, they are not stringent enough to prevent interference to amateur reception.

RSGB leaflet *Interference to Amateur Radio Reception* (EMC 04) contains information on identifying sources of interference. Some notes taken from this will be found in Chapter 4, Part 2.

In general, interference to reception falls into two categories. The first is simply the overcrowding of the radio spectrum, about which amateurs can do little except to urge the use of good operating practice, coupled with good receiver design [1]. The second is incidental local interference, caused by the proliferation of electrical and electronic equipment. This has been called 'incidental' because it is not caused by a specific communication signal but is generated as a by-product of some other electrical activity. A great deal can be done to alleviate this type of interference, and the causes and remedies form the subject of this chapter. Unless the contrary is indicated, the term 'interference' is used here to refer to incidental interference.

Interference or static?

For many years the main source of incidental radio interference was impulses of electromagnetic energy caused by rapid discharges at sparking contacts, such as motor commutators or the ignition circuits of motor vehicles. Such discharges were often called *man-made static* because of their similarity to natural static electrical discharges of thunderstorms etc.

More recently, the simple classification has been blurred by the fact that many sources involve electronic switching which has characteristics of both impulse and continuous-wave interference. The modern trend is to refer to all such activity simply as *radio frequency interference* (RFI) or sometimes as *man-made noise*.

Fundamentals

As with any other type of radiation, the emission of interference involves the acceleration of electric charges. Basically, the important factors are the number of charges and how fast they move or, in radio terms, the magnitude and rate of change of current.

The rate at which this energy is released can vary from a short burst of energy from a switched circuit to the continuous output from an oscillator. As a general rule, short impulses generate interference over a wide bandwidth, while the nearer a source approaches a continuous oscillation, the narrower becomes the bandwidth. Underlying this is a fundamental principle which ties together the duration of signals and their bandwidth – in effect you cannot have short pulses and narrow bandwidth.

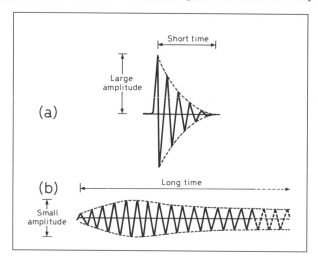

(a)

(b)

Fig 7.1. (a) Transient energy released in a circuit with a low *Q*. (b) Response of a high-*Q* circuit to a short RF pulse. Amplitude builds up and decays relatively slowly

The rapid release of energy

This occurs when the current in a circuit is switched, either by a mechanical switch or by some form of electronic device, and is usually known as *impulsive interference*. The radiating circuit will consist of the leads associated with the switched circuit and any other wiring which may be capacitively or inductively coupled to it.

A circuit that has been shocked into oscillation will oscillate with an amplitude which decays exponentially and will have fallen to a negligible value after a time equal to about 2*Q* cycles.

When a short-duration signal arrives at a narrow-band circuit, such as the IF of a receiver, the short burst of energy is converted into a smaller-amplitude signal spread over a relatively long time (Fig 7.1).

The continuous release of energy

This is where an oscillation is maintained by a supply of external energy – as in almost any oscillator used in radio work. In an ideal case the bandwidth of the oscillation will be negligibly small.

Nowadays the most common sources of interference are digital devices such as computers or games machines, and these almost always involve a clock oscillator of some sort. The oscillator itself will be a narrow-band source (or rather a series of narrow-band sources, since harmonics will be present), but this will be mixed with a large number of signals generated by switching transients in the myriads of gates in the processor and the input/output circuitry. The result is a broad-band mess, which has the characteristics of transients and of continuous signals, and almost anything in between.

Continuous high-speed data signals can give rise to a pseudo-random spectrum which sounds similar to white noise at the receiver. This may become a greater problem in the future as the use of high-speed digital links over long cable runs becomes more common. This is considered in more detail later in the chapter.

Transferring the energy

The generation of interference is only half the story; equally important is the path by which it arrives at the receiver. The mechanisms by which interference gets out of a piece of equipment are very similar to those by which breakthrough gets in. This is not surprising since the same basic rules of physics apply. There are two ways that interference can find its way out.

(a) *By direct radiation from the point where it is generated.* Generally the conductors inside the offending equipment are short and do not make very good radiators except where the frequency is relatively high – a wire has to be a significant proportion of a wavelength to make an effective antenna. This means that directly radiated interference is usually more troublesome at frequencies above 30MHz.

(b) *By conduction.* Interference can be conducted to the outside world through any leads which are connected to the equipment. Once outside, the interfering signals can either be radiated or may be carried for considerable distances along the wire. In this case, it is not just a simple case of conduction along a wire; usually the fields are confined between the conductor and earth, forming a crude transmission line. A transmission line of this type will radiate a good deal of the energy supplied to it, so that both conduction and radiation are taking place at the same time. It is possible for interference to be carried out through the mains supply by the live and neutral conductor acting as a transmission line. It is more usual, however, for the signal to travel as a common-mode signal, treating the live and neutral as if they were one conductor and using earth as the return path. It is also possible for interference to be propagated as a common-mode signal using all three mains wires (live, neutral and earth) as one conductor and the true earth as the return path.

When considering how radiation takes place from leads coming from the equipment, it is important to remember that the electric charges don't just appear from nowhere. The energy causes the charges to move from one place to another and back again. Very often the two places are an external lead and the capacitance of the equipment to earth. The lead is then acting as a very crude earthed antenna.

Dealing with interference

In most cases it is possible to prevent interference being generated but usually this will involve some modification or additions to the offending equipment. To avoid constantly repeating dire warnings about the risks of modifying equipment, particularly if it belongs to other people, it will be assumed that two general rules are taken for granted.

1. Don't carry out internal modifications to anything unless you know what you're doing – particularly where safety is concerned. Always play safe.
2. Never attempt internal modifications on equipment which is not your own. Where external modifications such as connecting filters are required, they should be carried out by the owner – helped where necessary by the amateur.

Impulsive interference

Where mechanical contacts are concerned, there are a number of well-tried remedies based on the principle of absorbing the energy which would otherwise be released when the contact is broken. The energy is initially stored in the magnetic field, due to the normal operating current flowing in any inductance which may be present in the circuit, and in many cases this will be considerable. When the contact is broken, the magnetic field collapses and a large voltage appears for a short period as the contacts open, causing a spark. RF currents are exchanged between the inductance and capacitance in the vicinity of the contact, using the ionised air of the spark as a bridge.

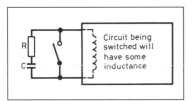

Fig 7.2. A resistor and capacitor used to absorb the energy released when contact is broken

The traditional way of absorbing the energy is to connect a resistor and capacitor across the contacts as in Fig 7.2. This effectively 'quenches' the spark by dissipating the unwanted energy in the resistor; there is an added advantage of reduced contact wear. The capacitor should be between 0.01 and 0.1µF, and the voltage rating must be several times the voltage being switched. Special capacitors rated for use on AC mains are available, and these must always be used where mains voltages are involved. Devices containing a resistor and capacitor in one encapsulated unit can be purchased from component suppliers. Another approach is to use a semiconductor surge-suppression diode or voltage-dependent resistor. It is most important to use the correct type of device and to follow the advice in the manufacturer's data sheet.

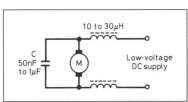

Fig 7.3. Suppressing a small low-voltage DC motor

Small, low-voltage, DC motors can be suppressed by using a shunt capacitor of between 0.05 and 1µF and series ferrite-cored chokes of 10 to 30mH, as in Fig 7.3. The chokes are more effective at higher frequencies, and may not be required if only low frequencies are involved. Mains motors are best dealt with by using one of the many mains filters which are available in the suppliers' catalogues. This should be installed as close to the machine as practical.

A very nasty form of impulse interference can be generated at unintentional spark gaps caused by bad connections or by insulation breaking down. The actual mechanism in any particular case is likely to be complicated by the unknown variables which are part and parcel of EMC investigations. A brief diversion into history will highlight the principle.

Fig 7.4. A spark transmitter converts low-frequency energy to RF energy

The spark transmitter (Fig 7.4) operated by converting energy stored in a low-frequency inductance into RF energy. The AC power usually came from a generator at a frequency of about 500Hz, and the effective inductance of inductor L1 and transformer T1 would be more or less resonant with capacitor C1, depending on the design requirements. When the low-frequency energy across C1 reached a sufficient voltage in each cycle, the spark gap would break down, and the energy stored in C1 would then oscillate in the RF circuit, C1 and L2. The oscillatory energy would be coupled to the antenna in the usual way. The similarity to interference

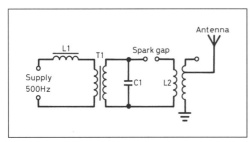

generated by sparking at power transformers or other inductive circuits is obvious. The solution is to correct the fault causing the sparking, though in many cases all the amateur can do is to track down the source and report the problem to the appropriate authority. A similar situation occurs in the cyclic release of short bursts of energy in thyristor control circuits, but in this case the remedy is to fit a suppressor. Suitable devices are readily available from component suppliers, and the correct type should always be used – this is not an area for making do with doubtful components.

Interference from electronic equipment

In most cases it is relatively easy to reduce the leakage of interference from a piece of apparatus at the design stage – it is really a matter of good engineering practice. Good decoupling and the provision of a substantial ground plane for the common 0V rail is a good start. The object is to prevent external leads having energy coupled into them from shared return paths, and so acting as antennas (Fig 7.5). Ideally, interference-generating circuits should be completely screened. The screen should be connected to the common 0V point through a path which has the lowest possible impedance. All leads should be decoupled where they pass out through the screen.

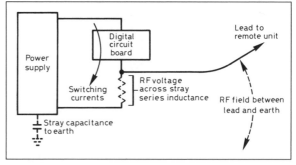

In situations where interference reduction is a major factor, for instance where digital control circuits are actually part of the receiver, special attention should be paid to screening and feedthrough capacitors should be used on all leads. (It is important to choose the correct value – too large a capacitance will distort fast digital signals.) So far as possible, the screen should be continuous and where there are any joints there must be good electrical contact along the mating surfaces. Unfortunately most interference to amateur reception is from equipment which is already installed and remedial action is likely to be limited to simple measures to improve matters outside the equipment.

Fig 7.5. External lead, nominally at 0V, acting as unwanted antenna

The emissions which trouble radio amateurs most are those generated by fast switching operations. Emissions from narrow-band sources such as oscillators are a nuisance but if they only occur on a single specific frequency they are at least tolerable. Very-low-frequency sources, rich in harmonics, can be a much more serious problem.

A good example is TV time-base noise where the situation is made worse by the fact that there is a large amount of energy involved. An interference source which has come on the scene more recently is the *switch-mode power supply* (SMPS). Again, large amounts of energy are involved and EMC is a major design factor. Emissions from such sources can extend up to 30MHz and above.

A substantial part of the emissions from this type of source takes place via the leads attached to the equipment, and common-mode choke techniques described below will usually reduce emissions in the HF bands. One of the problems is achieving sufficient choking effect, particularly at lower frequencies. Switch-mode power supplies are very efficient and much smaller and lighter than conventional supplies. They are widely used in TV sets and other household equipment.

Common-mode and differential mode interference

Common-mode and differential currents were mentioned in Chapter 5 in connection with breakthrough. Fig 5.8 shows the two modes. In a similar way, emissions from a lead can be due to either of the two modes or a combination of both. Common-mode currents are the predominant cause of interference in domestic situations. Differential-mode currents occur where there are large circulating currents which generate a voltage between two conductors or between a single conductor and its 0V return. Interference escaping by the mains leads often involves both differential and common-mode current, and proprietary mains filters usually attenuate both modes.

Differential-mode emissions on signal and control lines are fairly easy to attenuate at the design stage but tend to be difficult to deal with outside the equipment unless some form of plug-in filter can be devised. The principle is to drop the interference voltage existing between the wires without affecting the wanted signal. Where the interference frequencies are not widely different from the signal frequencies, this requires careful choice of component values.

When a pair of wires, very close, together carry differential signals, the field generated by the 'go' current in one wire is cancelled by the 'return' current in the other. The point about a balanced system is that the currents are identical. Any unbalance will cause the current to be greater in one wire than the other so that cancellation is not complete. The uncancelled portion of the current gives the effect of a current travelling along both wires in the same direction, as if the wires were one conductor, or in other words a common-mode current. Problems can arise where the interfering signal is fed directly into some other piece of equipment but more often the problem is radiation caused by the balance being degraded, either by an unbalanced load or because the wires themselves are not close together throughout their length.

The conductors for balanced transmission systems are often twisted together, as in the unscreened twisted pair (UTP) used for data links. If the twist or the disposition of the pair is not perfect, then the imperfectly balanced differential currents give rise to common-mode currents. This is known as *mode conversion*.

The quality of the line in this respect can be expressed as the ratio between balanced currents and common-mode currents which are generated by imperfections in the line. This is often called the *balance of the line* and expressed in decibels at a specific frequency. A typical figure for twisted pair might be 35dB at 10MHz.

There are several ways of looking at how unbalanced systems cause interference but it all comes down to the fact that any RF current in a conductor will radiate unless it is cancelled by an equal and opposite current in a conductor which is so close, in terms of a wavelength, that the two opposing fields effectively occupy the same space.

ains filters

ains filter can be very useful tools in the EMC moury. There are a large number of proprietary vices available, mainly advertised as preventing sturbances on the mains from entering computs and similar equipment, but they can be effec- /e against RF interference entering or leaving ra-

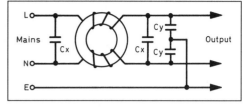

Fig 7.6. Mains filter with balanced inductor (the action of the coil is similar to a very large number of turns of two-core lead on a ferrite ring)

o equipment. Simple filters consist only of capacitors but more compli- ited devices include inductors, usually in a balanced arrangement as in g 7.6. Most filters do not include any inductance in the mains earth line it there are some more expensive ones which do. A number of devices so include semiconductor surge suppressors which serve to limit mains ɔikes.

It is not unusual for interference to appear on the mains lead as differen- al currents as well as the more usual common-mode situation. This is robably the commonest type of differential-mode problem in domestic quipment. When considering a mains filter, make sure that it contains omponents to suppress both differential and common-mode currents. ome mains filters are sold with a simplified circuit diagram, and if this ndicates that it contains an arrangement similar to Fig 7.6, then the filter vill probably give a reasonable degree of attenuation to both modes. The nductor usually consists of two independent windings wound on oppo- iite sides of a ferrite core. The windings are connected so that the fields cancel for the mains current, so that the core is not saturated by the supply current but provides an effective impedance to common-mode interfer- ence. The choke works in conjunction with the two capacitors to earth (Cy in Fig 7.6) to give common-mode attenuation while the capacitors Cx give differential-mode attenuation. The Cy capacitors are limited in size for safety reasons. Too large a value would give unacceptable leakage cur- rents to earth. The values of Cx are much larger, though in this case the effective series impedance of the filter is much less, consisting of the leak- age inductance of the choke plus any internal impedance of the source. Differential-mode currents tend to be more of a problem at lower frequen- cies in circuits where large currents are circulating, such as switch-mode power supplies. Mains filters are generally more effective at lower fre- quencies up to about 30MHz. If a mains filter is being considered as an interference reduction measure, it is worth trying a ferrite choke made by winding the mains lead on a ferrite ring as described elsewhere (Chapter 3, Fig 3.6, and in Chapter 5, Fig 5.5), before buying a mains filter. A ferrite choke of this sort has the advantage of reducing common-mode currents on all three conductors (live, neutral and earth). It may be more effective, particularly at higher frequencies, and will certainly be much cheaper.

Interference from digital installations

In the first edition of this book the computer installation was used as a way of focusing discussion of the causes and cures of interference from digital equipment and interconnecting leads. Since then, home computer installations have changed a great deal but a computer and peripheral units still make a good basis for discussion of RFI from a digital installation. A

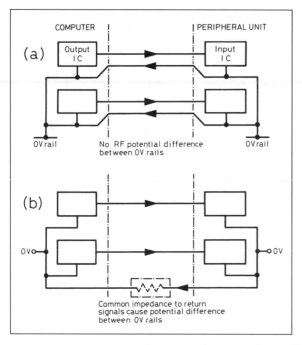

Fig 7.7. Common return impedance causes PD between computer and peripheral unit 0V rails. (a) Individual signal and return lines. (b) Only one return path

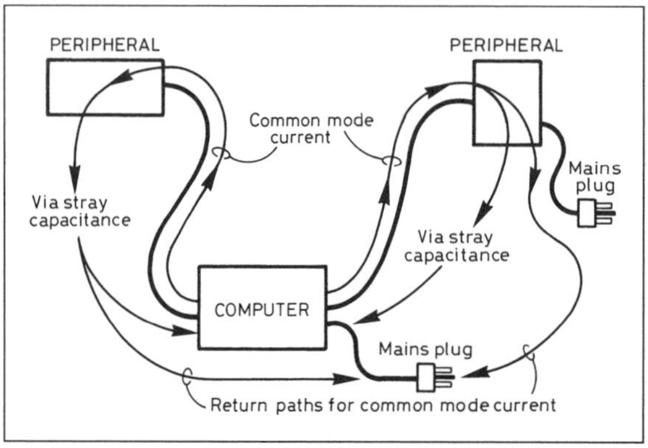

Fig 7.8. Common-mode current paths

more detailed discussion of the interference problems of PCs and how to deal with them will be found in Appendix 6 – 'Radio Frequency Interference from Computers' (taken from reference [2]).

At HF most interference is caused by the external leads acting as antennas. These antennas are energised by interference voltages developed across common impedances, generally along the lines illustrated (rather simplisticly) in Fig 7.5. There are a number of variants of this theme, and it is not too much of an exaggeration to say that most interference problems stem from poor 0V rail/grounding practice (in this context the terms '0V rail' and 'ground' have the same meaning).

When data signals are passed to a remote part of an installation, the current will go out from the computer on one wire and come back on another. If the wire going out and the one coming back are very close together, as in a twisted pair, the fields due to the outgoing current and the return current almost cancel. As seen from outside, the pair of wires appears to carry negligible current and radiation is minimal. It is good practice to arrange for the signal and return wires in a ribbon cable to be adjacent to one another; this is not ideal but does give a reasonable degree of field cancellation.

Where several signals share a common 0V return, the impedance of the wire will be common to all the return currents, and the potential across this impedance will cause the 0V rail of the peripheral unit to be at a different potential from that of the computer. Not only are the signal and return currents not properly cancelled but, more importantly, interference is injected into the 0V system (Fig 7.7).

The overall effect is that residual (common-mode) currents flow from the computer to the peripheral and then return via any available path. This could be the mains or any stray wiring which may be capacitively coupled to either unit. These currents wandering all over the place will, of course, radiate interference (Fig 7.8).

Ferrite common-mode chokes

The simplest approach is to increase the impedance to common-mode currents by using ferrite chokes, in exactly the same way as described in Chapter 5 for dealing with breakthrough. When looking at breakthrough it was convenient to look at the choke as forming the series element of a potential divider; in the present case it is easier to think of the choke raising the impedance of the path, so that the common-mode current is reduced (Fig 7.9).

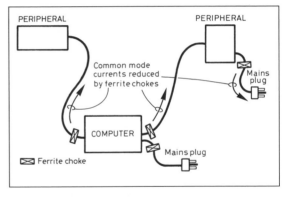

In many installations the cables will be unsuitable for winding on to ferrite rings. Clamp-up ferrite cores or ferrite rods are a possibility. It is possible to purchase special clamp-on ferrite devices for ribbon cable, but at most amateur radio frequencies their effectiveness is limited. To achieve a reason-

Fig 7.9. Reducing common-mode currents using ferrite chokes

able degree of attenuation, the cable must form several turns on the core. The inductance is directly proportional to the length of ferrite through which the wire passes, and proportional to the square of the number of turns.

This means that you get more attenuation by winding several turns on a relatively narrow ring than by using one turn on a thicker ring. (Every time the wire passes through the ring counts as one turn, so a ferrite ring simply slipped on to a wire counts as one turn.)

Screened leads

Where a screened lead is used to connect a peripheral to a computer, the screen has two functions. As might be expected, it does reduce radiation by forming an electrostatic screen around the conductors but, more importantly, it provides a low-impedance path back to the source for the common-mode currents which would otherwise leak back by devious routes.

Screened leads can be purchased for standard peripherals on a modern PC. They should have good-quality braid which is properly terminated at the connectors.

The important thing about screening is not so much the nature of the screen but where it is connected. It must be taken to a point which is as near as possible at true 0V potential at each end. Modern computers and peripherals have connector shells at 0V (ground) potential. In simpler equipment which has no external metalwork at ground potential and a two-core mains lead, it must be appreciated that the manufacturer did not anticipate 0V/ground connections being brought out from the case, and this will be reflected in the design of the mains power supply. Think carefully before attempting any modifications, and if in doubt seek expert advice.

Under no circumstances connect anything to the chassis/0V rail of equipment which is not isolated from the mains by a suitable double-wound transformer. In particular remember that domestic TV sets, still occasionally used as monitors, often have the chassis live to earth.

Before going to the trouble of fitting screening, try 'strapping' the 0V rails on the computer and the peripheral together with a short length of braid. If this reduces the interference then you are on the right track. Improvements may not be noticeable if other peripherals are still connected. They should be disconnected or similarly 'strapped'.

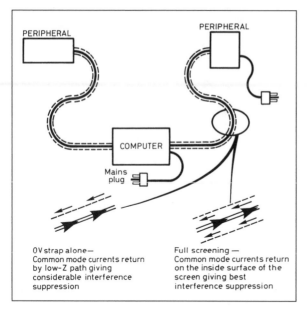

0V strap alone— Common mode currents return by low–Z path giving considerable interference suppression

Full screening — Common mode currents return on the inside surface of the screen giving best interference suppression

Fig 7.10. Confining common-mode current by 0V rail strapping and screening

In some cases 'strapping' may cure the problem but, if screening is required, there is a choice of using either special screening materials available from component suppliers or household aluminium cooking foil. The easiest way to make a contact with an aluminium screen is to include an uninsulated 'drain wire' inside the screen. In effect, wrap the screen over the cable, leaving the 'strap', which we have just been discussing, inside (Fig 7.10).

Screening the case

Some years ago, screening the case of a plastic-cased computer with spray-on conductive paint was a popular anti-interference measure. Improvements in computer EMC design have made this largely unnecessary, and it is not recommended for application to a modern computer. It may be practical for home-built equipment where a plastic case has been used though, if there is a choice, it would be better to start with a metal case and avoid the problem altogether. Before committing yourself consider the following.

(a) It is unlikely to effect a significant improvement unless the connections to peripherals have already been dealt with. The analogy about blocking up one hole in a colander has been used before, and applies very much in this situation.

(b) The unsatisfactory 0V conditions on the PCB of the equipment can cause RF voltages to be injected onto peripheral leads, even though the case may be otherwise adequately screened. RF currents flowing in the 0V track cause the two leads to be at different RF potential, as indicated in Fig 7.11, and therefore allow interference to be carried out of the enclosure.

Fig 7.11. Interference currents in the 0V track cause the 'ground' connections of the peripherals to be at different RF potential

(c) The screened case must be connected to the correct 0V point; ideally the ground plane of the circuit board. If this is not done, not only will the screening be ineffective, it may even make matters worse. The screen has a large area and can form quite an effective radiator of any interference which is accidentally fed to it (Fig 7.12).

Conductive spray paints are usually nickel based, and are available under various trade names. There are no difficulties in using the spray, providing the maker's instructions are followed, but it is most important to ensure that it only goes where you want it to – short-circuits could be very expensive. Some types of

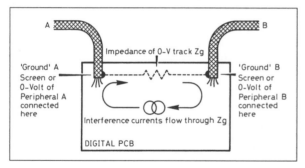

A

B

Impedance of 0-V track Zg

'Ground' A Screen or 0–Volt of Peripheral A connected here

'Ground' B Screen or 0–Volt of Peripheral B connected here

Interference currents flow through Zg

DIGITAL PCB

plastic may require special primers. If the spray leaves a shiny finish, make sure that the reflection of heat inside the case does not cause overheating. Don't be tempted to block up ventilation holes. It is important to remember that paints can flake off, with the consequent risk of causing serious damage.

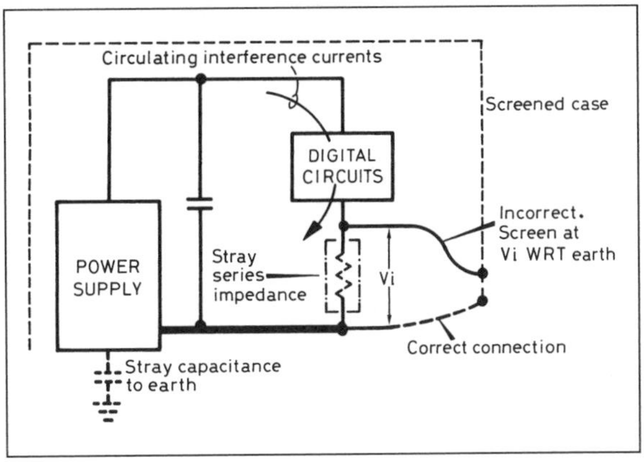

Connecting a computer installation to a transceiver

In this context the transceiver is just another peripheral unit and the underlying anti-interference procedures are the same.

(a) Try to arrange that all the 0V/ground rails of the various units are at the same RF potential. Where screened leads do not already do this, use short lengths of braid to link together convenient 0V points.

(b) Use ferrite chokes to minimise common-mode currents on inter-unit cables and mains leads.

Fig 7.12. Incorrect connection of screened case. Screen is at interference voltage V_i with respect to earth

In addition it is most important to make sure that all received signals come through the antenna feeder and are not getting in through stray paths in the station wiring.

Further information on computer RFI will be found in Appendix 6. In extreme cases it is possible to use the cancelling techniques discussed later to reduce interference generated by a computer controlling a transceiver. For the EMC investigator, though, this seems a bit defeatist – rather like a football club that avoids being beaten by getting a carpenter to board up the goal!

High-speed digital signals on unscreened twisted pair

The previous paragraphs have emphasised the importance of good screening. One area of digital engineering practice goes completely in the reverse direction. This is the use of unscreened twisted pair (UTP) as a transmission medium between the parts of a digital system. Bit rates up to 100 megabits per second have been used. The system relies on the fact that it is possible to get high-speed signals over a twisted pair provided one is prepared to design for a fairly high transmission loss. At the time of writing there have been few reports of interference from such systems but if they become widely used there could be a serious problem. Emissions from twisted pair will be mainly from common-mode currents caused by mode conversion as described above when discussing differential and common-mode currents. The magnitude of the common-mode current will depend on the balance of the source and load, and also upon the balance along the line.

Emissions from high speed data links are often very broad-band, and may be pseudo-random, giving the effect of white noise. The casual listener may simply think that he is hearing the noise floor, and that there are no signals about, when in fact the S-meter is reading S7 or more.

PART 2 – DEALING WITH INTERFERENCE AT THE RECEIVER

What can be expected?

At any receiving antenna there is always a background level of noise, natural and man-made, and at HF and low VHF this sets the limit to the detection of weak signals. The intensity of this noise varies with location, frequency and time of day; Fig 7.13 gives some idea of the range of noise levels that can be expected.

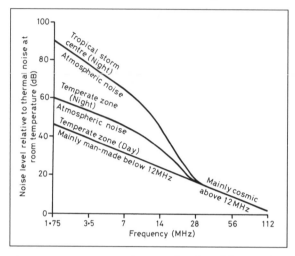

Fig 7.13. Typical background noise levels

At lower frequencies there is a marked difference between daylight and night-time conditions. This is simply a matter of different propagation conditions bringing man-made and natural noise from distant parts of the globe at different times. The natural noise comes from lightning discharges and similar phenomena, which are always taking place somewhere or other in the world. The majority of this interference is impulsive but, as frequencies rise above the HF band, the noise becomes more 'white' and is indistinguishable from front-end noise of the receiver. At these frequencies the noise comes mainly from space and is usually called *cosmic noise*. This becomes less as the frequency rises, until above about 100MHz the receiver noise starts to predominate, even with good, low-noise, front-end designs. In temperate zones the noise during the day on the lower HF bands is predominantly man-made, and in a typical location may be some 20 to 40dB above the thermal noise.

Any locally generated interference simply adds to this background noise which effectively sets the 'bottom line' of interference reduction. It is perhaps worth repeating the well-known fact that there is no point in designing an HF receiver with a noise figure of better than about 10dB, unless it is to be used with a very poor antenna. In all practical cases the external noise will predominate. If you are designing your own HF receiver it a good idea to consider trading off sensitivity for dynamic range; quite a lot of what seems to be interference on HF is actually due to intermodulation in the receiver [1].

The effect of noise

White noise is fairly well behaved in engineering terms, and calculation of noise levels and bandwidths are straightforward. The noise power is proportional to the bandwidth, so that the noise power doubles if the bandwidth is doubled. This is one reason why Morse code, which can be copied in a bandwidth of less than 100Hz, has an advantage over speech which requires a bandwidth of about 2.5kHz. The ratio 2.5kHz to 100Hz is equivalent to 14dB. (One of the most interesting things about CW is that a good operator is able to focus his (or her) attention on the signal, providing an excellent filter at no cost.)

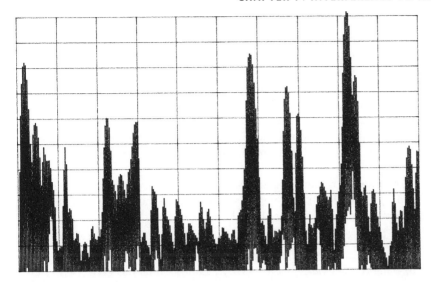

Fig 7.14. Plot taken in the 9kHz IF bandwidth of a measuring receiver tuned to 7.025MHz. Resolution bandwidth 100Hz; vertical scale 5dB/division; horizontal scale 1kHz/division. The bottom line of the graticule represents −15dBµV (−122dBm) at the receiver input. The antenna was an inverted-V dipole

If the spectrum of an active HF amateur band is examined, it will be seen to consist of a floor of noise similar to white noise and a number of peaks. Added to this, there are bursts of noise, many of which are relatively short in duration, occurring every few seconds. The peaks may be genuine signals or they may be intermodulation products or discrete emissions from interference sources. A typical example might be the 7MHz amateur band received on a dipole in a reasonably quiet suburban location around about midday. In an audio bandwidth, the floor of the noise might be in the region of −110dBm, with discrete peaks occurring every few hundred hertz across the band. To anyone listening on a receiver with a wide bandwidth, the general effect would be of a noisy band, and it might be assumed that a high level of RFI emissions on HF is tolerable because of the high ambient noise level. This is an incorrect picture, because signals with a narrow bandwidth, such as CW or other slow digital modes, can be picked out between the peaks. The short bursts of noise will not significantly affect the reading of signals, providing the correct techniques are used (sophisticated processing techniques in the case of computer-generated signals or lots of practice in the case of CW!).

Fig 7.14 illustrates HF amateur band conditions. The plot is taken from a spectrum analyser connected to the IF output of a measuring receiver tuned to 7.025MHz. The IF bandwidth of the receiver is the 9kHz CISPR bandwidth normally used for HF EMC measurements. This is displayed at 1kHz per division, with a resolution bandwidth of 100Hz. The plot was taken on a Sunday morning in a typical suburban location.

Planning a station for minimum interference

Interference reaches the receiver either by direct radiation or by a combination of conduction and radiation. The vicinity of any amateur station will be cluttered by electrical wiring such as mains supply, telephone or other utilities. There will also be unintentional conductors in the form of pipes or structural metalwork. This means that interference generated at any particular location is likely to travel at least part of the way by a path involving a conductor of some sort. As previously discussed, signals can travel considerable distances using electrical wiring as a transmission line. In effect the electromagnetic energy is propagated between the wire and earth, though the situation is so indeterminate that it would be unrewarding to attempt to analyse it in any depth. Depending on the conditions, the wiring will also radiate energy, effectively acting as as a grounded antenna. In engineering terms the situation is an untidy collection of unknown factors, but so far as the present problem is concerned the message is simple. Keep your receiving antennas as far away as possible from house wiring.

The rules for minimising interference are the same as for reducing breakthrough (Chapter 3), and the reasons are much the same. Good receiving antennas for the HF bands should be:

(a) horizontally polarised, as interference radiated from house wiring is predominantly vertically polarised;
(b) balanced because, just as poorly balanced antennas give rise to radiation from feeders, they will also allow signals to be picked up by the feeders;
(c) compact, so that neither end comes close to house wiring. Looking at Fig 3.1 (Chapter 3) from the receiving point of view, the electric charges, which are the interference currents flowing in the house wiring, induce equal but opposite charges in the end of the wire close to the house.

On VHF, conditions are different, because at these frequencies the background noise is becoming negligible. In this case the antenna should be as efficient as possible, and should be mounted as high as practical.

The similarity between transmitting and receiving antenna requirements is well known, and there is a general rule in radio engineering that good transmitting antennas make good receiving antennas. Like all good rules this has an exception, at least so far as HF receiving antennas in suburban gardens is concerned. The exception is due to the high level of background noise on the HF bands, which has no effect on transmission but is a very significant factor in reception.

Since on HF the minimum receivable signal is determined, not by the receiver sensitivity, but by the ratio between the background noise and the wanted signal, it follows that the efficiency of the antenna is not of primary importance. This means that for reception it may well be worth mounting a relatively inefficient antenna in a good location that gives minimum local interference pick-up.

The active antenna

This is a concept that has been around for some time but has only become really practical since the advent of modern semiconductor devices with good intermodulation performance. Active antennas can be either balanced or unbalanced but, where interference reduction is the aim rather than simply convenience, a dipole configuration is the best choice. Fig 7.15 shows the outline of an active dipole, along with the equivalent circuit. A typical length for the elements might be between 1 to 2m, which is short compared to a wavelength over the whole of the HF band, and very short indeed at frequencies such as 1.8MHz. By way of illustration, think of a dipole with elements 1m long operating on 10MHz. At this frequency, each element looks like a large capacitive reactance – in the region of 2kΩ – in series with a very small resistance. For the present purpose the resistance can be neglected. If the dipole were connected directly to a 75Ω feeder, nearly all the signal voltage would be dropped

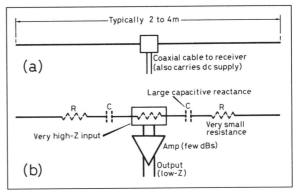

Fig 7.15. An active dipole and equivalent circuit

across the series capacitive reactance and only a very small fraction would appear across the feeder, and hence be fed to the receiver input. In the active antenna the elements are connected to active circuitry which presents a very high impedance to the elements. A second function of the circuit is to amplify the signal voltage developed across this high impedance and to match it to a low-impedance coaxial feeder.

If the active dipole with 1m elements is receiving signals on 10MHz, the actual signal voltage picked up will be considerably less than that which would be picked up by a full-length half-wave dipole – roughly about a fifth – but looking at the noise levels of Fig 7.14 shows that, in terms of practical signal to background noise, this will have hardly any effect. A dipole of this type is, of course, untuned and will operate satisfactorily over a very wide range of frequencies – typically from medium wave to above 30MHz.

The secret of the design of an active antenna lies in providing these functions without introducing intermodulation problems, and it is for this reason that active antennas tend to be rather 'thirsty'. Generally good intermodulation performance and high current consumption go together. It is quite practical to build a home-brew active antenna, but achieving the required performance can be tricky. It is advisable to use a published design, at least as a starting point.

There are a number of active antennas on the market but this is an area where it pays to be careful and to study the specification before committing yourself. The main thing to look for is sensibly quoted intermodulation figures – at least the second- and third-order intermodulation performance should be quoted. A review of a commercial active antenna suitable for amateur use will be found in reference [3].

The advantage of the active antenna is that it is compact, and so can be mounted high up and away from local interference sources. If it is to be used with a transceiver, it is essential to ensure that in no circumstances can the transmitted power find its way to the active antenna. This will involve some form of switching by relays or possibly PIN diodes, and great care is needed to ensure that it is fail-safe.

Interference which gets past the antenna

Before coming to the conclusion that the interference is being picked up in the antenna, check that it is not sneaking in through devious routes. The most obvious is interference coming into the receiver through the mains, possibly as a differential signal between live and neutral but more likely as a common-mode signal.

The usual check for mains-borne interference is to disconnect the antenna – preferably replacing it with a dummy load – and see if the interference goes away. It is possible for interference to find its way in by routes involving the antenna feeder (or other cables connected to the receiver) acting in conjunction with the mains. Because of this, a better check is to operate the receiver (or another one of similar sensitivity) from batteries and to see if the interference is still present. During the test all associated mains equipment should be disconnected. Many modern receivers or transceivers can be arranged to operate from battery supplies, so this test is much easier than it would have been a few years ago.

If interference is coming in through the mains, the solution is a commercially available mains filter or a home-made ferrite choke as described in Part 1. In some instances interference can be introduced into a receiver by a similar process to that by which it leaks out of a computer: using common-impedance paths. Examine the station layout and ensure that everything associated with the receiver has a common 0V system – in effect this means connecting everything to a common 'earth' point by the shortest possible leads.

Specific action against interference

When all the possible good radio housekeeping measures have been taken, there could still be an intolerable level of interference from some specific local cause. Let us suppose that there is nothing that can be done at the source and that the only course is to alleviate the interference at the receiving end. For this to be done it is necessary to exploit some difference between the unwanted and the wanted signals, so that one can be reduced without affecting the other too much. There are two possible differences to consider: the first is amplitude and the second is phase.

Noise limiters and blankers

Noise limiters have been around for decades (since well before the Second World War) but the blanker is more complex and has only become popular with the advent of modern semiconductor receivers. Both techniques are only suitable for alleviating certain types of interference: impulse signals of large amplitude and short duration, such as those from car ignition circuits or similar sources.

The limiter is simply a clipper circuit which chops off the large-amplitude signal at some reasonable level while letting the wanted signals through unaffected. In traditional designs the limiter comes after the IF amplifier and this inevitably reduces its effectiveness. By the time the large-amplitude impulse has reached this point it has already been through the IF filter and will have become smaller in amplitude and longer in duration, as in Fig 7.1.

The *noise blanker* also works on impulsive interference but in this case the large-amplitude, short-duration signal is picked off at an early stage in the amplifier chain before the narrow IF filters. Fig 7.16 shows the block

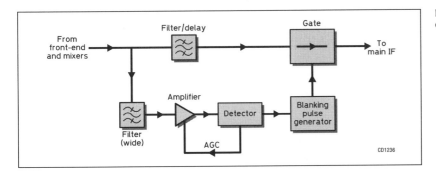

Fig 7.16. Block diagram of a noise blanker

diagram of a noise blanker. The signal from the front end and mixer circuits is split into two parts. The first part going through the filter/delay which provides some selectivity and also delays the signal by a small amount. This small delay allows for the time it takes for the second signal to pass through the filter, amplifier and detector, and to generate the blanking pulse, so that the gate is closed just as the interference spike arrives there. AGC is applied to the amplifier to enable the blanker to operate over a wide range of signal levels.

The noise blanker is very effective in certain circumstances but nevertheless suffers from a number of drawbacks. One of these is that the length of the blanking pulse is a compromise which is set by the designer to cover the most likely situations. It is assumed that the duration of the interference impulse is very short (because it has not been smeared out by the high-Q circuits of the IF amplifier) so the blanking pulse is made short enough for the effect on the wanted signal to be negligible. As a result, the blanker only works well with interference which consists of sharp spikes [4]. A more serious problem is that, in order to preserve the sharpness of the impulse which will generate the blanking pulse, the pulse generating circuits must operate in a relatively wide bandwidth. This means that large signals which are outside the pass band of the main IF come within the pass band of the blanker amplifier and reach the circuits which generate the blanking pulse. This can cause severe intermodulation effects. Many receivers have an adjustable noise blanker threshold which enables the threshold to be set to a level which optimises the blanking without giving intermodulation problems.

Interference cancelling

Cancelling is not so well known as limiting or blanking, which is surprising since it is a very powerful technique. It has two big advantages: first, it will work with any type of interference and, second, it does not require any modification to the receiver (or transceiver) itself. For amateur operation, interference cancelling is more common on the HF bands, though the same technique can be used at VHF.

The canceller works by utilising the difference in phase between the wanted signal and the interference. If two receiving antennas are set up some distance apart and the same signal is received on both, then the phase relationship between the currents in the two antennas will depend on the direction from which the signal comes (Fig 7.17(a)). If the two outputs from

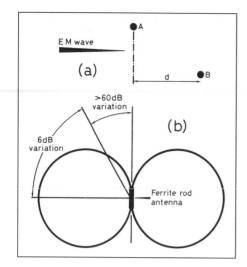

Fig 7.17. (a) An electro-magnetic wave arriving at two antennas. The signal at B will be delayed in phase by the time taken for the wave to traverse the distance d. (b) The response of a ferrite-rod antenna. The change of signal strength near the null is quite large. Away from the null the change is quite small

the antennas are adjusted to be exactly the same in amplitude and exactly 180° out of phase, then, if they are added together, they will cancel, leaving almost no residual signal. The key to a practical canceller lies in the word 'exactly'; if the phase and amplitudes are not just right, most of the cancelling effect is lost. This is very similar to the loop antenna, or the far more familiar ferrite rod antenna widely used for direction finding. The null is very sharp but away from the null the signal strength does not change much (Fig 7.17(b)). In practical amateur reception it is most unusual for two independent signals to have exactly the same null, even if they come from more or less the same direction – on HF most wanted signals arrive at the receiving antenna by a sky-wave path, while the majority of local interference comes along the ground.

In an interference canceller the gain and phase of the signals in the two antennas are adjusted, using two control knobs, until the interference is nulled out, leaving the wanted signal more or less unaffected. How much the wanted signal will be affected depends on the relative directions from which the two signals are coming and the distance between the two antennas [5]. As a rule of thumb, for interference coming from a fairly long way off (several wavelengths away), the antenna spacing should not be much less than one quarter-wave at the frequency of operation, though much smaller spacing can be used if some degradation of reception is acceptable. Where the interference source is much closer, the situation becomes very complicated, and it is simpler not to think in terms of antennas and nulls but of picking up interference to use as a cancelling signal.

The main difficulty in designing a canceller is achieving the required adjustment of phase and amplitude. The latter is a matter of amplification and/or attenuation, which is not too difficult in practice, but the phase adjustment requires some ingenuity. Phase can be varied by using tuned circuits and exploiting the fact that the phase of the circulating currents in a tuned circuit change, relative to the exciting signal, as the circuit is tuned across resonance. A more convenient method is to use an arrangement where a signal is split into two parts, one part being shifted in phase by 90° relative to the other part; the two parts are then recombined. By adjusting the amplitudes of the shifted and unshifted signals, it is possible to achieve any phase shift between zero and 90°. By inverting (changing by 180°) either or both signals, any required phase shift is possible.

A design for a canceller using this principle was described some years ago in *QST* by W1ETC [5]. This circuit illustrates the technique very well, and will form a good basis for experiments with cancelling. The block diagram and circuit are reproduced in Figs 7.18 and 7.19. The 90° phase shift is achieved by using a length of coaxial cable cut to be a quarter-wave at the frequency of interest – not forgetting to allow for the velocity factor of the cable. Fortunately, in practice there is a fair amount of latitude in the cable length so that it is possible to cover more than one band with a particular length. It may be wondered why the relatively high-power amplifiers are

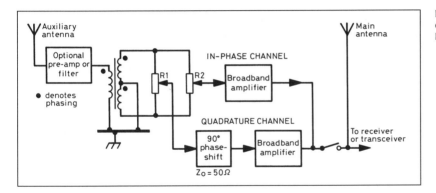

Fig 7.18. Block diagram of a canceller (*QST* October 1982)

used in a receiving circuit; this is an example of using high-power devices to minimise problems from intermodulation – as mentioned previously in connection with active antennas.

Where the requirement is to eliminate local interference, one of the antennas is usually the main station antenna, and the other (the auxiliary antenna) is a relatively simple arrangement, sited to pick up the interference as well as possible. If more controlled experiments are to be carried out, the wide bandwidth and inherent matching of an active antenna make this a good choice for the auxiliary antenna.

All this talk of exactly adjusting the phase and gain may give the impression that cancellers will only operate in ideal conditions. This is far from the case: in fact they will give a good account of themselves in almost all situations – the only requirement is that there must be sufficient amplitude/phase adjustment to cover the range of signal to interference

Fig 7.19. Circuit diagram of the canceller. R1/R2: linear carbon potentiometers. T1: 5 trifilar turns. Core: Palomar F37-Q2 or Amidon FT37-63. Note that the circuit around RLA (R5, D3, R4 and the 2N4401 transistor) should be adapted to suit the available relay. The circuit shown is suitable for receive only or for a low-power transceiver. For high power a more substantial relay will be required

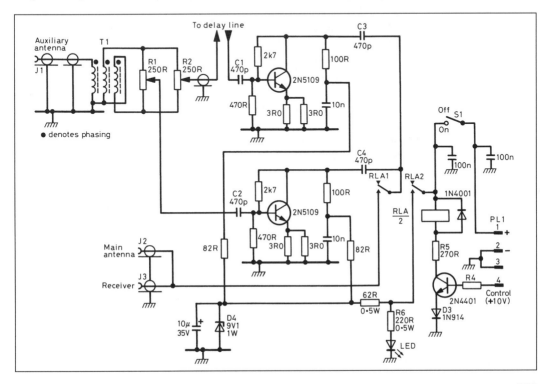

conditions. It is also important to remember that, by its very nature, such a device can only cancel one signal at a time. If the interference is coming from more than one source, or arriving at the station by more than one route, as with ionospheric signals, the cancellation will be limited. In good conditions cancellers can be extremely effective, giving nulls of 60dB or more.

Pseudo-random data signals which give the effect of white noise can be cancelled, but have the difficulty that there is nothing distinctive to listen to. The best technique is to use the S-meter to get as deep a dip as possible. Hopefully by then the noise will have reduced to a level where signals will be audible, and final adjustment can be made for best signal and minimum noise.

The one type of interference which the canceller will not cope with is natural static. This is because the crashes of natural static come from different locations, so that even if it were possible to cancel one crash, the adjustment would not be suitable for the next one, and it would get through more or less unaffected.

Information on HF cancellers has appeared in a number of articles including reference [6]. A design for a VHF canceller can be found in references [7] and [8]. Commercially manufactured interference cancellers are available, but there is no unanimity about what to call them, so it is important to make sure that the device you are purchasing is what you are looking for.

REFERENCES

[1] 'Dynamic range, intermodulation and phase noise', P E Chadwick, *Radio Communication* March 1984.
[2] EMC column, *Radio Communication* December 1996 and February 1997.
[3] Equipment review, P J Hart, *Radio Communication* June 1982.
[4] 'In practice', *Radio Communication* July and August 1996.
[5] 'Electrical antenna null steering', J Webb, *QST* October 1982.
[6] 'Technical Topics', *Radio Communication* March 1993.
[7] '2 metre interference reduction system', T S Day, *Radio Communication* April 1992.
[8] '4m/6m interference reduction system', T S Day, *Radio Communication* September 1992.

SUMMARY – DEALING WITH RECEIVED INTERFERENCE

Actions at source

Impulsive interference

(a) Absorb the released energy in some form of 'quenching' circuit (Figs 7.2 and 7.3).

(b) For mains-operated motors and similar devices, fit a mains filter as close to the source of the interference as possible.

Interference from digital equipment

(a) Avoid common-mode (interference) currents on leads to external units by using good 0V/ground practice. Where possible, provide a dedicated 0V return for each outgoing signal.

(b) Reduce common-mode currents by fitting ferrite chokes on external leads (Fig 7.9).

(c) Provide low-impedance return paths for common-mode currents by connecting the 0V rails of peripherals back to the 0V rail of the source (Fig 7.10).

(d) Fit screening, where appropriate, but make sure that the screen is connected to the correct 0V point.

(e) Be careful. Incorrect connections could be very expensive and, MORE IMPORTANTLY, MAY BE DANGEROUS.

Actions at the receiver

(a) Make sure that the interference is coming through the antenna. Eliminate any pick-up at the receiver or through the mains before proceeding to further measures.

(b) Use a noise limiter or blanker. These are only effective where the interference has impulsive characteristics.

(c) Use interference cancelling. This will work with almost any type of interference. Best results will be achieved where the interference comes from a specific source some distance away. Where cancelling is to be used to eliminate very local interference, it is worthwhile experimenting with the siting of the auxiliary antenna. In many cases a simple wire strung up near the source of interference will be satisfactory.

8 | The social side

I N DISCUSSING the technical aspects of EMC, it has been emphasised that the principles underlying EMC problems are relatively simple and predictable. In real life things seem complicated only because of the large number of unknown factors.

A philosophically minded physicist might dispute any claim to absolute predictability, but everyone agrees that at the practical engineering level things are predictable (provided that everything is known about the conditions), even though we may jokingly suspect the operation of that well-known law that states that if things can go wrong, they will, and always at the most inconvenient time.

The social side of EMC problems is quite different; people do not always act in a predictable way. Perhaps this is just as well; it would be a very dull world if we could be sure of how our friends and relations would react on every occasion.

The other person's point of view

How should one deal with a difficult neighbour who is upset because breakthrough is spoiling his favourite TV programme? The response is immediate – there is no specific way, it all depends on the circumstances. A good starting place is to understand the neighbour's point of view. This is not easy, and can be a salutary experience since it involves seeing amateur radio, which we (rightly) see as being something special, through the eyes of someone who sees it as just another hobby.

Two hundred years ago Robert Burns wrote 'To a Louse, On Seeing One on a Lady's Bonnet at Church'. A curious subject for a poem, one might think, and one which gives an interesting sidelight on life in the late 18th century. It contains some very well-known lines which put our problem in a nutshell.

> *O wad some Pow'r the giftie gie us*
> *To see oursels as others see us!*
> *It wad frae monie a blunder free us*
> *An' foolish notion:*

Weighing up the situation

The only way to tackle the personal aspects of EMC complaints is by assuming that the people involved are basically reasonable – even though they may be angry or possibly rude at the outset. Unfortunately this approach will not always work; as we all know, there is a small percentage of people who are just not rational. Before concluding that your neighbours come into this category, consider the following points.

(a) We are all likely to take up strong positions if we have been annoyed by what we consider someone else's thoughtless action. It is a great mistake to let a situation get to the stage of real anger before doing anything about it. Most EMC problems can be solved with reasonable give and take, but once the diplomatic approach has been abandoned the chances are greatly lessened. This applies both ways: if you think you are suffering undue interference from some gadget a neighbour has installed, first make sure of your technical facts and then go and have a word with them. Don't wait until you are really cross about it.

(b) Aggression often masks frustrations which are quite unconnected with the problem in hand. This is a well-known fact of human nature. We all know people for whom nothing is ever right. It is not uncommon for people to go so far as to move house because they can't stand the neighbours, only to find that in a few weeks they are quarrelling with their new neighbours. They may just be unlucky, of course, but the problem may be with themselves. In dealing with neighbours of this type, the best course is to use subtlety; if you can find out what is really upsetting them, it may be possible to improve relations to a point where radio problems are easily dealt with. It is a truism that most people are better for knowing, and you may find that your awkward neighbour is not so bad after all. Even if they turn out to be completely unreasonable you haven't lost anything, and at least you have gained in experience!

(c) Expectation of trouble sometimes causes amateurs to take up a negative attitude to their neighbours, even if no complaints have been received. If you set off with an aggressive, isolationist attitude, then when trouble comes you are not going to have many friends. In an extreme case the awkward person of point (b) might be yourself. Listening to comments on the air and at club meetings it is evident that some amateurs almost take a pride in not knowing their neighbours. The choice is up to the individual, of course, but a friendly smile and a few minutes chat cost nothing and makes dealing with any future EMC problems so much easier.

Dealing with complaints of breakthrough

Let us imagine that a neighbour has come to complain about interference, and that he is quite cross about it. (To avoid having to keep printing 'he or she' all the time, a man has been assumed, though it could just as easily be a woman). As has already been said, the approach in any particular case will depend very much on circumstances, but the following suggestions will at least be a starting point.

Getting off to a good start

(a) Try to keep your temper. If you keep calm and reasonable at this stage it will pay handsome dividends later.

(b) If possible, conduct the discussion sitting down. This helps to make the situation seem more normal.

(c) Explain that most cases of interference are due to breakthrough but occasionally the amateur station may be at fault. If he cannot give you times and dates which enable you to make a diagnosis, offer to carry out tests (see Chapter 4). If the fault is due to harmonics or other spurious emissions from your station, admit it, apologise, and keep off the offending bands until you have put the trouble right.

If the problem is breakthrough

(a) Find out if the susceptible equipment is CE marked. If it is, then explain it should have a reasonable degree of immunity but that the inherent immunity may be degraded by an installation problem. This could be a faulty antenna connector or down lead, or more likely an unsuitable booster or distribution amplifier (Chapter 5 and Appendix 5).

(b) Even if the installation is satisfactory the immunity may not be adequate in all circumstances. It may be a case for the 'special mitigation measures' (See Chapter 3).

(c) Have copies of information sheets, such as the RSGB's *Radio Transmitters and Domestic Electronic Equipment* [1], *Radio Transmitters and Home Security Systems* [2] or *Radio Transmitters and Telephones* [3], ready to hand so that you can go straight to them.

(d) Ask yourself whether you are practising good radio housekeeping (Chapter 3). If you are doubtful, resolve to do something about it but keep your thoughts to yourself at this stage.

(e) Offer to help but make sure that it is understood that this is a goodwill gesture, not an obligation.

(f) Do it as quickly as possible. Nothing impresses a sceptical neighbour so much as being able to fix the trouble in a prompt and business-like way.

Two general points

(a) Don't deliberately run down a neighbour's equipment, whatever you may think. Be positive and talk in terms of EMC requirements in the modern domestic environment.

(b) If possible, end the interview on a friendly note. Try to bring the conversation round to everyday matters – children, grandchildren, cars, football or anything you can think of which has no connection with radio.

The Authorities

In the UK the Authority governing the use of all types of radio is the Radiocommunications Agency (RA). So far as amateurs are concerned the function of the Agency is described in the *Terms, Provisions and Limitations Booklet* (BR68) that accompanies the amateur licence. BR68 is updated from time to time. The comments below refer to the issue of March 1995.

Most amateurs are aware of the RA's two main powers in policing amateur radio. These are:

1. To inspect an amateur station, for the purpose of verifying compliance with the terms of the licence.
2. To instruct an amateur station to cease transmission and close down immediately if the problem is considered sufficiently serious. In practice this would only happen if the station was causing interference by transmitting spurious emissions outside the amateur bands or if the station was being deliberately operated contrary to licence conditions, such as abuse of repeater or packet facilities or broadcasting propaganda. The reasons are always confirmed in writing.

Less well-known and much more open to misinterpretation is the RA's power to take action against an amateur station if interference is being caused by "undue" local field strength generated by the station (BR68 4.3). An amateur can be requested to modify his operating practice to reduce the local field strength. If the amateur does not voluntarily comply with the request, the RA can issue a Notice of Variation (NoV) which modifies the amateur's licence, making the change of operating practice obligatory. The restriction could involve a reduction in transmitted power or ERP and might in some cases be coupled with restrictions on the type of antenna that can be used.

Needless to say the problem here is the interpretation of "undue". Paragraph (l) of the Notes at the end of BR68 sets out the policy in more detail. The RA has stated that it will not carry out such action until all factors have been taken into account. In many cases the RA has supported amateurs who have been accused unreasonably of being at fault. Inevitably, however, there will be cases where interpretation is disputed. Members of the RSGB can ask for the EMC Committee to discuss their case with the RA. However, to do this the Committee must have a clear written request from the amateur. (For reasons of confidentiality the RA cannot discuss a third party's affairs without their express permission.) When asking the Committee for assistance, sufficient details should be given to enable an estimate of field strengths to be made. These should include:

- A description of the antenna.
- A plan showing the property boundaries, the location of the transmitting antenna and the susceptible equipment.
- Information on the frequency bands and modes in use, and the maximum power in each case.

The role of the Committee in such cases is to ensure that the amateur gets a fair deal within the prevailing regulations. The emphasis has to be on fairness. The Society cannot support cases that are obviously unreasonable. To do so would undermine its negotiating stance in genuine cases.

Making an official complaint
It is important to make sure that complainants understand that they have the right to go via the official channels. In the UK anyone may report a suspected source of interference by filling in Part A of form RA179, obtainable from the Radiocommunications Agency. No charge is made for this, and the Agency will investigate the suspected source at their discretion. Where an amateur is named as the suspected source the, local staff of the

Agency may visit the station and carry out an inspection. If they find that it is being operated within the terms of the licence they will take no further action – other than to inform the complainant and suggest they look at the immunity of their own receiving installation. If the complainant wishes officers of the Agency to visit their premises to investigate an interference problem then Part B of RA179 must be filled in and the appropriate fee paid. Part B has a section which must be filled in by a competent person, such as a TV dealer, to show that they have not been able to cure the problem.

When telling your neighbour this, do not forget to point out that the majority of cases of interference from amateur stations are due to breakthrough, and that with a little co-operation the problem can most likely be solved without the delay and expense of calling on experts to tell him what is general knowledge in amateur radio circles. (If your general knowledge is flagging a bit, revive it by reading Chapters 3, 4 and 5 again!)

Breakthrough to non-radio devices and unprotected services

Electrical devices which do not use radio are not "wireless telegraphy apparatus" as defined in the Wireless Telegraphy Acts, and are therefore not able to claim protection from radio interference. This includes things such as audio equipment, conventional telephone equipment and alarm systems. Generally speaking, interference problems should be taken up with the supplier or installer. However, devices purchased since 1996 should comply with the EC EMC immunity standards and carry the CE mark on the device itself or the packing or instructions for use. (The enforcement of CE marking and the conformance of products are the province of the Trading Standards Officers). The same applies to devices such as wireless baby alarms and security systems which use radio but are not a protected service. In the UK, the RA will not become involved in such cases, unless there are special circumstances, but it must be remembered that the comments made above on BR68 and "undue field strengths", are equally applicable to problems involving such devices.

Tenancy agreements

Amateurs who operate from rented accommodation may find that there are clauses in their tenancy agreement restricting activities such as the erection of antennas. Where there is a choice, it is obviously desirable to look for a property that does not have such restrictions. For many amateurs occupying local authority or housing association property, there may be no option but to go along with the agreement and the consequent restrictions.

Many authorities and associations are prepared to allow variations to restrictions on antennas for modest structures, but the snag is that interference complaints from neighbours can cause the permission to be withdrawn.

In many tenancy agreements there is a 'nuisance' clause, which makes "not causing a nuisance to neighbours" a condition of the tenancy. There have been cases where amateurs have been instructed to cease transmission and threatened with eviction if they do not comply. The legal situation here is unclear, but it seems reasonable to assume that the landlord cannot prevent a tenant with a valid amateur licence from transmitting in general terms, because 'transmitting' could cover anything from a few milliwatts to full legal power on frequencies from top band to microwaves. It is likely, however, that they could insist that the amateur does not cause a nuisance by so doing. No doubt legal arguments can be put forward as to what constitutes a nuisance, but by the time the situation has reached this stage most amateurs will have found that the neighbour relations have become intolerable.

Experience has shown that most cases of this type end either with the amateur giving up altogether or agreeing to a compromise. The compromise might involve the landlord having the immunity of a susceptible communal alarm or TV system improved if this is causing problems, and on the amateur's part an undertaking to operate with appropriate power levels and modes. Once a working relationship has been established the amateur can work to improve his position by assisting neighbours with any problems which may arise, so that power can gradually be increased.

This is really an extreme case of operating in difficult circumstances, as discussed in Chapter 3, p15.

If things get out of hand

If things get really bad, don't be provoked into doing anything rash – seek expert help. Most national societies have an organisation for dealing with EMC problems, and will advise their members in cases of difficulty. In the UK EMC advice is available to RSGB members from EMC co-ordinators who give routine advice on EMC matters. In difficult cases the co-ordinators can call on the help of committee members specialising in the particular type of problem.

Threats of legal action are not uncommon, but are usually just a ploy without serious intent. If you should receive a solicitor's letter, send a copy of the letter, along with the relevant facts, to the EMC Committee Chairman.

The co-ordinators' telephone numbers are published in the *RSGB Yearbook* [4] and also from time to time in *Radio Communication*. The telephone number of the current EMC Committee Chairman can be obtained from RSGB Headquarters.

Setting up a new station

There are two main reasons for setting up a station in a new location: moving house or a brand-new licence. In addition to this, there are always amateurs going back on the air, often after a lapse of many years. Veterans will be only too aware of the pitfalls, but a few suggestions may help newcomers to avoid a serious confrontation.

The first and most important point is to be patient. Don't put up an ugly, 'EMC unfriendly' antenna straight away, and then go on the air on full power for hours at a time. First read Chapter 3 and then think carefully about your situation. If you think you are likely to have problems, start with an antenna arrangement which minimises the risk of breakthrough and keep the power down for the first few weeks while you get the feel of the situation. Any complaints which do arise are likely to be fairly mild and easily dealt with without souring relations.

It is a good plan to put up your antenna a few weeks before you actually put the station together. The sight of an amateur antenna is often enough to bring complaints of all sorts of interference problems. It is important to make the maximum possible capital out of such situations, which are an ideal opportunity for discussing possible sources of interference. Even the most sceptical neighbour will agree it cannot be you if there is nothing connected to the antenna. Don't lose a golden opportunity by being high-handed.

Choosing a house with EMC in mind

Very few of us are in a position to make amateur radio operation a prime factor in choosing a new house but in many cases it will be a secondary issue, so that it will be useful to look at a few of the factors involved. From the transmitting point of view, choose a garden shaped so that it is possible to arrange antennas a reasonable distance from your own house and neighbouring houses (Chapter 3). For HF operation, the further away the antennas are, the better; the provision of feeders is a minor problem compared to interference. A nearby block of flats may indicate a potential risk of interference to a TV distribution system.

From the reception viewpoint, avoid locations that can be expected to have a high local man-made noise level. At one time this was fairly simple because most noise came from industrial premises, electric railways or power lines. Noise still does come from such sources, of course, but nowadays some very nasty noise sources in the form of computer systems and other electronic apparatus can turn up even in the most peaceful residential areas.

Though not strictly an EMC issue, the most important point to check is that there are no restrictions on antennas or other constructions on the property under consideration – other than normal planning permission (see 'Tenancy Agreements' above).

When you are on the receiving end

The boot is now on the other foot, and it is up to the amateur to decide whether the problem is serious enough to warrant doing anything about. All locations suffer from man-made noise to some extent, and minimising the effects is part of good radio housekeeping.

From the official point of view, amateur radio is not a 'protected service', and this means that amateurs do not have a right to protection from interference. Exactly how this is interpreted varies from country to country and administration to administration but, as a general rule, the authorities will not be interested unless the interference affects broadcast radio or television inside the normal service area.

In the UK, where there is interference to broadcasting and the source is known, then, like anyone else, the amateur may report the fact to the regional office of the RA using form RA179 (Part A). At the time of writing, this service only applies to VHF radio and TV broadcasting.

Amateur signals are on the whole much weaker than broadcast signals and the RA cannot put resources into tracing interference to them. Nevertheless if an amateur can be precise in identifying a source of interference, the RA may be able to investigate, though they emphasise that the 'leisure' use of radio cannot be a priority.

Interference from domestic equipment

Very little is likely to be achieved without the co-operation of the owner, and it is in situations like this that being on good terms with your neighbours really counts. It is fairly common nowadays for a small business to be carried on from a private house, so that the distinction between a residential and a commercial neighbourhood becomes blurred. Interference from fax machines and other office machinery can propagate considerable distances via the telephone lines and it is sometimes very difficult to find the source. To make matters worse some equipment is operational 24 hours a day. Fortunately computerised telecommunications equipment tends to get out of date fairly quickly, so that old equipment which is not compliant with the new EMC regulations should become increasingly rare. This will at least get rid of the worst offenders, but even compliant equipment can still pose a threat to amateur operation. The technical aspects are as discussed in Chapters 7 and 9, with the emphasis on preventing interference from entering the mains or the telephone lines. If the interference is so severe that it is causing problems to broadcast radio, it may be possible to obtain official assistance, as discussed in the previous paragraph.

When considering the regulatory aspects of interference it is important to bear in mind the difference between the EC EMC regulations, which are Europe-wide requirements regulating the EMC performance of equipment being sold throughout the community, and the powers of the RA to regulate interference in the UK. The former are primarily a matter of the product quality (EMC performance in this case) and the avoidance of 'barriers to trade', while the latter are statutory powers to control interference which may occur, for any reason, in the industrial or domestic environment.

Interference from commercial installations

Sometimes interference is received from computer installations in business premises or public service organisations. The first thing is to find out where the interference is coming from and, if possible, some estimate of the signal strength (Chapter 4). When you are sure of your facts, give some thought to whom you should contact. Generally it is better to contact someone fairly senior in the organisation, but if you are going to contact the head office of a firm it would be courteous to let the local manager know. Unless you are a persuasive talker, it might be better to write rather than telephone. With public services there is usually an officer in each district who deals with communications and he (or she) would be the person to contact. In most cases it should be possible to get their name and the address of their office by ringing the 'enquiries' of the organisation in question. In your letter or telephone call give as much information as possible: frequencies, times, what the signal sounds like etc.

The person you contact may not have a great interest in amateur radio but he will almost certainly be interested in security. This is the important thing to emphasise. Data leakage can be picked up by unscrupulous people and used for malicious, possibly criminal, purposes. It would not need to be sophisticated hacking – a simple change of signal format might indicate the 'status' of machines or alarms within the premises. Cases have been reported where the information displayed on a computer screen has been picked up and displayed some distance away, simply by decoding the interference radiated. All in all, the firm or organisation would be well advised to keep their signals in their proper place. One very important point: don't try to decode the signal yourself and don't suggest that you might try. This would almost certainly be illegal; all the amateur should do is to examine the signal to ascertain whether it is an amateur signal or not.

References

[1] *Radio Transmitters and Domestic Electronic Equipment*, leaflet EMC 01, available from the RSGB.
[2] *Radio Transmitters and Home Security Systems*, leaflet EMC 02, available from the RSGB.
[3] *Radio Transmitters and Telephones*, leaflet EMC 05, available from the RSGB.
[4] *RSGB Yearbook*, RSGB.

9 Some specific EMC problems

Telephone equipment

The old electromechanical telephone of yesteryear has now all but disappeared from the scene, to be replaced by a bewildering array of electronic telephones and ancillary equipment. Telephones account for a substantial number of amateur EMC problems, simply because there are so many of them around.

Breakthrough to telephone equipment

The immunity of telephone equipment in Europe has improved as the EMC regulations have become effective but it will be some time before the full benefits are evident. At present telephone equipment is tested to the 1992 Generic immunity standard EN 50082-1:1992, but a new, tougher, Generic standard will come into force in the near future [1]. It is understood that equipment may still be tested to the old standard until the year 2001. It seems likely that, some time in the future, telephone equipment will come under the Information Technology Equipment (ITE) immunity standard, EN 55024.

Telephone breakthrough is tackled in much the same way as breakthrough to other types of equipment. The interference will almost always be common mode, and it is really a question of applying the techniques described in Chapter 5 as is most practical in the circumstance. The procedure can be summarised as follows:

(a) First check your radio housekeeping to see that you are not inviting trouble by poor antenna siting.
(b) Fit ferrite chokes on the lead to the telephone as close to the instrument as possible. Winding the lead on to a ferrite ring is the most popular method of making a choke but split-core or rod chokes can also be used.
(c) If the interference seems to be getting in from the external overhead lines (through the *line jack*), a proprietary filter may be fitted between the line jack and the lead to the telephone equipment.

Most households have extension telephones connected by plugs and sockets to the line jack provided by the telephone company, and these may involve quite long lengths of interconnecting cable. At the start of the investigation, unplug any extension units and their cable, leaving only the instrument near the line jack connected. Clear any breakthrough on this, and then reconnect the extension leads and telephones one by one, dealing

Photo 9.1. Telephone with BT Freelance RFI filter (lower left)

with breakthrough problems as they arise. If it is suspected that the RF is entering as a common-mode signal on the lines coming into the house, a ferrite ring choke should be tried close to the line jack. In some cases it may be necessary to re-route vulnerable extension leads but usually the liberal use of ferrite chokes will prove effective. The ferrite chokes are basically the same as those used for breakthrough to other types of equipment. Where connectors are too large to pass through the cores, a split core can be used. See Appendix 3.

Proprietary filters are available for fitting directly to the line jack. Unfortunately the only ones available at present are intended to protect against AM broadcast signals, and become less effective as the frequency increases. Typical filters contain chokes of a couple of microhenry or so in series with the four terminals normally available for domestic use. Because they use individual chokes these filters will give protection against differential as well as common-mode RF currents, These filters are quite effective at 1.8 and 3.5MHz, giving less rejection as the frequency rises, though some benefit may be obtained even up to 30MHz [2]. Photo 9.1 shows a BT Freelance filter. Because of the increasing use of digital signalling on telephone lines it is likely that proprietary filters with better HF performance will become available in the near future.

In general, it is not permissible to carry out any internal modifications to telephone equipment, even if it is your own property. There are rules about equipment being approved for connection to telephone lines, and most telephone authorities (including those in the UK) do not permit unofficial modifications to anything connected to their lines. If privately purchased telephone equipment is abnormally susceptible to interference, then the supplier should be contacted as discussed under 'Intractable cases' in Chapter 5. In the case of equipment rented from the telephone company or administration, the problem should reported to the appropriate engineering department. There are standard EMC modifications which their technicians will carry out – usually free of charge. Alternatively they may exchange the telephone for a type which has better immunity.

Emissions from telephone equipment

Telephone ancillary units, such as answering machines and fax machines, contain logic circuits, usually controlled by a microprocessor so that some emission of clock frequencies is to be expected. Radiation directly from the equipment is a possibility, but a much more serious problem can occur where emissions find their way on to the telephone lines. The interference can then be carried long distances – hundreds of metres in some cases. A typical situation might be where a local resident is running some sort of data bureau from home, with equipment connected to the telephone lines and operating 24 hours a day. Cases of this sort can be very hard to track down. Even if the source can be found it may well be that the equipment in use is compliant with the relevant standards, so that there is no obligation on the part of the owner to do anything about it. This is a situation where tact and persuasion will be required (See Chapter 8).

In many cases the only practical course of action is the reduction of common-mode currents by fitting ferrite rings as described for reducing computer emissions (Chapter 7). If the emissions are leaking on to the telephone lines, a proprietary filter of the type mentioned above for breakthrough reduction may give some relief on the lower HF bands, though a ferrite ring choke on the lead close to the master line jack would probably be as effective.

If neither of the above procedures is effective and it is considered that the emission levels are greater than can reasonably be expected, then the supplier of the equipment should be contacted. Before doing this, it is a good idea to check with your national society to see if the particular item is a known troublemaker, and if so what action has been taken in previous cases. In the UK this should be done through the RSGB's EMC co-ordinator scheme.

Cordless telephones

Most cordless phones currently in use in the UK operate on a fairly simple duplex system, known officially as the *CT1 system*. The base station transmits on a frequency around 1.7MHz and receives on a frequency in the region of 47.5MHz, while the handset does the reverse. Only a small number of frequencies are available, reliance being placed on the use of narrowband frequency modulation (NBFM) to minimise the effects of interference. In practice, the signals received by any base station/handset pair is likely to be larger than signals from other units in neighbouring houses. In an NBFM system the largest signal will capture the channel, effectively eliminating weaker interfering signals. To prevent a particular base station being used by someone else's handset, the pairs of units have a digital access code built in to the control circuitry. Some cordless 'phones suffer quite severely from hum and other extraneous noises; and it may be necessary move away from specific noise sources when using the handset.

There is obviously a risk of interference from transmitters operating in the 1.8MHz and 50MHz bands, but in fact this does not seem to be a serious problem at the present time. This may be because high-power operation on these bands is not all that common. In addition, there is an awareness on the part of the public that this type of cordless telephone system is subject to disturbances, and they are prepared to put up with a certain amount of interference.

If trouble is experienced, first check that it is not due to direct breakthrough into the audio circuits. If it is, consider where ferrite chokes can be fitted – as discussed above for an ordinary telephone unit. If interference only occurs when operation on 1.8MHz or 50MHz is taking place, then it is probably due to the transmitted signal getting past the front-end tuning on the cordless telephone. Check the following points.

(a) Is the 1.7MHz wire antenna on the base station arranged to best advantage?
(b) Are the 47MHz whip antennas on the base station and handset properly extended?

(c) Is it possible to resite the base station to provide better communication to the place where the handset is most often used?

There are a number of illegal cordless telephones around, using incorrect frequencies and in some cases using quite high power. If you are suffering interference from one of these, a polite word with the owner is clearly in order.

Security systems

Breakthrough to security systems has become a problem in recent years. Experience has shown that the standard breakthrough measures, such as ferrite chokes and by-pass capacitors, are rarely effective. By far the most usual cause of breakthrough to security systems is poor immunity in the passive infra-red sensors (PIRs). The solution is to replace the offending units with ones which are more immune to RF signals. Occasionally the control panel has been found to have insufficient immunity but this is unusual. Up-to-date information will be found in leaflet EMC 03, *Dealing with Alarm EMC Problems* [3].

Most security systems are professionally installed, and it is up to the installer to ensure that it is sufficiently immune to operate in the environment in which it is installed. (There is a British Standard for security systems, BS 4737, which makes reference to environmental conditions including electrical interference.) A well-installed system with suitably immune PIRs is unlikely to be affected by an amateur station practising reasonable radio housekeeping.

If a complaint of breakthrough to a security alarm system is received, it is advisable to be open with the complainant and to carry out checks to see exactly what the problem is. As in all breakthrough problems, check your station and your radio housekeeping before going any further. Once you are sure of the problem, advise the complainant that the installer should be approached, and give them a copy of the RSGB's leaflet EMC 02, *Radio Transmitters and Home Security Systems* [4]. Whether the amateur or the complainant should approach the installer depends on circumstances, but it is worth remembering that it is the neighbour who has the complaint – they have paid for something which is not functioning correctly.

All new installations should be using CE marked units, including the PIRs, though the mark may not always be on the unit itself. It could be on the instruction or on the packing.

Satellite and cable TV

Most cases of amateur radio interference to television are due to breakthrough caused by RF currents being picked up by the antenna coaxial feeder and interconnecting leads. In general, satellite and cable TV are no different. Wherever parts of an installation are connected together by long leads, these will act as unwanted antennas, usually using capacitance to earth to complete the circuit as described in Chapter 5. Fig 9.1 gives an idea of how interfering currents might flow in a typical satellite TV installation. The procedure for combating the unwanted common-mode currents is the same as for any breakthrough situation, but unfortunately satellite and cable TV installations are so variable that it is not practical to give detailed suggestions. The best thing to do is to read Chapter 5 and then decide where best the ferrite chokes can be fitted in the particular installation.

In addition to breakthrough, satellite and cable TV have their own special problems, involving both received and radiated interference.

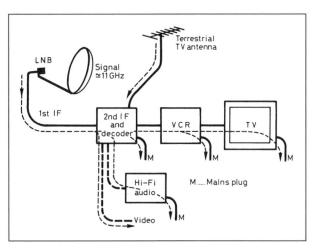

Satellite TV

The signal from the satellite is at a frequency in the region of 11GHz and this is focused by the dish on to the low-noise block (LNB). The LNB contains

Fig 9.1. A satellite TV receiver installation (dashed lines indicate possible paths for common-mode currents on coaxial braid and other leads)

an RF amplifier, mixer, local oscillator and IF amplifier. The local oscillator is fixed in frequency, using a dielectric resonator oscillator (DRO), which can be compared in function to a crystal oscillator except that it operates at microwave frequencies. This local oscillator beats with the incoming 11GHz signal to generate a first IF output in the range 950 to 1750MHz. (It is probable that this will extend upwards towards 2000MHz as the bandwidth of LNBs is increased to accommodate more satellite stations.) The output of the mixer is amplified and passed down a coaxial cable to the indoor part of the installation. Special 'satellite TV grade' coaxial cable with low loss and improved screening should be used to reduce losses and also to minimise the risk of interference from other services. Users of the 1250MHz amateur band will recognise a potential threat here, since this band actually falls inside this first IF band. Fortunately the 1250MHz band involves the use of highly directional antennas, as high up as possible, so that it may be that the problem will not prove as serious as it might at first sight seem. An additional mitigating factor is that satellite TV uses FM with very wide deviation (13MHz upwards, depending on the system), whereas the energy of most amateur signals is confined to a relatively narrow band.

All LNBs are similar in their first IFs but the handling of the signal in the indoor unit varies considerably and several second IFs are in use. It is unlikely that the nominal frequency of the second IF will fall in an amateur band, but it is important to remember that the IF has a bandwidth of many megahertz to suit the deviation of the system, so that it is quite possible that an amateur band might come within the pass band. It is possible for the harmonic of an amateur transmitter to get into the first or second IF stages, but generally this will not happen unless the harmonic is far larger than it should be.

Encoding and decoding systems are in use by system operators to counter unauthorised reception, and this means that most installations include some form of decoder. These involve high-speed digital signal processing and the consequent risk of radiating interference. In general the causes and cures are similar to those discussed in Chapter 7 with regard to computers.

As with any radio or electronic equipment, a well-installed system is

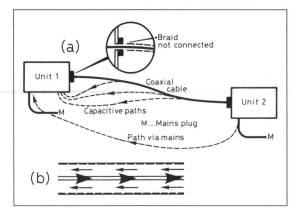

Fig 9.2. (a) Broken braid connection cause the current which would normally flow on the inner surface of the braid to return by random paths. (b) In a correctly connected coaxial cable the currents balance, giving no external field

much less likely to give trouble than one which has been thrown together without thought, using the cheapest possible materials. The vulnerable part of all complicated installations is the interconnections, particularly the RF and screened audio or video leads. Make sure that all connectors are correctly fitted and the braid is making good contact. In many cases an installation will appear work satisfactorily even if the braid is not contacting the connector at all. When this happens, the currents which should flow on the inside surface of the braid (in effect balancing the currents on the inner conductor) return by random paths existing between the units. These paths may be through supply cables or through stray capacitance. The net result is that the normal 'go-return' balance which is inherent in coaxial cables is lost, and the stray return paths form a common impedance which 'couples' to the outside world, allowing interference to be radiated and breakthrough to find its way into the system (Fig 9.2).

TV distribution systems

These have come into prominence in recent years as more complex systems, often operating in conjunction with satellite TV, have come into use. Actually TV distribution has been around for decades and many blocks of flats have been fitted with outlets fed from a single antenna and amplifier. These systems have been a thorn in the flesh of many amateurs over the years. Problems occur when the amateur signal gets into the antenna amplifier unit, causing overloading and consequent cross-modulation. The resulting interference affects every TV set in the block, and needless to say generates a great deal of ill-feeling.

There are really only three practical actions that the amateur can take.

(a) Make sure that the trouble is definitely not due to transmitter defects – harmonics or other spurious emissions as dealt with in Chapter 6. It is well worth while spending time and effort in making sure of this point.
(b) Ask yourself (and give yourself honest answers) whether you are practising good radio housekeeping (Chapter 3).
(c) Advise complainants that the interference is due to a defect in the cable TV installation and suggest that they contact the organisation managing the flats. Explain that there is nothing you can do at your end to prevent the interference, but that you are willing to co-operate in any tests which may be required.

Cable TV (CATV)

Large-scale cable TV systems covering whole towns are now becoming established in the UK. Modern systems use optical fibres to bring the signal to cabinets in the street, but from there distribution to customers' houses is usually by coaxial cable. Carrier frequencies are in the VHF and UHF

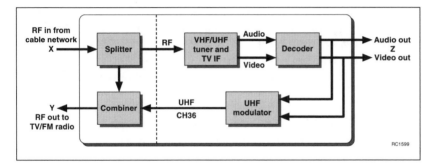

Fig 9.3. A typical set-top converter box for cable TV

bands. At one time it was usual for cable operators to avoid the 144 and 432MHz amateur bands, but recently reports of problems on these frequencies have become more common. Fortunately most systems in the UK are underground, and leakage from the cable system itself is rare. When it does occur it usually indicates some sort of discontinuity in the braid of the coaxial cable. The most common place for this to happen is at junctions or connectors. In most cases there will not be much that the individual can do, except to trace the location of the leakage as far as possible and then to report it to the appropriate service provider.

Reducing interference to CATV

An item on CATV appeared in the EMC column of *Radio Communication* [5]. It included some good advice on reducing CATVI and the following notes are taken from this source.

In some cases, particularly at HF, amateur signals in more than one band cause breakthrough on all cable and terrestrial channels. When this happens it is more likely that the amateur signals are getting into the TV itself than into the converter box. This can normally be tackled by fitting a suitable filter, braid breaker or ferrite ring at the TV antenna socket. In other cases, amateur transmissions in the 2m or 70cm band only affect one or two cable channels which use frequencies within the amateur band. To deal with this it is useful to know something about how the converter box works.

Fig 9.3 shows a simplified block diagram of a typical set-top converter box. RF comes in from the cable network at point X. The vision carrier frequencies are normally exact multiples of 8MHz, from around 56MHz up to 672MHz or higher. The cable distributes the normal terrestrial TV channels above 470MHz but these are not on the same frequencies as the equivalent off-air broadcast signals. The cable also distributes FM radio broadcasts in Band 2 (88 to 108MHz) but, again, these are not on the same frequencies as their local off-air equivalents.

The converter box has a VHF/UHF tuner which can tune to any of the cable channels and a decoder for those channels which are scrambled. The received audio and video outputs are normally available on two 'phono' sockets at point Z. These signals are also re-modulated onto a UHF carrier which is output at point Y for connection to the TV antenna socket. The combiner and splitter allow the terrestrial channels and FM broadcasts to bypass the converter and go straight to the TV and/or FM radio even if the converter box is switched off.

If the TV has a SCART input, connect the audio and video outputs of the converter box (point Z) to the TV via a screened phono-to-SCART cable. Select the SCART input on the TV and unplug both ends of the coaxial cable from the converter box to the TV antenna socket. If breakthrough was only affecting one channel and is reduced or eliminated when using the SCART, this suggests that the RF is getting into the converter box via its RF output cable. Fit a suitable filter at point Y and reconnect the coaxial cable between the TV and the converter box. Use a length of well-screened cable such as CT100, making sure that the cable screen is well grounded to all-metal coaxial connectors at each end.

Use RSGB Filter 3 at point Y to reject signals in all amateur bands 1.8 to 144MHz. This filter will also block the Band 2 FM radio broadcasts coming from the cable network, however. If the FM broadcast signals are required, Filter 2 and Filter 1 can be used together to let through FM Band 2 and block the amateur HF bands. If 432MHz breaks through on one cable channel with the RF cable connected but not when using the SCART connection, try a Filter 8 at point Y. This blocks all amateur bands 1.8–440MHz but also blocks FM Band 2 signals. (See Appendix 3 – 'Filters' for details of the RSGB filters.)

In some cases of HF breakthrough, a ferrite ring may also be required on the incoming cable at point X. This requires a length of coaxial cable with F-type connectors wound about 10 times through a ferrite ring or 15–20 turns through a ferrite yoke ring core. (See Appendix 3 for more information on ferrite chokes). Some cable TV operators do not like anyone to touch the incoming connection from the cable network to the converter box so it is advisable to get the company's engineer to fit such a ferrite ring.

Video signal distribution by existing telephone systems

At the time of writing interest is being shown in the distribution of high-speed digital signals by means of the existing telephone distribution system. This is generally known as *VDSL* (very-high-speed digital subscriber line) The principle is that optical fibre links would feed street cabinets known as Optical Network Units (ONUs), and these would supply typically 300 customers using the ordinary telephone pairs which may be up to 1km long. The system would permit transmission rates of from 12 to 26Mb/s downstream (from ONU to customer) and about 2Mb/s upsteam (customer back to the ONU). It would use frequencies up to about 10MHz.

There are two problems from the EMC point of view:

1. Leakage of signals from the telephone pairs could raise the noise level on the lower HF bands.
2. The system could suffer from breakthrough from amateur stations.

Amateur radio involves small-signal reception in the lower HF bands, in the ordinary domestic environment, and could be affected by VDSL systems. There are several transmission systems which could be used, and at least one of them can be engineered to leave notches in the transmission spectrum. This would make it possible to minimise emissions in the amateur bands, and also hopefully reduce breakthrough problems. Standards for VDSL are still under consideration.

It is worth noting that, with the exception of CT1 cordless telephones, amateur radio is the only service which involves the reception of low-level signals at the lower HF frequencies in the domestic environment.

Mobile operation

So far as amateur radio is concerned, 'mobile' almost always means some form of motor transport, and in this case it has been assumed that it is a car, though it could just as well be any other type of vehicle – the problems will be basically the same. Change is likely to take place in both technical and the regulatory aspects of automotive radio and electronics in the near future and the latest information is best obtained in the various journals, in particular the EMC column of *Radio Communication*. The RSGB has also published a leaflet entitled *Automotive EMC for Radio Amateurs* (leaflet EMC 06). This is currently at edition 1, but will be updated as required [6].

There are two ways in which EMC factors affect mobile operation:

(a) interference to reception caused by electromagnetic energy generated in the engine and ancillaries;
(b) interference by radio transmitters to electronic systems controlling the engine and ancillaries.

The first of these is as old as mobile radio itself. Leafing through old copies of amateur journals will turn up articles on interference suppression going back to the days when 160m was the popular mobile band – and a mobile antenna really added something to a car! These traditional sources of interference are well known, and suppression techniques are covered in other handbooks [7]. In recent years this type of interference has become less important for a number of reasons. One is that nowadays many cars have a broadcast radio fitted as standard, so that at least basic interference suppression is built in. Another factor is that the majority of amateur mobile communication now takes place on VHF FM, which is inherently less susceptible to impulsive interference than SSB or AM. The immunity of an FM receiver to impulses (or any other AM signal) is due to the action of the limiter. Sets vary in the degree of limiting designed into the system. If a particular radio seems to suffer unduly from interference, suspect a lack of signal at the limiter caused by a fault or a design weakness.

On SSB and AM the effect of impulsive interference can be greatly reduced by the use of a good noise blanker. A blanker operates by using the very short impulses of interference to operate a gate in the receiver IF as described in Chapter 7, and its performance is dependent on a number of factors, including the ability of the receiver front-end to handle large impulses. The effectiveness of blankers varies considerably, so it is worthwhile trying the noise blanker in a practical test before deciding on a transceiver for mobile use.

RF interference to electronic control systems has become a major consideration in mobile radio; not least because the possible safety aspects attract publicity. Basically, the problem is caused by RF energy being picked up in the wiring of the car and entering the logic of the control circuits. The effects can vary from specific faults, such as failure of door locks or erratic flashers [8], to complete failure of the microprocessor engine control. Fortunately (from the amateur's point of view) the increasing use of mobile transceivers for leisure and commercial purposes has meant that EMC is becoming an important feature of vehicle design. The biggest problem is HF operation, where the cable harnesses can form quite efficient antennas.

When considering a mobile HF station it should be borne in mind that high-power HF operation may not be practical in any particular car. It is also worth sparing a thought as to whether it is wise to be so close to antennas radiating high powers. All in all, this is probably another case where moderation will pay dividends. Keeping the power down to reasonable levels (perhaps 25W mean power) on both HF and VHF would seem a sensible compromise.

The various metal assemblies in a car may not be in good RF contact, and bonding various parts can result in a reduction of received noise and in improved immunity. Be careful of course, and don't be fooled into thinking that 12V is safe. Short-circuits can cause nasty burns, and bursting batteries are not unknown.

Co-locating transceivers

Operating transmitters and receivers in close proximity has always been a problem, but it has come into prominence in the last few decades as radio systems have become more complex. The design of co-located radio systems is a special branch of radio engineering, and the satisfactory operation of so many amateur repeaters bears witness to how well the principles can be made to work in practice. There is plenty of information around on co-location for VHF and UHF systems, both amateur and commercial [9] and we will confine our discussion to 'unengineered' situations where it is a case of making the best of what is available, rather than designing the system to suit.

A practical example might be a special-event station where it is desired to operate two HF transceivers (on several HF bands) and one transceiver on each of the 144 and 432MHz bands.

Fundamentals

The unwanted interaction between co-located transceivers is just another case of interference, and falls into the two main categories: unwanted emissions by the transmitter and unwanted reception by the receiver. Where modern, well-designed equipment is being used, most of the problems will stem from various sorts of unwanted reception – generally breakthrough, due simply to the fact that very large signals are being radiated close to antennas which are being used for reception on another band. There will of course be spurious emissions, whatever transmitter is being used, but these are unlikely to fall into the amateur bands and if they do it is usually possible to avoid the frequencies which are affected. The one serious exception to this is harmonics. There is really no chance of being able to reduce harmonics to a level where they will not cause trouble, and the only solution is to plan the station to avoid one transceiver operating on the harmonic of another. In practice this means co-operation between the operators of the various transceivers.

A much more important problem is overloading of receivers by large signals. All receivers have spurious responses, and the reduction of them is a major factor in modern receiver design. Reviews of transceivers in amateur journals devote considerable space to discussion of the large-signal performance. A typical example is reference [10]. In most cases it will be a question of using available equipment, but if there is any choice then it is obviously best to choose a transceiver with a known good large-signal performance.

The whole strategy of co-location is to reduce the amount of unwanted signal getting into the transceivers, and this is really a matter of planning and good radio housekeeping.

Guidelines for HF operation

(a) Plan the frequencies and antennas so that everyone concerned is quite clear which antennas are to be used on which frequencies. Think of the antennas that are to be used simultaneously as being in different groups. A simple arrangement would be to have a low-frequency group and a high-frequency group. Keep the antennas in different groups as far apart as possible. Low-frequency antennas should be arranged to be the most distant since feeder losses will be less. Minimise losses by ensuring that the distant antennas are well matched. For a 3.5 or 7MHz dipole with a VSWR of less than about 2:1, 100m of UR67 or RG213/U would be quite reasonable. Where long feeder lengths are used, don't forget to check the VSWR at the antenna end of the feeder, otherwise very misleading results can be obtained.

(b) Avoid antennas which use earth as part of the antenna system – practically this means avoiding antennas tuned against ground.

(c) Use balanced antennas and choose antennas which do not have normal resonance in the other group of frequencies. A dipole is a good choice but don't forget that a 7MHz dipole has a resonance at 21MHz.

(d) Try to avoid antennas in the different groups running parallel to one another.

(e) Pay particular attention to feeders. In many cases coaxial feeder with a balun at the antenna end is a convenient arrangement. Where the station layout permits, a non-resonant dipole with tuned feeder can be used. In temporary locations, 300Ω ribbon is simpler to use than open-wire feeder but if possible the type with slots cut away in the insulation should be used. This type of antenna and feeder may seem a strange choice but it has the advantage that it can be made to have a fairly high Q, and so helps to increase the isolation of the transceiver at unwanted frequencies.

(f) Always use a manual ATU with each transceiver, even if the antenna in use does not need one to achieve a match. An ATU will help to increase the isolation but more importantly a manual ATU will also reduce the chance of two transceivers attempting to operate on the same band. This point is most important. Serious damage could be done to a transceiver if it is switched to the same band as a transmitter and the antennas are close together. This is a special risk with modern semiconductor equipment: not only are semiconductor devices more vulnerable but the ability to switch from band to band at the press of a button makes accidents more likely.

Guidelines for VHF operation
(a) Keep the VHF and UHF antennas as far away as possible from each other and from the HF antennas.
(b) Plan operation to avoid third harmonics from the 144MHz band causing trouble at 432MHz.
(c) If band-pass filters are available, they will greatly increase the isolation.
(d) Use dedicated VHF and UHF transceivers, well designed and well screened. Transverters are almost certain to give problems when co-located with HF equipment.
(e) It is quite possible that HF signals may be picked up on the antenna coaxial cable of VHF equipment, causing a classical breakthrough problem. A ferrite ring choke fitted to the cable near to the transceiver should reduce the unwanted signals but if not a ferrite choke in the mains lead can be tried. If the trouble persists, then the station layout should be reconsidered and possibly changes made to the HF antenna or feeder arrangements.

Make sure that all RF connectors are correctly fitted and that they are fully mated. Passive intermodulation products (PIPs) can cause unexpected interference problems where several transceivers are co-located, and care should be taken to ensure that all connections and antenna fixings are clean, tight and free from corrosion. Use ferrite ring chokes on ancillary leads and microphone cables to reduce unwanted RF currents.

When operating co-located transceivers, moderation pays handsome dividends. Don't be tempted to run excessive power, particularly on the HF bands, and keep the microphone gain on all the transceivers at a reasonable level to avoid overdriving and consequent splatter.

References
[1] 'EMC' column, *Radio Communication* April 1997.
[2] 'EMC' column, *Radio Communication* October 1993.
[3] *Dealing with Alarm EMC Problems*, leaflet EMC 03, available from RSGB.
[4] *Radio Transmitters and Home Security Systems*, leaflet EMC 02, available from RSGB.
[5] 'EMC' column, *Radio Communication* December 1997.
[6] *Automotive EMC for Radio Amateurs*. Leaflet EMC 06, available from RSGB.
[7] *Radio Communication Handbook*, 5th edn, RSGB, 1976.
[8] 'EMC Matters', *Radio Communication* December 1991.
[9] *The ARRL Antenna Book*, 16th edn, ARRL, Chapter 17.
[10] 'The Peter Hart Review', *Radio Communication* October 1997.

1 Protective multiple earthing (PME)

WHEN a potentially dangerous situation could arise, but in practice is very unlikely to do so, misunderstandings and false ideas can lead to suggestions being made which are much more dangerous than the small risk which they are intended to avoid. These notes have been compiled to clear away some of the mystery surrounding PME and to put it into its proper perspective. *As with any aspect of electricity supply, anyone who does not have the necessary knowledge should take advice from a qualified electrician or consult their Regional Electricity Company (REC).*

Summary

Q *What difference does PME make to an amateur station?*

A If an RF earth is used it must be connected to the (PME) earth bonding point at the consumer unit, using a conductor of at least 10mm². Amateurs should also be aware that external parts of the station, such as antennas and their associated metalwork, could under certain rare fault conditions rise above earth potential (see 'The practical risks of PME', paragraph (c), below).

Q *What is bonding?*

A Bonding, more correctly called *equipotential bonding*, is the connection of metalwork within the building to the earth bonding point (usually at the consumer unit). This includes services such as gas and water pipes, central heating and structural metalwork.

Q *Is bonding special to PME systems?*

A No, bonding is required in modern conventional installations but it is considered more important in PME installations, and more stringent conditions apply.

Q *Where can I get information about bonding?*

A The IEE Regulations [1] are a formal statement of the requirements. The IEE also publish the *IEE On-site Guide* which explains the applications of the regulations to practical situations [2].

Q *Should I disconnect the mains earth from my radio equipment, and rely on the RF earth?*

A No, definitely not! This can only be done in very special circumstances. (See 'What you can do if you have a PME installation', paragraph (b), below).

What is protective multiple earthing?

Protective multiple earthing (PME) systems started to be installed on a wide scale in the mid 'seventies. If your house is more modern than this, it is likely that it is wired on this system. Older houses may have been changed to PME if the supply system in the area has been renovated.

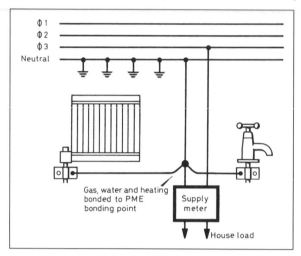

Fig A1.1. Protective multiple earthing

In a PME system, the main earthing terminal of an installation is connected to the neutral of the electricity service at the consumer's premises (Fig A1.1). All metallic surfaces within the building, including gas pipes, water pipes, central heating systems and accessible structural steelwork are bonded together at the consumer unit; this gives the consumer an earth of very high reliability and of low impedance.

Under normal circumstances a small voltage may appear between a PME earth and the true earth potential measured outside the building as a result of voltage drop in the neutral of the electricity supply company's system. Under very rare fault conditions, such as a rupture of the neutral conductor on the supply company's system, a higher potential difference may appear which could, in theory, rise to phase-to-neutral voltage (240V). Because all the metalwork in the building is bonded together, the shock hazard is minimised because everything is at the same potential - even though this may be different from the outside earth potential.

It is permissible to connect other means of earthing to the main earthing terminal of the installation provided certain precautions are taken. Where a low-impedance earth, such as might be used in an amateur radio installation is connected to the earth system, a very large current could flow down the earth wire in the unlikely event of rupture of the neutral (Fig A1.2). This current could be as high as several tens of amps and could be a fire risk.

Fig A1.2. A ruptured supply neutral could cause a large current to flow in a low-resistance RF earth

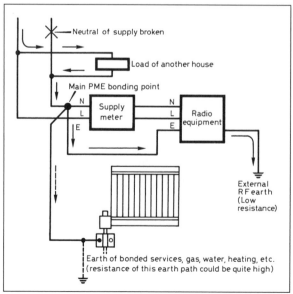

How to identify a PME installation

In theory a PME installation should have a notice close to the meter and distribution panel, indicating that it is PME. Of course one cannot rely on this, because it may have been detached or for some reason or other may not have been fitted. If there is no notice and you have any doubts, get a qualified electrician to have a look at the supply arrangements, or contact your Regional Electricity Company (REC) for advice.

The practical risks of PME

(a) In PME systems the supply authorities take great care to ensure that supply faults such as ruptured neutrals do not occur, and that if they do the risk of serious accident is minimal. In practice, serious accidents due to supply faults on PME systems are very rare – so rare that there are no real cases to discuss, and the following notes are based on purely hypothetical considerations. The fact that the risk is insignificant is, however, dependent on sensible precautions being taken where an installation is non-standard – for instance, if an RF earth is being used for a radio station.

(b) The risks from a PME installation stem from the possibility of a ruptured neutral in the supply to the consumer's premises. The break in the neutral could occur anywhere in the supply, and could affect just one house or several houses, depending on the supply arrangements. This could cause the neutral, and the mains earth which is bonded to it, to rise above the 'true' earth potential. To avoid the possibility of metalwork inside the house being at a different potential from the mains earth (which in this case is at neutral potential), the IEE regulations state that all metalwork such as central heating systems, water pipes, gas pipes etc should be securely bonded to the neutral at the PME bonding point near the consumer unit, as in Fig A1.1. In the unlikely event of a ruptured supply neutral, the current which would normally return via the neutral will attempt to return by way of all the other earthed conductors – including the RF earth to amateur radio equipment (Fig A1.2).

(c) Any conductor which is connected to bonded metalwork inside the house, and which passes out though the walls to the outside of the house, could rise to a significant potential with respect to the true earth, should a ruptured neutral occur. In a properly installed PME system, the risk of a severe shock from such metalwork is very small. However, a relatively mild shock could have a secondary effect such as causing someone to jump back or fall from a ladder.

(d) If a ruptured neutral were to cause a significant voltage to exist between the neutral/mains earth and the true earth, the existence of a fault will be revealed by the drop in the supply voltage between live and neutral. In other words, the mains voltage will have dropped, the loss being roughly the same as the voltage between the neutral/mains earth and the true earth. This is doubtless another reason why accidents are very rare – any faults on the supply are likely to be reported and corrected very quickly.

How PME affects the radio amateur

(a) If an RF earth connection is brought into the house and connected to the metalwork of equipment which is otherwise earth-free, a hazard is created because under the supposed supply fault conditions a voltage could exist between metal connected to the RF earth and the other metalwork inside the house which is bonded to the supply neutral.

(b) If an RF earth is connected to apparatus which is itself earthed to the mains earth system, then in the case of the supposed fault, very large currents (eg several tens of amps) could flow through the mains earth system and down the RF earth lead, giving rise to a fire risk.

(c) There is a general requirement, arising out of (a) and (b) above, that any external earth (in our case the RF earth) should be bonded to the PME bonding point using a conductor of not less than 10mm^2. This prevents a significant difference in potential existing and also provides an adequate path for prospective fault currents. Further information on bonding can be found in the IEE Wiring Regulations [1], and the *IEE On-site Guide* [2].

(d) Antennas which are effectively connected to the equipment metalwork, and therefore to the mains neutral/earth, are conductors passing through the walls of the house as mentioned in 'The practical risks of PME', paragraph (c), above. While the risk of severe shock is small, it is a wise precaution to ensure that such metalwork is out of normal reach, or suitably insulated.

Avoid touching antennas, earths or any external metalwork bonded to the PME bonding point if there is an obvious fault on the electricity supply, for instance if the voltage is much lower than normal. This could indicate a neutral-to-earth potential problem on the supply.

What you can do if you have a PME installation

There are four options:

(a) The proper procedure is to bond the RF earth to the PME bonding point at the consumer unit. The earth bonding conductor must be at least 10mm^2 (7/1.35mm) and all parts of the RF earth must be of suitably heavy conductors, in order to ensure that mechanical damage to the earth system will not lead to excessive current density in the event of a fault.

If the station is installed with EMC in mind, following the recommendations of Chapter 3, then RF currents entering the mains earth system through the bonding conductor should not be a problem. If it is, the station 'radio housekeeping' should be reviewed. In some instances interference may be brought into the station through the mains earth.

If it is necessary to prevent radio frequency currents from entering or leaving the main PME earth system, the RF earth can be isolated from the PME earth (so far as radio frequencies are concerned) by winding the bonding cable round a stack of ferrite rings, as described for a typical ferrite ring choke in Chapter 5. The high current capacity makes the bonding cable inflexible so that it may be necessary to use fewer turns and more cores to achieve the required inductance. Needless to say the arrangement must be mechanically and electrically sound, and its function as a low-resistance, high-current-capacity bonding conductor must not be impaired.

(b) It is possible to operate a station with an earthing system independent of the PME installation but this is not a safe option unless you have a room where all the electricity wiring can be on an independent earthing system. The reason for this is that metal-work connected to the PME earth and the non-PME earth system could be at different potentials and to avoid the danger of shock must be separated by at least two metres. (A little thought will show that it is not really practical to have the two earth systems in the same room because it would be necessary to ensure that

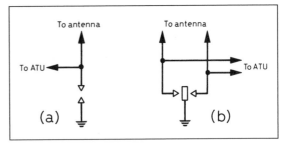

Fig A1.3. Using spark gaps or gas-discharge device to give lightning protection. (a) Single-wire antenna; (b) balanced feeder

earthed portable items on the different systems could not come within 2m of each other). If an independent earthing system is used, a residual current circuit breaker (RCD) is essential, and the new earth arrangements would have to be to IEE Regulations standard and suitably marked as a safety earth. Take advice from a qualified electrician before considering this solution.

(c) Likewise it is possible to have the PME removed from the whole house installation, but this is most definitely a job for the professional.

(d) It is possible to operate a station without an RF earth. This is common with VHF installations and is possible, under the right circumstances, on HF.

Earth-free antenna systems

It is possible to make an HF antenna system that has no connection to any outside earths. The metalwork of the station *must* be connected to the mains earth in the normal way, including the case of the ATU and the braid of any coaxial feeders. Wires coming into the house from outside must have a DC connection to the metal work of the station and hence to mains earth or, where this is not practical, the antenna arrangement must be such that there is no chance of any part coming into contact with the earth outside. Any parts of the antenna which is within reach from the ground should be insulated.

Because no external earth is being used, particular care must be taken to avoid RF currents passing into the mains earth system. This means that balanced antennas are essential, except perhaps for very low power. In particular, any sort of antenna which tunes against earth should be avoided (see Chapter 3). For low-power operation the use of a suitably insulated counterpoise might be considered.

Lightning protection with an earth-free antenna

As discussed in Chapter 3, where an antenna system is earth-free then we have the problem of discharging voltages caused by static build-up, and by surges caused by nearby direct strikes, without actually connecting the earth to the antenna system. This can be achieved by using spark gaps or gas-discharge devices, as indicated in Fig A1.3. (It should be noted that this will not protect against a direct strike. If such protection is thought to be necessary, then lightning protection for the whole property should be considered [3].)

Information on the use of gas-discharge devices will be found in references [4] and [5], and constructional details for spark gaps can be found in references [6] and [7]. The spark gaps or gas-discharge devices must be installed outside the house and in a PME installation there is the added requirement that they should be constructed and protected as if mains voltages were involved. Under the supposed supply fault conditions this might be the case. Where gas-discharge devices are used, they must be capable of handling the currents and voltages which may exist under any fault conditions.

References

[1] *Regulations for Electrical Installations*, 16th edn, The Institution of Electrical Engineers.

[2] *IEE On-site Guide*, The Institution of Electrical Engineers.

[3] BS6651, *Code of Practice for Protection of Structures against Lightning*, British Standards Institution.

[4] 'Lightning and EMP protection of amateur radio equipment', G R Jessop, *Radio Communication* December 1982.

[5] 'Lightning and your antenna', G R Jessop, *HF Antenna Collection*, RSGB.

[6] *Radio Communication Handbook*, 6th edn, ed D Biddulph, G8DPS, RSGB, 1994.

[7] *ARRL Antenna Handbook*, 16th edn, ARRL, Chapter 4.

Acknowledgement

The author wishes to acknowledge the assistance of the Electricity Association in the preparation of this appendix. The Association was supplied with a copy of the appendix, and asked to comment on the aspects which come within its province. They were good enough to supply the following:

"The Electricity Association, which is responsible for publication of *Engineering Recommendation G12/3 – National Code of Practice on the Application of PME to Low Voltage Networks*, agrees with the references in the appendix which are particular to mains supply and the provision of earthing facilities from PME systems. Regional electricity supply companies (RECs) publish their own guides on the connection and use of PME earthing facilities and these should be consulted by consumers."

Appendix

2   Lightning

This appendix is taken from an article in Radio Communication, *January 1984, by Alan Martindale, G3MYA. The last paragraph and references have been added after discussion with the author.*

Introduction

If, like my wife and I, you are one of the millions of people who show a certain amount of trepidation every time those black heaps of cumulo-nimbus loom large, read on. We live on one of the highest points in the small Suffolk town of Leiston, and we have had one or two close encounters of the charred kind since we moved here 26 years ago.

Our apprehension is fuelled by memories of an incident in 1959 when my top-band antenna became a lightning victim. We had been warned on the radio that there would be some electrical storms that day, so before I left for work I disconnected my equipment and grounded all the antennas. This seemed like a good idea at the time, and I was under the impression that this was the correct way to protect your installation from the ravages of lightning – how wrong can you be?

The predicted storms arrived after lunch, and did their thing with rain and heavenly pyrotechnics, and passed on their way. After the storm had gone by and the sun was shining, my wife looked out of the kitchen window to make sure the rain had stopped, and as she did so there was a most vivid flash accompanied by a tremendous crash and roar.

From what my wife told me when I got home, and from subsequent studies, I have no doubt that this was a positive lightning strike, which is the most violent type of all.

A quick inspection of the antenna system soon revealed a total absence of the top-band antenna and a close inspection of the ground revealed a few tiny copper balls – a direct strike! This unplanned metamorphosis of my antenna left me completely bemused and wondering how to protect my system from heavenly fireworks. I did not find an answer until comparatively recently, when the secretary of the lpswich Radio Club suggested that I fill in some idle moments in a study of lightning and give a talk on protective measures to the members – that's how I got really interested.

The first problem I encountered was the difficulty of finding any suitable learned literature on the subject in the English language. My quest was eventually rewarded by my local library with a work by Dr R H Golde entitled *Lightning Protection* (published in 1973 by Arnold at a (then) price of £6) to which I attribute most of the knowledge I have since acquired on the subject.

Thunderstorms – their formation and performance

In order to face an enemy, it is always a good idea to have a basic understanding of his physiology and habits – in military parlance this is called an 'appreciation' – so I will start this appreciation with the lightning's home base – the thunderstorm itself.

In the UK, thunderstorms fall into two basic categories which have quite different beginnings and are not readily confused with each other. Both are the result of very turbulent air which, by its very nature, collects electrical charges from frictional contacts within the air itself, with surrounding objects, and with water vapour in particular. These charges distribute themselves in a very orderly manner throughout the storm centre so that the top of the storm is positively charged with respect to its base.

The first of the two categories is the 'frontal' storm that heralds the arrival of cooler air on a cold front. It is triggered by the sudden upheaval of warm, surface air by the approaching cold air. This has the effect of lifting the warm air very quickly and creating an assisted thermal situation as the warmer air is replaced by the advancing cold air. All this activity is quite violent and frequently creates a *squall-line* that is often accompanied by quite severe, but short-lived electrical activity.

The more familiar type of storm is the one that appears late on a summer's afternoon and seems to hang around for hours grumbling and banging for what seems to be an age. These summer storms are again the result of rising warm air, but this time not assisted by the approach of cooler air. This time the rising air is the result of summer heat over warm, most ground creating thermals beloved of gliding enthusiasts. These thermals, however, are really quite fierce. They rise to many thousands of feet and lift huge quantities of water with them in the form of vapour, which condenses as it cools and forms those massive thunderheads known as *cumulo-nimbus*. This massive conglomeration of thermals is due to the fact that there is not usually much wind at the time, thus allowing these thermal columns to become much more concentrated. This lack of wind also accounts for the fact that summer storms tend to hang around for some time.

Both types of storm produce lightning of all descriptions. Frontal storms seem less active, but this is mostly due to their rapid transit over the ground and the fact that the line of storms is at right-angles to the passage of the front, thus allowing storm activity to pass relatively quickly. The summer storm, however, moves very slowly, is usually much larger – covering a greater ground area – and contains more than one storm centre to each storm.

Lightning – what it is, how it is produced, and types of stroke

While it is not easy to quantify all the components of a lightning stroke, a lot of research has been done, and by a combination of scientific measurement and educated observation it has been possible to come up with some interesting figures. For instance, the average peak current in a cloud-ground stroke is about 25kA. That is for a negative stroke, but the sort of current encountered in a positive stroke has been known to peak at over 270kA!

When it comes to measuring the actual amount of electricity discharged in a single stroke, the task is much more difficult, but certain scientific techniques have come up with some very reliable figures, based on measurement and calculation. For instance, by measuring the damage to aircraft or other metal surfaces, it is possible to re-create the same current in a controlled discharge and, by measuring the distance of travel and dissipation of heat en route, to come up with a reasonable estimate. From these and similar measurements, such as oscilloscope traces measuring current in certain selected lightning conductors, it is estimated that the average total discharged during the life of a single storm centre is around 1,000 coulombs. With an average of about 20 to 30 discharges per storm centre, this would put an average stroke's total discharge at around 40 coulombs. If we assume the average storm centre to resemble a capacitor of about $25\mu F$, with a charge of 1000C the charge potential will be of the order of $(V = Q/C)$ 40MV. To put this into perspective as potential energy, it represents an energy of 40GJ or (in terms of the domestic electricity supply) enough latent power to supply the average household for two years. Remember that one storm can, and usually does, consist of several storm centres.

One aspect of thunderstorms which can be measured accurately is the voltage gradient between cloud and ground, and results of research in this field (no pun intended!) produce some hair-raising figures (that pun was intentional!). On any day of the year there is always a space charge between the ground and the atmosphere, with the ground normally being negatively charged with respect to the air above it. On a warm, summer day this charge is around 100V/m, somewhat less on a cooler day. These figures go completely haywire when there are thunderstorms about!

As mentioned earlier, a thunderstorm carries a heavy static charge with positive at the top and negative at the bottom. In fact, the base of the thundercloud becomes so negatively charged that it is much more negative than the ground, thus reversing the normal voltage gradient and doing it in a most convincing way. With the base of a thundercloud at about 2km above ground and the top some 6–7km high, it is the charge across the bottom 2km that most interests us at this stage.

As a charged-up cu-nim approaches, the standing voltage gradient declines, momentarily disappears and then reappears with reversed polarity and increases very quickly. When the storm centre is still some 5km distant, the voltage gradient has climbed to 5000V/m, and directly beneath the storm centre it rises to a shocking 20,000V/m! It is when this gradient gets so steep that you feel its effects by your hair 'standing on end', and at the same time sweat glands are stimulated.

Looking at the voltage gradients, Fig A2.1 shows the gradient on a normal summer day, and Fig A2.2 the gradient under and in a thundercloud over flat ground. In residential areas of course, flat ground is broken by obstructions such as trees and buildings (not to mention our antennas!) and Fig A2.3 shows the effect of obstructions in the electrostatic field between cloud and ground. Where an obstruction occurs, there is some local

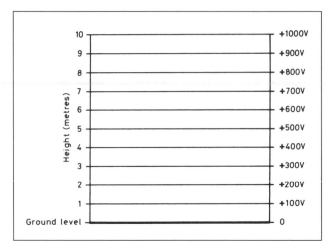

Fig A2.1. The normal voltage gradient on the bottom 10m of the atmosphere on a normal, warm summer's day

compression of the voltage gradient, especially at the corners of electrically earthed structures and other protrusions. Flagpoles, masts and chimneys all tend to cause tight compression and the effects of this will be discussed later. Fig A2.4 shows the extreme compression of the voltage gradient at the tip of a very sharp pointed object, such as a lightning conductor, and it will be seen how easy it is to get a breakdown of the insulation factor of air. This results in local ionisation, which appears as a pale blue glow and is sometimes called *St Elmo's Fire*. Another place where one can see ionised air in connection with a thunderstorm is along the leading edge of a very active squall line, but this pale blue line is not often visible.

Now to the actual anatomy of lightning itself, and there is literally more to this than meets the eye! For our example we will take the common ground stroke, known as the *negative stroke* because it originates in the negative region of the cloud, and which is the most documented of all the lightning phenomena.

As explained above, there is already a steep voltage gradient between the base of the cloud and the ground, though this in itself is not sufficient

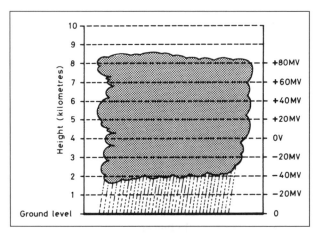

Fig A2.2. The average voltages encountered in the bottom 10km of the atmosphere in the area of an active thundercloud

for the insulation property of air to break down and the air to ionise – it needs some help. Beneath the cloud is an area of extreme turbulence, and this is constantly causing local high charges to be generated. This causes separation of air molecules, and the positively charged ones (those that have temporarily lost an electron) are lighter and travel upwards towards the highly negatively charged cloud base. This, in turn creates local imbalances in the overall voltage gradient and suddenly there is a path of about 20m where the gradient is so steep that ionisation occurs between a point at the cloud base and a positively charged packet of air about 20m or so below it. This ionised path now brings the cloud base potential down by 20m at the leader tip (the ionised track is called the *leader*). This means that another packet of positively charged air within about 20m will cause the leader to continue its course – possibly two more packets will be targets for the leader, which will split as many ways as it pleases. Not all leader tips continue to find sufficient targets on which to continue, so they just fizzle out, while the more prosperous ones continue on their erratic path towards the ground (see Fig A2.5).

In addition to the positively charged packets of air caused in the undercloud turbulence, there are also packets being formed by local ionisation down at ground level – where small coronal discharges are taking place at the tips of lightning conductors and other projections. All these little packets rise and join the throng, making sure that there is a steady supply of 'tag-points' for the leader tip. Eventually, this tip reaches a point about 40m above the ground. As the leader is a track of ionised air, it has a very low resistance, so it effectively brings the potential of the cloud base to a point just 40m from the ground.

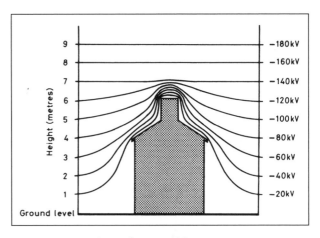

Fig A2.3. The effects of the high voltage gradient beneath a storm centre on ground obstructions. Note the tight bunching at chimney corners

So far, the leader has been travelling downwards from the cloud base at a velocity of around 10^5m/s, and is clearly visible as a pale blue, jagged, luminescent line. The reason we do not actually notice it is because it only takes about two thousandths of a second to complete its downward path before it is totally outshone by the main discharge. But, before that can happen, one final leap is required to complete the ionised path between the cloud and the ground. From its vantage point some 40m above the ground, the leader tip selects the shortest (electrical) path to ground potential and bridges it with the final bit of ionisation to complete the circuit between cloud and ground.

We now have a low-resistance connection between two points of many megavolts, and the only thing that can possibly happen is that a current will flow in an effort to neutralise that potential difference. The main discharge actually travels in the opposite direction to the leader, ie from the leader tip via the shortest electrical route back to the point of origin of the leader. The actual amount of current depends on the resistance of the path and the potential across it (Ohm's Law). If it had its way, the discharge would be a perfect square wave, but the ionised path, being a single conductor of finite length, also has inductance. This inductance shapes the return stroke, thus allowing it to build up to maximum as it generates a

Fig A2.4. The effect of a tall, sharp object in the high voltage field beneath an active storm centre. The tight bunching often leads to a local breakdown of air insulation at the tip, causing ionisation at that point

colossal magnetic field around it, and dying away as the field collapses at the end of the discharge. Fig A2.6 shows the profile of a ground stroke (negative) as measured on a special lightning conductor connected to an oscilloscope. Even so, the leading edge of the *return stroke* (as the main discharge is called) reaches the cloud just 22 ten-thousandths of a second after the leader started its downward journey. To put it another way – it's all over in a flash!

In the introduction I mentioned a positive ground stroke which made

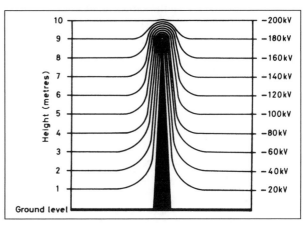

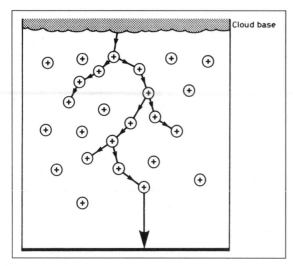

Cloud base

Fig A2.5. Track of a leader, showing its movement to the nearest positive air packet, and dying leader tips

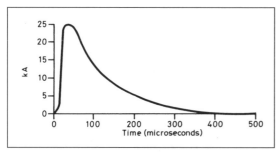

Fig A2.6. Profile of a negative ground stroke

Fig A2.7. Profile of a positive ground stroke

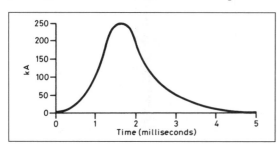

itself known to me in 1959. When a storm cloud is almost spent, there is less electrical activity as most of the charge has been discharged, either to ground or between clouds. The internal turbulence dies down and the positively charged air tends to mass at the top of the cloud. This now creates a new situation where the main potential difference appears, not at the base of the cloud, but at the top; this is all the residual charge, which amounts to something like almost half the original charge. As the top and base of the cloud tend to travel over the ground at varying speeds, there sometimes comes a point when the easiest way to discharge this huge charge at the top of the thunderhead is to do so to ground rather than in the cloud itself. This creates a positive stroke and works in exactly the reverse order to the more common negative stroke, with the leader starting its journey from the ground and the return stroke actually travelling the commonly thought route from cloud to ground. This is the mighty 'tail-ender' that often takes you by surprise when you think that a summer storm has safely passed. A profile of the positive stroke appears in Fig A2.7.

Another variant of the common negative ground stroke is the multiple stroke, and it also has an interesting anatomy. It starts out in exactly the same way as a normal negative ground stroke, but one return stroke is not enough to neutralise the potential across the leader track. With all the turbulence and the damage caused by the return stroke, the track needs re-ionising in order to permit a further discharge. A fresh leader sets out and follows the remnants of the original path for most or all of the way, creating a freshly ionised track for a further discharge. This new leader travels much faster than the first one, at the same speed as the main return stroke, in fact, and it is known as a *dart leader*. However, during the course of a multiple stroke, the entire storm is travelling laterally and it quite often happens that – after a few multiple strokes – the next dart leader finds a more acceptable ground target so that it ionises a fresh path for the next and subsequent discharges. To the unaided eye this looks as if the lightning has split and struck two or more places at the same time. This is not so, but because the strokes are in such quick succession it looks like a split stroke. This is what is commonly known as *fork-lightning*, for obvious reasons. Up to 26 successive discharges have been recorded in a multiple stroke, taking almost half a second to complete.

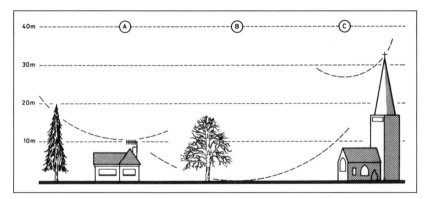

Fig A2.8. Three alternatives for the leader to find its final track to ground. At 'A' the fir tree and the TV antenna are most at risk; at 'B' the round tree or the ground itself seem most likely, while at 'C' the top of the church spire is an obvious choice. The significant thing is that prior to arriving at these three points, ground conditions have little effect on the track

Going back to our primary leader for a moment, it might help to put things in perspective if we take a further look at the last 40m when the final breakdown of the remaining gap occurs. As the last leap is over a distance of about 40m, and the actual insulation breakdown point of air is between 3 and 5kV/cm, a short calculation based on 4kV/cm gives a breakdown voltage between leader tip and ground of about 16MV! That is a fair old 'tickle' in anyone's language, and it helps one to realise just how insignificant are Man's efforts when compared with Nature's gentler activities. Incidentally, cloud-to-cloud strokes are thought to resemble negative ground strokes, but it is difficult to verify this. The common name for cloud-cloud strokes is *sheet lightning*.

Other factors which influence the strength of a lightning stroke are the nature of the ground potential at the point of strike. This means the physical nature of the object struck – its conductivity and the conductivity of the ground connected to it. For instance, a chimney that has not been used and is dry is not a very good conductor, but one that has been used and contains an internal coating of soot (carbon) is a good conductor and is more likely to attract a direct strike. Likewise a tree in winter when the sap is low is not so attractive as it is in the summer when it is full of sap and greenery.

Fig A2.8 shows how a leader selects its target for the final connection of the ionised track; it would be better if it could be shown in 3-D, but a cross-section of typical ground gives some idea of the situation. The important thing is that when the leader tip reaches the 40m point it will immediately go on to the most advantageous ground potential, and that means the point of least resistance (including the intervening air) and that normally means the highest point at earth potential within striking distance. Down to the 40m point from the cloud base it is not affected so much by what is on the ground, unless that ground structure is giving off a good supply of ionised air packets to guide the leader in.

Some facts and figures on thunderstorm activity in the UK

In assessing the need for protection from electrical storms, the following information may help to make up your mind – or, conversely, it may only serve to confuse you even further! By scientific observation it has been established that, on a nationwide basis, there are 10 days in the year when there are thunderstorms in the vicinity of any one place. They need not be directly overhead, only within clearly audible range. Of course this is an average which is subject to differences in location and counts from year to year, but these figures have been calculated over a long period and from a large variety of locations. My own recollection seems to differ quite substantially from this, but then mine is subjective while the quoted figures are objective.

Allowing for the fact that not all storms are overhead and that most storms consist of more than one storm centre, it is calculated that 10 storm centres pass directly overhead in any one year (on average!). However, seasonal variations, preferred storm paths and other stray phenomena could double this figure, so we will assess the risk on the basis of 20 storm centres passing overhead per year.

In the UK and similar temperate regions, each storm centre produces about 20 or 30 strokes during its average life of 30 to 60 minutes. Of these strokes, less than half (about 40%) are cloud-to-ground strokes, and of these ground strokes about 95% are negative type.

Each storm centre covers a ground area of about $4km^2$. If the storm centre were to remain perfectly stationary during its active life, it would produce 2.5 ground strokes/square kilometre, but on average a storm centre travels across the ground at a speed of 50km/h so its ground strokes are distributed over an area of $100km^2$. This gives an average of 0.1 ground strokes/storm centre/square kilometre. Multiply this by 20 storm centres/year and this leaves us with two ground strokes/square kilometre/year.

Now let us take a look at an average domestic property of about 20 × 50m or an area of $1000m^2$. One thousand such properties would fit into $1km^2$, which means that the chances of a direct strike on a single property works out at once every 500 years! We all know what happens to averages and statistics, but I think it is wise to try and get the whole thing into perspective.

Of course, radio amateurs do tend to tempt Providence a bit by putting things up high in the sky with good electrical connections to a point not too dissimilar from earth potential – this must increase the risk of a strike on our property, to the relief of our neighbours! If, in our quest for better radio communications, we do put up such electrically attractive devices, it is in our own interest to do something to protect them.

It is important to note that nothing short of full lightning protection of the antenna installation and adjacent property will give protection against a direct strike. Further information can be found in reference [1]. If the requirement is only to discharge high voltages which may build up on feeders etc then spark gaps or gas-discharge devices may be used. Information on the construction of spark gaps and the use of gas-discharge devices may be found in many places including references [2–5].

References

[1] BS 6651, *Code of Practice for Protection of Structures against Lightning*, BSI.
[2] *Radio Communication Handbook*, 6th edn, RSGB.
[3] *ARRL Antenna Handbook*, 16th edn, ARRL, Chapter 4.
[4] 'Lightning and EMP protection of amateur radio equipment', G R Jessop, *Radio Communication* December 1982.
[5] 'Lightning and your antenna', G R Jessop, *HF Antenna Collection*, RSGB.

3 Characteristics of some filters and ferrites

This appendix is a report on work carried out by Dave Lauder, G0SNO, at the request of the RSGB's EMC Committee. The performance of the filters and chokes has been measured under defined conditions, and comments made on their effectiveness. The author is professionally involved in EMC, mainly in the field of education and training, and has written the EMC column in Radio Communication *since August 1996.*

THE filters and chokes described are for use with broadcast radios, TVs or other affected equipment. They are not suitable for use at the output of an amateur transmitter.

Table A3.1 summarises the characteristics of various filters and ferrites for EMC use on various amateur bands. For an explanation of common-mode (in-phase) and differential-mode (anti-phase) signals, see Chapter 5 and also later in this appendix. Common-mode signals can be caused by amateur transmissions on any band where the braid of a TV antenna co-axial cable, rather than the antenna itself, acts as a receiving antenna for amateur signals, particularly at HF where a UHF TV antenna itself is not an efficient receiving antenna.

In the 'stop-band loss' column, the bar graphs represent the minimum filter loss in a particular amateur band to the nearest 5dB. The higher the stop-band loss, the better. One square represents 10dB which may cure minor breakthrough, but in most cases 20dB, 30dB or more may be required. Six squares represent 60dB or more.

In the 'pass-band loss' column, the bar graphs represent the loss in the UHF TV band to the nearest 1dB. The lower the pass-band loss, the better. In the case of the HPF2, the pass-band includes the FM radio broadcast band (Band 2, 87.5 to 108MHz) as well as the UHF TV band. Many of the filters have 'N/A' in the FM broadcast pass-band loss column which means 'not applicable', ie the filter is not suitable for passing this band.

Where the UHF TV signal strength is high, a loss of 3 to 5dB may not be noticeable but, if the signal is weak, then even a 2dB loss could give a slight but noticeable increase in noise on the picture.

In some cases, the pass-band loss of a filter varies in different parts of the UHF TV band, particularly on the lowest channels. In this case, the relevant curve on Figs A3.10 to A3.14 should be examined to find the loss for the UHF TV channels used in a particular area. (See Appendix 7 for vision carrier frequencies of UHF TV channels).

For ease of reference, all figures, photos and the table are grouped at the end of this appendix.

Filters

For each filter, the principal characteristics are described, together with equivalent circuits and measured response curves for a typical filter. The responses are subject to some variation between samples of the same type, particularly in the case of the home-constructed filter. The test methods are described later.

Home-constructed high-pass filter and braid-breaker

Circuit and layout: see Fig A3.19.

Response curves: see Figs A3.1, A3.2, A3.11 (pass band), A3.16 (common mode).

Type: balanced L-C high-pass filter (UHF TV) with braid-breaking.

Pass band: Bands 4 and 5 (UHF TV).

Loss in pass band: typically 0.5–2dB.

Braid-breaking action: capacitive.

Remarks: This filter is simple but should be used with caution as it is a balanced filter used in an unbalanced feeder. It has good rejection of HF differential-mode signals but rejection of common-mode signals is not as good as a transformer-type braid-breaker. As its roll-off below 470MHz is not particularly sharp, this filter is not particularly effective at 144MHz. For improved rejection at 144MHz, the five-element, home-constructed, high-pass filter shown in Chapter 5 can be used.

Fig A3.1 shows the response of this filter and the AKD HPF1 in a test circuit with a common ground between the input and output. This test bypasses the capacitor in series with the braid and gives sharp resonances which are unlikely to occur in practice at the frequencies shown. Fig A3.2 shows the response of the two filters with a 'floating' source (see 'Test methods' later).

AKD HPF1 high-pass filter

Equivalent circuit: see Fig A3.20.

Response curves: see Figs A3.1, A3.2, A3.11 (pass band), A3.16 (common mode).

Type: L-C high-pass filter (UHF TV) with braid-breaker.

Pass band: Bands 4 and 5 (UHF TV).

Loss in pass band: typically 0.5–2dB.

Braid-breaking action: capacitive.

Remarks: Similar performance to home-constructed filter above but slightly better stop-band performance. See notes in previous section regarding test methods.

AKD HPF2 high-pass filter

Equivalent circuit: see Fig A3.21.

Response curves: see Figs A3.3 (stop band), A3.12 (pass band).

RSGB description: Filter 2, HPF for FM Band 2.

Type: L-C high-pass filter (FM broadcast).

Pass band: Bands 2 (FM radio broadcast), up to 4 and 5 (UHF TV)

Loss in pass band: typically less than 1dB in most of Band 2 (2.5dB at 87.5MHz), 1–3dB in Bands 4 and 5.

Braid-breaking action: none.

Remarks: It is intended for reducing breakthrough on FM broadcast receivers (87.5–108MHz), particularly from HF signals but is also useful for rejecting 50MHz signals. It is only effective against differential-mode signals as it has no braid-breaking action, but an HPF2 with a BB1 or ferrite common-mode choke can be used together if this is required.

AKD HPF6 high-pass filter

Equivalent circuit and appearance: see Fig A3.22.

Response curves: see Figs A3.4 (differential mode overall), A3.13 (pass band).

RSGB description: Filter 8, six-section for UHF TV.

Type: Six-section L-C high-pass filter (UHF TV), sharp cut-off.

Pass band: Bands 4, 5 (UHF TV).

Loss in pass band: typically 1–3dB (Channels 21–40), 1–2dB (Channels 41–68).

Braid-breaking action: None.

Remarks: The HPF6 is a high-performance filter with a very sharp cut-off below 470MHz and is specifically designed for reducing breakthrough from the 430–440MHz amateur band. It also has very good rejection of all lower amateur bands. If a UHF TV masthead preamplifier is in use, the HPF6 should be mounted in a weatherproof box between the antenna and the preamplifier.

Trace B on Fig A3.4 shows the measured response of an HPF6 with 40dB loss at 435MHz. If the coaxial plug on the flying lead was grounded to the metal case of the filter, the response improved, as shown in trace C with 50dB loss measured at 435MHz.

Mutek XBF700 television band stripline filter

Appearance: see Fig A3.23.

Response curves: see Figs A3.5 (differential mode overall) and A3.13 (pass band).

Type: stripline band-pass filter (UHF TV).

Pass band: Bands 4, 5 (UHF TV).

Loss in pass band: typically 2–3dB, channels 24–65, rising to 9dB on channel 21, and 4dB on channel 68.

Braid-breaking action: none.

Remarks: This is the only filter tested with a stop band which includes 1.3GHz. It is also useful at 430–440MHz and good on the 144MHz band and below. The pass-band loss rises at the top of Band 5 and at the lower end of Band 4, particularly on channels 21 and 22. The XBF700 is a stripline filter PCB (size 145 × 57mm) which requires the addition of connectors or flying leads and a case.

The loss measured above 1GHz is affected by stray capacitive coupling between the input and output of the filter. The result shown in Fig A3.5 is likely to be representative of the performance of the filter in practice, although better performance may be measured using an improved test set-up.

AKD BB1 braid-breaker

Equivalent circuit: see Fig A3.24.

Response curves: see Figs A3.6 (differential mode overall), A3.14 (pass band), A3.16 (common mode).

RSGB description: Filter 1, braid-breaker.

Type: 1:1 transformer braid-breaker.

Pass band: below 10MHz to over 1GHz.

Loss in pass band: typically 2dB over most of its range but 3 to 4dB at UHF channels 50–68.

Braid-breaking action: 1:1 transformer.

Remarks: The BB1 is a transformer-type braid-breaker which is more effective against common-mode signals picked up 'on the braid' than a capacitive braid-breaker such as the HPF1. The BB1 is particularly effective at HF. The braid-breaking action diminishes at VHF due to interwinding capacitance of the transformer, with only 7–8dB loss to common-mode signals in the 144MHz band. A BB1 can be cascaded with other filters such as HPF2, HPF6 or XBF700 which do not have any braid-breaking action, although the total pass-band loss is then the sum of the pass-band losses (in decibels) of the two filters.

Although not intended as a high-pass filter, the differential mode response of a BB1 starts to roll off below 10MHz, with some attenuation to differential-mode signals in the 3.5 and 1.8MHz bands.

A BB1 can also be effective on the 1.8, 3.5 and 7MHz bands in reducing HF interference produced by TV line timebase harmonics and switch-mode power supply harmonics by preventing these from being radiated by the braid of the TV antenna cable.

Where a braid-breaker is required with negligible insertion loss to differential-mode signals at all frequencies, a common-mode choke may be used (see 'Ferrites' sections below). A suitable type of common-mode choke can be a more effective braid-breaker than a BB1 at VHF, but the BB1 will generally be more effective at HF.

AKD HPFS high-pass filter (special)

Equivalent circuit: see Fig A3.25.

Response curves: see Figs A3.6 (differential mode overall), A3.14 (pass band), A3.16 (common mode).

RSGB description: Filter 3, HPF & Braid Breaker.

Type: L-C high-pass filter with transformer braid-breaker.

Pass band: Bands 4, 5 (UHF TV).

Loss in pass band: typically 3–4dB (Channels 21–40), 4–5dB (Channels 41–68).

Braid-breaking action: 1:1 transformer.

Remarks: The HPFS is a BB1 combined with a high-pass filter. See BB1 section above for braid-breaking performance. The HPFS is a good all-round filter for all amateur bands up to and including 144MHz but it has negligible effect at 432MHz.

Due to the relatively high pass-band loss, the HPFS is not suitable for areas where the TV signal strength is low. For the lowest possible pass-band loss, the home-constructed filter shown in Chapter 5 can be used, in conjunction with a ferrite ring choke (if required). See also the section on ferrite rings below.

Another filter with identical electrical characteristics to the HPFS is sold by Maplin Electronics and Waters & Stanton as 'Global HP-4A'.

AKD RBF1/70cm notch filter

Equivalent circuit: see Fig A3.26.

Response curves: see Figs A3.7 (differential mode overall), A3.15 (pass band).

Type: series-resonant trap between inner conductor and braid.

RSGB description: Filter 5, notch tuned to 435MHz.

Pass band: Bands 4, 5 (UHF TV).

Loss in pass band: typically 2–5dB (Channels 21–30), 1–2dB (Channels 31–68).

Braid-breaking action: none.

Remarks: The RBF1 is called a 'radar blip filter' because it was designed to notch out airport radar signals on UHF TV channel 36. The RBF1/70cm version is pre-tuned to 435MHz, although it is possible to adjust the tuning if necessary by means of a trimmer capacitor which is accessible through a hole in the plastic sleeving under the label. A non-metallic trim tool should be used to avoid detuning, as neither side of the trimmer capacitor is grounded. The RBF1 also has a high-pass action with useful rejection of HF differential-mode signals.

AKD TNF2 tuned notch filter range

Equivalent circuit: see Fig A3.27.

Response curves (VHF): see Figs A3.8 (stop band), A3.15 (pass band), A3.17 (common mode).

Response curves (HF): see Figs A3.9 (stop band), A3.15 (pass band), A3.18 (common mode).

AKD type	RSGB description
TNF2/2 metres	Filter 4, notch tuned to 145MHz
TNF2/70MHz	Filter 7, notch tuned to 70MHz
TNF2/50MHz	Filter 6, notch tuned to 50MHz
TNF2/10	Filter 10, notch tuned to 28MHz
TNF2/15	Filter 15, notch tuned to 21MHz
TNF2/20	Filter 20, notch tuned to 14MHz

Type: L-C notch filters in series with inner conductor and braid.

Pass band: Bands 4, 5 (UHF TV).

151

Loss in pass band: typically 0.5–2dB (Channels 21–40), 2dB (Channels 41–68)

Braid-breaking action: Resonant, only at tuned frequency.

Remarks: Each filter provides rejection of differential-mode and common signals over a certain range of frequencies only. These have low insertion loss in UHF TV Bands 4 and 5 but a high insertion loss in Band 2 and are therefore not suitable for passing FM broadcast Band 2 signals. For amateur bands below 14MHz, tuned notch filters are not generally used as a high-pass filter/braid-breaker will normally be equally effective.

The test methods used to obtain Figs A3.8, 3.9, 3.17 and A3.18 are different from the test methods used by the manufacturer of the filters. This may be why some of the notches measured do not coincide exactly with the specified amateur bands. Nevertheless, in most cases there is still a good level of attenuation in the specified band. See later for details of test methods.

In general, this type of filter should only be used if no other type is suitable as it can cause 'mode conversion' of common-mode signals to differential mode. This may increase breakthrough of certain signals well away from the notch frequency. In particular, the TNF2 type of tuned notch filter is not recommended for use at the input of a UHF TV preamplifier or a distribution amplifier as it may increase rather than decrease the unwanted signal or may cause the amplifier to oscillate.

Home-constructed five-element high-pass filter

Equivalent circuit: see Chapter 5, Fig 5.11.

Response curves: see Fig A3.10.

Type: High pass.

Pass band: Bands 4, 5 (UHF TV).

Loss in pass band: 1dB or less.

Braid-breaking action: none.

Remarks: Constructional details for this filter are given in Chapter 5. It has a sharper roll-off below 470MHz than the filter shown in Fig A3.19 with about 60dB of attenuation at 144MHz. It does not have any braid-breaking action but can be combined with a ferrite ring (see below).

Antiference TVI/U

Response curves: see Fig A3.10.

Type: High pass.

Pass band: Bands 4, 5 (UHF TV).

Loss in pass band: 1dB or less.

Braid-breaking action: none.

Remarks: This filter is housed in an all-metal case only 1.75in (45mm) long. It is quite widely available from electrical shops and DIY warehouses. It is intended to reject 27MHz but is useful on all amateur bands up to 70MHz. It has poor rejection of 144MHz, however.

Ferrite chokes

Various types of ferrite cores can be used to make common-mode chokes on coaxial cables, mains cables and audio cables etc. These chokes introduce a series impedance to unwanted common-mode signals picked up from a transmitter but have negligible effect on the wanted differential-mode signal in the cable.

The ferrite rings currently available from RSGB are Fair-Rite type 2643802702. They have an inside diameter of 0.9in (22.85mm) and a width of 0.5in (12.7mm). These are made of grade 43 material and are also sold by Amidon Associates as FT140-43.

For maximum impedance on the lower HF bands, at least 12–14 turns on one or two cores are recommended. As the inductance is proportional to the number of turns *squared*, six turns on *four* cores are equivalent to 12 turns on a single core. At about 10MHz and above, stray capacitance in parallel with the winding starts to become significant and can be reduced in two ways:

(a) By winding the turns in two halves as shown in Fig A3.30, taking care that all the turns are threaded through the hole *in the same direction*. This allows the ring to be wound to full capacity so there is no loss of performance on the lower HF bands.
(b) By winding the ring as shown in Fig A3.31, that is, only about two-thirds full with the ends of the winding kept apart. This has the disadvantage of reduced performance on the lower HF bands due to the reduced number of turns.

At VHF, stray capacitance becomes particularly important and performance may be improved by winding the ring only half full.

TV antenna cables

A ferrite ring choke on a TV antenna coaxial cable can be used on its own to reduce HF breakthrough due to pick-up of signals on the braid of the coaxial cable or it can be used in conjunction with any high-pass filter which does not have built-in braid-breaking. Although the ring core is not a true transformer-type braid-breaker, it can give excellent results on most HF bands if enough turns are used. It also has the advantage of a lower pass-band loss than the transformer type. The additional loss introduced at UHF is small, typically 1dB or less, due to loss of the additional cable and connectors. This is clearly an important factor in areas where UHF TV signals are weak.

There are two ways to make a common-mode choke using coaxial cable. If standard low-loss cable is used, it should not be wound tightly as the sharp bending will damage it. Instead, it should be left loose as shown in Photo A3.2. As this loose winding is rather unsightly, it should only be used on a neighbour's TV or satellite system if there is no alternative. As there will only be room for six or seven turns, *four* rings are required to achieve the results shown in Fig A3.28 for 12 turns on a single ring.

An alternative solution is to wind a length of miniature 2.5–2.8mm diameter 75Ω coaxial cable such as RG179 or Maplin XR88V through a single ferrite ring. This cable is not compatible with standard coaxial plugs and sockets unless the outside diameter is increased using rubber sleeving. Even then, it is easily damaged, so a more robust solution is to house the ring in a small plastic box with coaxial sockets as shown in Photo A3.1. A metal box, a metallised plastic box or a box with a metal lid should not be used because even if the connectors are insulated from the box, the metal adds stray capacitance in parallel with the ferrite ring. The five-element, home-constructed filter (see Chapter 5, Fig 5.11) can also be housed in the same box if a Maplin Electronics type MB1 box is used (stock No LH20W). To fit the PCB slots in this box, the strip of Veroboard for the filter should be 22 holes long. It should be glued in place to keep it away from the ferrite ring.

A Fair-Rite type 2643802702 ring can easily accommodate 18 turns using less than one metre of cable. To reduce stray capacitance, the winding is wound in two halves, as shown in Fig A3.30. Self-locking cable ties secure the cable to the ring and the ring to the box. A 0.9m length of this miniature coaxial cable adds only about 1dB of additional loss in the UHF TV band. The impedance of this winding to common-mode signals is between curves B and C in Fig A3.28.

Cable TV

If amateur HF transmissions cause breakthrough on a cable TV system and other types of filtering have not cured the problem, it may be necessary to fit a ferrite ring on the cable to the RF input of the cable TV converter box but a UHF high-pass filter must NOT be included at this point. F-type connectors are required but F-type plugs cannot be fitted to miniature coaxial cable because the centre core of the coaxial cable acts as the centre pin of the plug. A boxed ferrite ring can be used with panel-mounted F-type sockets as shown in Photo A3.1. A Maplin H2855 ABS box (BZ72P) can be used but it is necessary to trim off the PCB mounting ridges where the F-type sockets are fitted. The sockets can be Maplin FE98G. A short length of coaxial cable with F-type plugs is also required. Maplin FE98X plugs are suitable but need to be fitted using a crimping tool. Alternatively, there is a screw-on type (FU04E) which does not require crimping.

Satellite TV

The download from the LNB (low-noise block converter) in a satellite TV dish carries the first IF at 950–1750MHz on older systems (950–1950MHz on newer systems) covering the Astra 1D satellite. The coaxial cable is normally fairly well screened with foil and braid so there should be little leakage of signals into or out of the cable. Nevertheless, the braid of the cable can act as a receiving antenna for amateur HF signals and can also radiate RFI generated by the digital electronics in some satellite receivers. Either problem can be tackled by winding the satellite downlead through a ferrite core near the indoor receiver. Other types of filter cannot be fitted in a satellite TV downlead as it also carries the DC supply to the LNB.

The boxed ferrite ring described above for cable TV might appear suitable for satellite TV but on the prototype model the loss increased significantly above 850MHz. The loss in 0.9m of miniature coaxial cable is about 2dB at 1800MHz but a much larger loss was caused by the mismatch of the panel-mounted F-type connectors which are only intended for use below 1000MHz. The mismatch introduced by two Maplin FE98G F-type sockets starts to become significant above 800MHz and can cause a loss of up to 20dB at some frequencies around 1800MHz.

Unless better-quality F-type sockets are available and are specified for use up to 2GHz, the best solution is to use a 1.5m length of 75Ω satellite TV cable such as CT100 type, threaded seven times through two or four Fair-Rite grade 43 rings as shown in Photo A3.2. Two F-type plugs should be fitted to the cable and an F-type straight coupler should be used to connect this to the satellite downlead. This coupler should be a high-quality type suitable for use up to 2GHz.

Clip-on cores

The split bead clip-on ferrite cores shown in Photo A3.3 are sold by Maplin Electronics as computer data line noise filters and are also available from other suppliers such as RS Components and Farnell Components. They are useful for cables which cannot be threaded through a ring core but it is important to ensure that the two halves of the core can close together without the slightest air gap. A core with a 13mm diameter hole such as Maplin BZ34M can accommodate about six turns of thin loudspeaker cable or eight turns of miniature coaxial cable (see Photo A3.3). Curve A in Fig A3.29 shows the characteristics which were measured with a six-turn winding on a Maplin BZ34M core. As these cores are primarily intended for EMC use at VHF, the performance of different manufacturers' products can vary significantly on the lower HF bands. With a multi-turn winding, a split bead offers poorer high-frequency performance than a ring core due to greater stray capacitance in parallel with the winding.

For a thick cable such as a SCART cable, which can only pass through the core once, the impedance of a split bead is typically 100Ω at 14MHz, rising to 200–300Ω at 144MHz. A single 'turn' on this type of core generally has little or no effect on the HF bands although it may damp a cable resonance if placed at a particular point on the cable. Three or four cores in series may start to give a useful impedance in some cases but over 100 clip-on chokes with a single turn would be required to achieve the same impedance as 18 turns on a ferrite ring!

Other types of clip-on ferrite core are available in the form of pairs of 'U'-shaped cores but these can be an expensive solution because typically four pairs of U-cores are required to achieve the same effect as a single split-bead core.

Yoke rings

A typical deflection coil assembly from the CRT in a TV receiver or computer monitor is shown in Photo A3.2. This assembly can be salvaged from a scrap CRT, taking care not to fracture the neck of the tube and not to remove the EHT connector as the tube may still be charged. The windings can be stripped off to reveal a ferrite yoke ring core with an inside diameter of 30–50mm depending on the size of the CRT. The ring is split into two halves which are clipped together. Although not intended for RF use, ferrite yoke rings normally have about the right permeability for amateur

EMC applications. Results can be somewhat variable but a 14-turn winding typically gives the characteristics shown by curve D in Fig A3.29 for any size of yoke ring. If possible, up to 20 turns should be used for HF. It is advisable to check the characteristics of a yoke ring core against a known good ferrite ring (See Chapter 5, Fig 5.7). Other types of scrap ferrite cores such as TV line output transformer cores have completely different RF characteristics and are NOT normally suitable for EMC use.

The main application for yoke ring cores is for choking SCART cables as these are thick and the connectors cannot be threaded through a ring. In some cases of HF breakthrough on a TV, video recorder or satellite receiver, a ferrite choke is required on the SCART cable in addition to other types of filtering. This can also be used to reduce RFI radiated by some types of TV via the SCART cable. A typical 1.5m long SCART lead is only long enough to allow about seven turns, however. The impedance would therefore be only one quarter of that shown by curve D in Fig A3.29.

Ferrite rods

An MW/LW ferrite antenna rod can be used to make a common-mode choke as shown in Fig A3.32. Curve C in Fig A3.29 shows the typical characteristics of a 25-turn winding on a ferrite rod 200mm long by 9.5mm diameter. This gives reasonably good results at 21MHz and above.

A ferrite rod should not be wound with semi-airspaced coaxial cable as the tight bend radius may cause the cable to collapse internally and short-circuit. A 25-turn winding requires about 1.2m of cable.

Test methods

A Hewlett-Packard 8591A spectrum analyser with tracking generator was used for the tests. A tracking generator is a signal generator which is built into a spectrum analyser and whose output frequency follows (tracks) the frequency sweep of the spectrum analyser. When the tracking generator output is fed via a filter to the spectrum analyser's RF input, the frequency response of the filter is displayed.

Due to the noise floor of the spectrum analyser and the additional attenuators used, measurements of filter loss greater than 60dB could not be made, hence losses greater than 55dB are not shown on the response curves.

Differential mode, 75Ω

Figs A3.33 and A3.34 show the test set-up for measuring differential-mode characteristics of filters which have transformer braid-breaking or no braid-breaking. The 50Ω output of the tracking generator is connected via a 10dB attenuator with 50Ω input impedance and 75Ω output impedance to the filter under test. Another attenuator with 75Ω input impedance and 50Ω output impedance is used to match the output of the filter under test into the 50Ω input of the spectrum analyser. The resistor values shown are designed to give a true 10dB power loss, for example 0dBm in 50Ω at the tracking generator output results in −10dBm in 75Ω at the output of the attenuator.

Above 600MHz, most of the filters tested allow some UHF signal to pass from the inner of the coaxial cable to the outside of the braid, resulting in standing waves on the outside of the cable. These standing waves cause variations in the apparent filter loss, depending on the exact cable length used. To give more repeatable test results, a ferrite clip-on choke is fitted to the output lead of the filter under test to attenuate such signals on the outside of the coaxial cable.

The arrangement in Fig A3.33 is used to give the 0dB reference trace, then the filter under test is plugged in as shown in Fig A3.34. For the 2dB/division pass-band loss tests, the reference trace is not perfectly flat but has up to ±0.25dB ripple at UHF. For the 2dB/division curves, the filter loss is the difference between the filter response trace and the reference trace.

When the filter is actually in use, however, the source and load impedances which are presented to it may be far from 75Ω, particularly at frequencies far outside the UHF TV bands. This means that its loss in practice may be significantly different from the test results.

Differential mode, 75Ω, floating source

Figs A3.35 and A3.36 show the test set-up for measuring differential-mode characteristics of filters which have an impedance in series with the braid as well as in series with the inner conductor. A BB1 braid-breaker is used to provide a 'floating' source, that is a source with neither side grounded to the chassis of the spectrum analyser. At HF, this is close to a true 'floating' source, but at VHF, and especially above 150MHz, the interwinding capacitance of the BB1 transformer makes the source 'float' less well. A clip-on ferrite choke was fitted to the output lead of the filter under test.

This test method was used when testing the HPF1, all the TNF2 range and the home-constructed high-pass filter/braid-breaker. The 0dB reference traces take account of the additional loss introduced by the BB1 so that the curves show only the loss of the filter under test. The filter responses are not shown below 10MHz because the response of the BB1 transformer starts to fall off.

If the test set-up shown in Fig A3.34 is used for filters with an impedance in series with the braid, the common ground between input and output short-circuits the impedance which is in series with the ground side of the filter, affecting the response of the filter. Fig A3.1 shows the response of two filters using the test method in the previous section but without the ferrite choke. Fig A3.2 shows the response with the 'floating source' test method, which is more likely to be representative of what happens in practice.

In the case of the tuned notch filters (see Fig A3.27), there is some interaction between the two tuned circuits L1/C1 and L2/C2, making it difficult to tune the filter so that it gives a differential-mode notch and a common-mode notch at the same frequency. In some cases the notch is not centred on the specified amateur band but the filter still provides a useful attenuation on the latter.

When the filter is actually in use, the differential-mode current on the inner conductor which flows through L1/C1 returns via the braid and L2/C2, except for a small proportion of the current which returns via stray capacitances external to the filter. The 'floating' source test models this situation with nearly equal but antiphase currents through L1/C1 and L2/C2. The two tuned circuits are in series as far as differential-mode signals are concerned, and this test shows a double notch response for some of the filters. In practice, the actual notch frequencies may also be affected by stray capacitances which are effectively in parallel with the tuned circuit L2/C2.

Common-mode filter test, 50Ω
Fig A3.37 illustrates the situation where unwanted signals are picked up by the outside of a coaxial cable braid acting as a receiving antenna. These unwanted signals appear to come from a source impedance which is not well defined but which could be hundreds of ohms, except in the case where the coaxial cable forms a resonant antenna for a particular amateur band. These unwanted signals flow via the chassis of the TV or other equipment and then to earth via capacitance and via the mains earth wire if any. Where there is no mains earth wire, there is still an RF path to earth via the mains due to capacitance from the chassis of the equipment to the mains live and neutral, and capacitance from these conductors to earth. (In PME installations, the mains neutral and earth are actually joined where the supply enters the house.) The 'load' impedance seen by common-mode signals is also not well defined but could be hundreds of ohms.

Amateur signals may also cause common-mode signals directly in the mains cable, either due to pick-up in the mains cable itself or in the mains wiring of the house. In such cases a common-mode choke is required.

In order to reduce the common-mode current resulting from this unwanted pick-up, it is necessary to introduce an impedance in series with the unwanted signal path without significantly affecting the wanted differential-mode signal flowing in the TV antenna cable, the mains cable or other cable. This common-mode impedance should be relatively large compared to the sum of the source and load impedances of the common-mode signal. This means that a filter which shows an attenuation of, for example, 20dB to common-mode signals in a 50Ω test circuit may give significantly less common-mode rejection in practice because the source and load impedances are likely to be greater than 50Ω near the affected equipment.

Unwanted common-mode (in-phase) signals are sometimes loosely referred to as being 'on the braid' of a coaxial cable, meaning that there is an RF voltage between the braid of the cable and earth, but the phrase 'on the braid' obscures the fact that there must also be an equal RF voltage between the inner and earth. The braid and the inner are connected together at the TV antenna by a low-impedance, folded-dipole element. Therefore, if there is a signal which is on the outside of the braid with respect to earth but which was not picked up by the TV antenna itself, then an equal or nearly equal signal must also exist on the inner with respect to earth, although it can only be measured at the ends of the cable. In any case, with a perfectly shielded coaxial cable, a signal outside the cable cannot pass through the shield and produce a potential difference between the inner conductor and the inside of the braid. To reduce common-mode currents it is therefore necessary to introduce an impedance in series with both the braid and the inner, either by winding the cable through a ring core or by using a filter which has impedance in series with both the braid and the inner.

Figs A3.38 and A3.39 show the test set-up for common-mode testing of filters which have any form of braid-breaking action. The 50Ω output of the tracking generator is connected to a 10dB attenuator with 50Ω input and output impedance. This attenuator also provides an approximate 50Ω termination for the tracking generator even when the impedance on the output of the attenuator is far from 50Ω, thus minimising standing waves in the input cable to the test jig. A second 10dB attenuator with 50Ω input and output impedances ensures that the filter under test is presented with a load impedance very close to 50Ω.

The input and output of the filter under test are terminated with 75Ω resistors to simulate the actual conditions of use, although in practice the source and load impedances may be significantly different from 75Ω at frequencies below UHF. The fact that the filter is designed to be used in 75Ω circuits is of little relevance to common-mode signals. The common-mode performance has been measured in a 50Ω circuit to be consistent with the test method in the next section.

In the case of the TNF2 range of tuned notch filters (see Fig A3.27), the two tuned circuits L1/C1 and L2/C2 are effectively in parallel as far as common-mode signals are concerned but in series as far as differential-mode signals are concerned.

Common-mode ferrite test, 50Ω

This type of measurement in the field of EMC is normally made with 50Ω source and load impedances. Fig A3.40 shows the test set-up for measuring the characteristics of common-mode chokes wound onto ferrite rings and other types of core. Fig A3.38 shows the configuration for the 0dB reference trace.

This test method is similar to the test method in the previous section except that where a ferrite ring is wound with coaxial cable, it makes no difference to the result whether the signal is driven onto the braid only or onto the braid and inner together.

As mentioned above, the source and load impedances for common-mode signals are not well defined and could be as high as several hundred ohms. Thus a common-mode choke which shows an attenuation of, for example, 20dB in a 50Ω circuit may give significantly less common-mode rejection in practice.

Any common-mode chokes with a measured loss greater than 20dB at VHF tend to be very sensitive to the stray capacitance of nearby conducting objects so that the repeatability of such measurements is poor. The test method used for common-mode tests on chokes and filters was not considered suitable for frequencies above 200MHz.

If a spectrum analyser with tracking generator is not available, the test jig shown in Fig A3.40 can still be used to make measurements at spot frequencies or to adjust the tuning of a tuned common-mode choke. The 10dB 50Ω attenuators can be omitted if only relative measurements are required. The signal source could be a signal generator or a steady signal

Photos

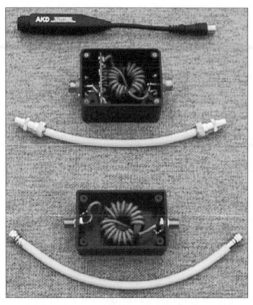

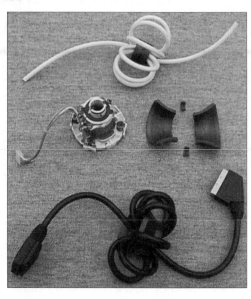

Photo A3.1. *Top:* AKD HPFS filter. *Middle:* Boxed ferrite ring choke and high-pass filter with coaxial connectors for UHF TV. *Bottom:* Boxed ferrite ring choke with F-type connectors for cable TV

Photo A3.2. *Top:* A length of 6.6mm diameter coaxial cable wound on to two Fair-Rite grade 43 rings. *Middle:* A scrap deflection coil assembly from a small CRT and a split ferrite yoke ring core from a larger CRT. *Bottom:* A SCART cable wound on to a ferrite ring core

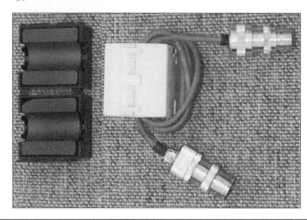

Photo A3.3. *Left:* Maplin BZ34M clip-on ferrite core with 13mm diameter hole. *Right:* A length of miniature coaxial cable wound on to a clip-on ferrite core

such as a beacon received by an amateur antenna. The signal level at the output of the test jig can be measured by any receiver tuned to the required frequency, provided it has an S-meter. Ideally the S-meter should have a large scale which has been calibrated in decibels relative to 1µV against a signal generator, or calibrated against a beacon or other source in decibels relative to the weakest signal detectable on the S-meter (S1 reading) using a calibrated variable attenuator. With a calibrated S-meter, the loss of various common-mode chokes can be measured in decibels. With a meter calibrated only in S-points, useful relative measurements can still be made to compare two different chokes at a particular frequency or to tune a tuned braid-breaker. (See also Chapter 5, Fig 5.7)

Table A3.1. Summary of filter performance

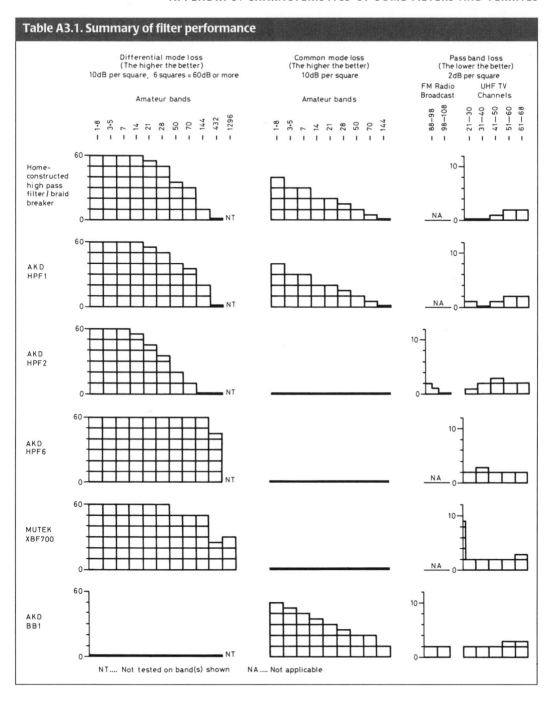

NT.... Not tested on band(s) shown NA.... Not applicable

Table A3.1 *(continued)*

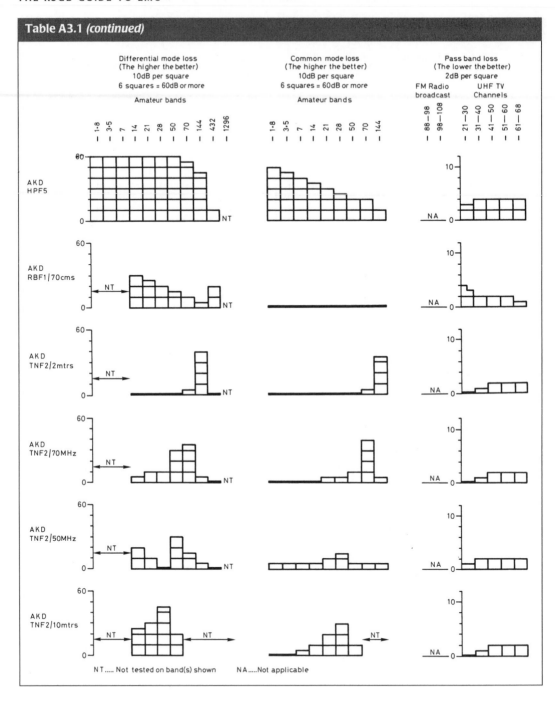

Differential mode loss (The higher the better) 10dB per square 6 squares = 60dB or more	Common mode loss (The higher the better) 10dB per square 6 squares = 60dB or more	Pass band loss (The lower the better) 2dB per square

NT..... Not tested on band(s) shown   NA.....Not applicable

Table A3.1 *(continued)*

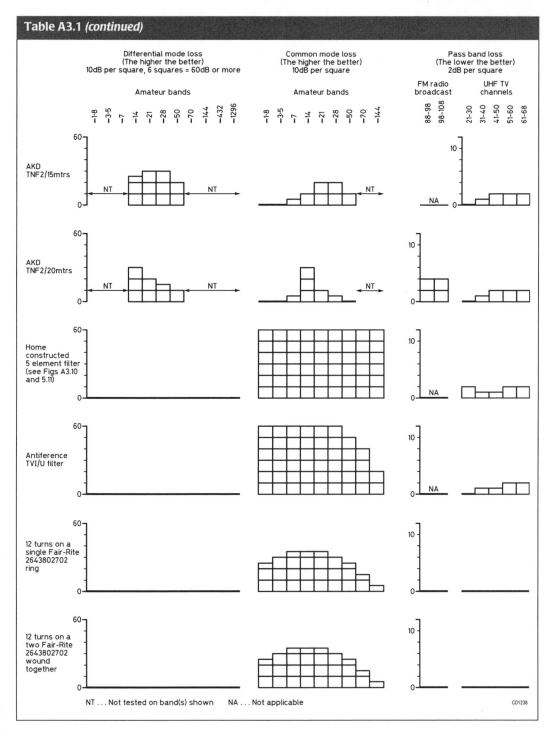

NT ... Not tested on band(s) shown   NA ... Not applicable

CD1238

Table A3.1 *(continued)*

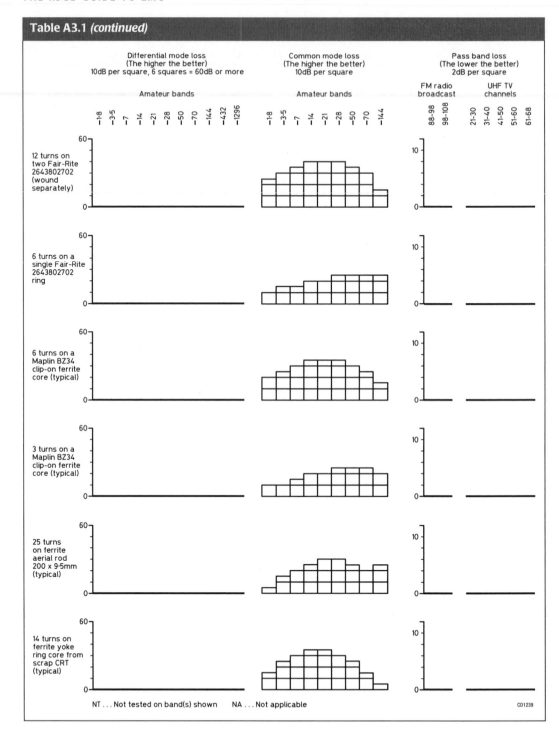

Differential mode loss (The higher the better) 10dB per square, 6 squares = 60dB or more	Common mode loss (The higher the better) 10dB per square	Pass band loss (The lower the better) 2dB per square

NT ... Not tested on band(s) shown   NA ... Not applicable

CD1239

Filter stop-band loss – differential mode

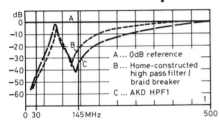

Fig A3.1. Home-constructed high-pass filter/braid-breaker and AKD HPF1, grounded source and load, 0–500MHz

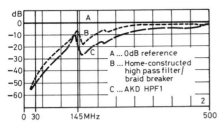

Fig A3.2. Home-constructed high-pass filter/braid-breaker and AKD HPF1, 'floating' source, 0–500MHz

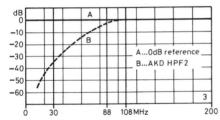

Fig A3.3. AKD HPF2, 0–200MHz

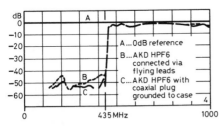

Fig A3.4. AKD HPF6, 0–1000MHz

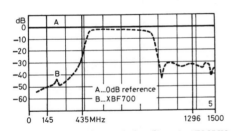

Fig A3.5. Mutek XBF700 stripline filter, 0–1500MHz

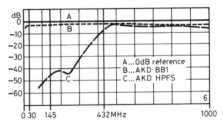

Fig A3.6. AKD BB1 and HPFS, 1000MHz

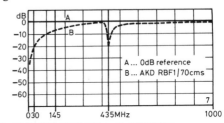

Fig A3.7. AKD RBF1/70cm, 0–1000MHz

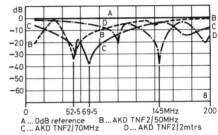

A ... 0dB reference   B ... AKD TNF2/50MHz
C ... AKD TNF2/70MHz D ... AKD TNF2/2mtrs

Fig A3.8. AKD TNF2/2m, TNF2/70MHz and TNF2/50MHz, 'floating' source, 0–200MHz

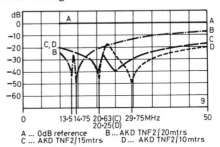

A ... 0dB reference   B ... AKD TNF2/20mtrs
C ... AKD TNF2/15mtrs D ... AKD TNF2/10mtrs

Fig A3.9. AKD TNF2/10m, TNF2/15m and TNF2/20m, 'floating' source, 0–50MHz

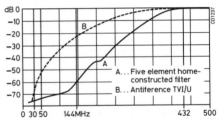

Fig A3.10. Five-element home-constructed high-pass filter and Antiference TVI/U, 0–500MHz

Filter pass-band loss

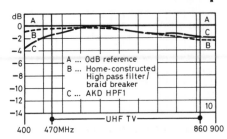

Fig A3.11. Home-constructed high-pass filter/braid-breaker and AKD HPF1, differential mode pass band, 2dB/division, 400–900MHz

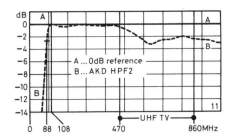

Fig A3.12. AKD HPF2, differential mode pass band, 2dB/division, 0–1000MHz

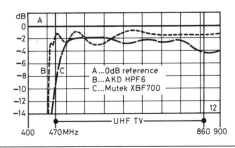

Fig A3.13. AKD HPF6 and Mutek XBF700, differential mode pass band, 2dB/division, 400–900MHz

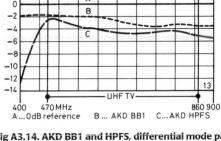

Fig A3.14. AKD BB1 and HPFS, differential mode pass band, 2dB/division, 400–900MHz

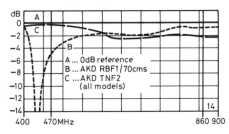

Fig A3.15. AKD RBF1/70cm and AKD TNF2 (all models), differential mode pass band, 2dB/division, 400–900MHz

Filter stop-band loss – common mode

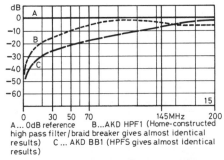

Fig A3.16. Home-constructed high-pass filter/braid-breaker and AKD HPF1, BB1 and HPFS, common mode, 0–200MHz

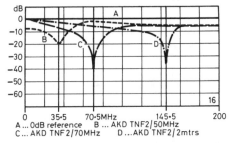

Fig A3.17. AKD TNF2/50MHz, TNF2/70MHz and TNF2/2m, common mode, 0–50MHz

Filter stop-band loss – common mode *(continued)*

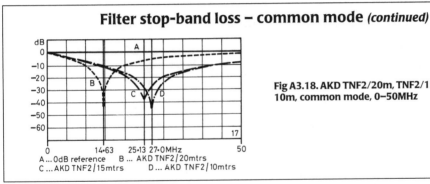

Fig A3.18. AKD TNF2/20m, TNF2/15m and TNF2/10m, common mode, 0–50MHz

A ... 0dB reference   B ... AKD TNF2/20mtrs
C ... AKD TNF2/15mtrs   D ... AKD TNF2/10mtrs

Equivalent circuits, appearance etc

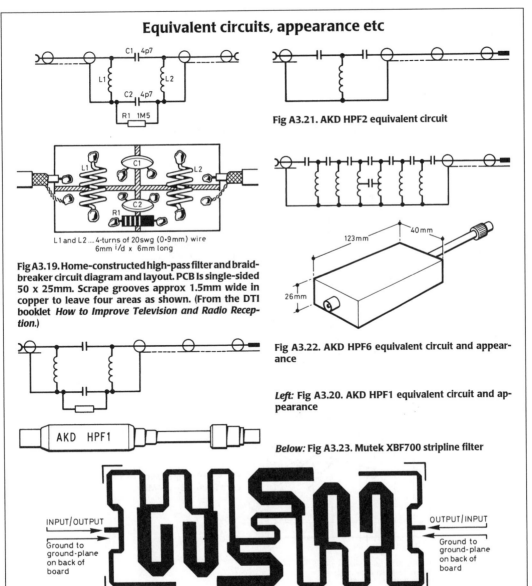

Fig A3.21. AKD HPF2 equivalent circuit

L1 and L2 .... 4-turns of 20swg (0·9mm) wire
6mm i/d x 6mm long

Fig A3.19. Home-constructed high-pass filter and braid-breaker circuit diagram and layout. PCB Is single-sided 50 x 25mm. Scrape grooves approx 1.5mm wide in copper to leave four areas as shown. (From the DTI booklet *How to Improve Television and Radio Reception*.)

Fig A3.22. AKD HPF6 equivalent circuit and appearance

Left: Fig A3.20. AKD HPF1 equivalent circuit and appearance

Below: Fig A3.23. Mutek XBF700 stripline filter

INPUT/OUTPUT

Ground to ground-plane on back of board

OUTPUT/INPUT

Ground to ground-plane on back of board

Equivalent circuits, appearance etc *(continued)*

1MΩ

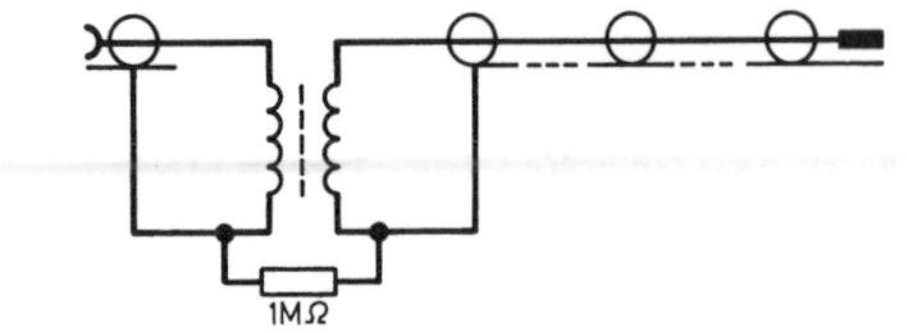

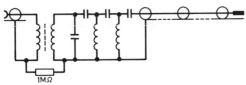

Fig A3.24. AKD BB1 equivalent circuit

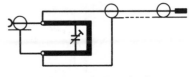

Fig A3.26. AKD RBF1 equivalent circuit

1MΩ

Fig A3.25. AKD HPFS equivalent circuit

C1
L1
L2
C2

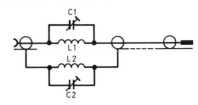

Fig A3.27. AKD TNF2 tuned notch filter range (all models) equivalent circuit

Ferrite chokes – common-mode loss

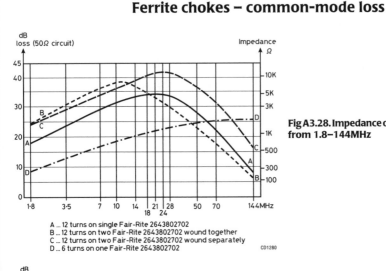

dB
loss (50Ω circuit)
Impedance
Ω
45
40
30
20
10
0
10K
5K
3K
1K
500
300
100
A
B
C
D
1·8
3·5
7
10
14
18
21
24
28
50
70
144MHz
A ... 12 turns on single Fair-Rite 2643802702
B ... 12 turns on two Fair-Rite 2643802702 wound together
C ... 12 turns on two Fair-Rite 2643802702 wound separately
D ... 6 turns on one Fair-Rite 2643802702
CD1280

Fig A3.28. Impedance of various ferrite ring chokes from 1.8–144MHz

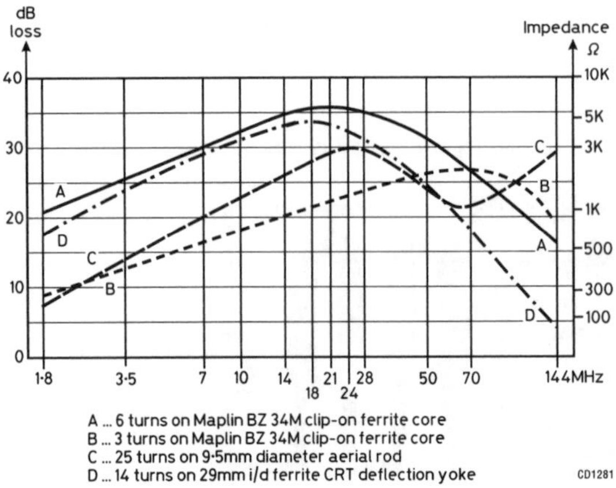

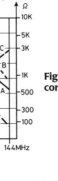

dB
loss
Impedance
Ω
40
30
20
10
0
10K
5K
3K
1K
500
300
100
A
B
C
D
1·8
3·5
7
10
14
18
21
24
28
50
70
144MHz
A ... 6 turns on Maplin BZ 34M clip-on ferrite core
B ... 3 turns on Maplin BZ 34M clip-on ferrite core
C ... 25 turns on 9·5mm diameter aerial rod
D ... 14 turns on 29mm i/d ferrite CRT deflection yoke
CD1281

Fig A3.29. Impedance of other types of ferrite core from 1.8–144MHz

Ferrite core details

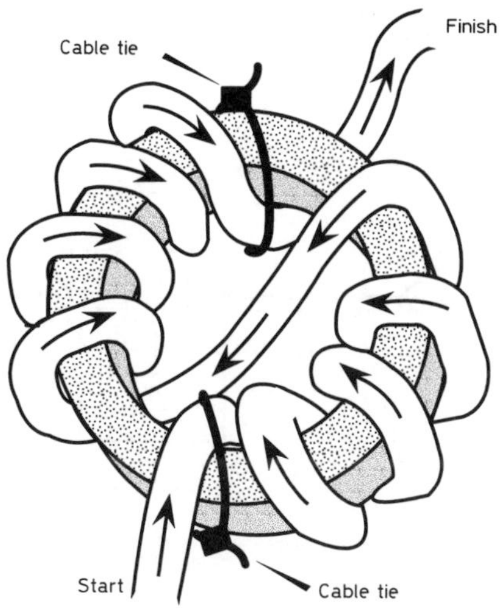

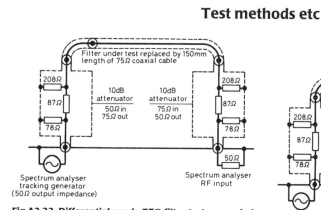

Cable tie

Finish

Start

Cable tie

Fig A3.30. Recommended winding for ring cores

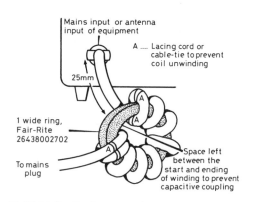

Mains input or antenna
input of equipment

A .... Lacing cord or
cable-tie to prevent
coil unwinding

25mm

1 wide ring,
Fair-Rite
26438002702

To mains
plug

Space left
between the
start and ending
of winding to prevent
capacitive coupling

Fig A3.31. Ferrite rings on mains lead or coaxial cable

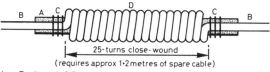

25-turns close-wound

(requires approx 1·2 metres of spare cable)

A .... Ferrite rod, 9·5mm dia   B .... Keep the two ends of the winding
separated especially at VHF   C .... Cable securely bound to ferrite
rod using cable-ties, lacing-cord, etc   D .... Loudspeaker cable,
mains cable, coaxial cable, etc

Fig A3.32. Common-mode choke using ferrite rod

Test methods etc

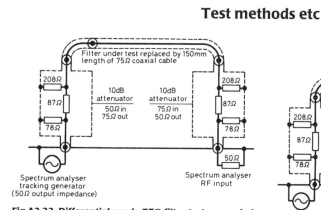

Filter under test replaced by 150mm
length of 75Ω coaxial cable

208Ω

87Ω

78Ω

10dB
attenuator
50Ω in
75Ω out

10dB
attenuator
75Ω in
50Ω out

208Ω

87Ω

78Ω

50Ω

Spectrum analyser
tracking generator
(50Ω output impedance)

Spectrum analyser
RF input

**Fig A3.33. Differential-mode 75Ω filter test, grounded
source and load, 0dB reference**

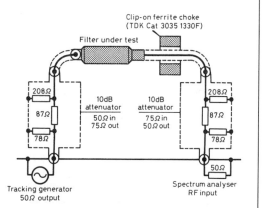

Clip-on ferrite choke
(TDK Cat 3035 1330F)

Filter under test

208Ω

87Ω

78Ω

10dB
attenuator
50Ω in
75Ω out

10dB
attenuator
75Ω in
50Ω out

208Ω

87Ω

78Ω

50Ω

Tracking generator
50Ω output

Spectrum analyser
RF input

**Fig A3.34. Differential-mode 75Ω filter test, grounded
source and load, measurement of filter loss**

Test methods etc *(continued)*

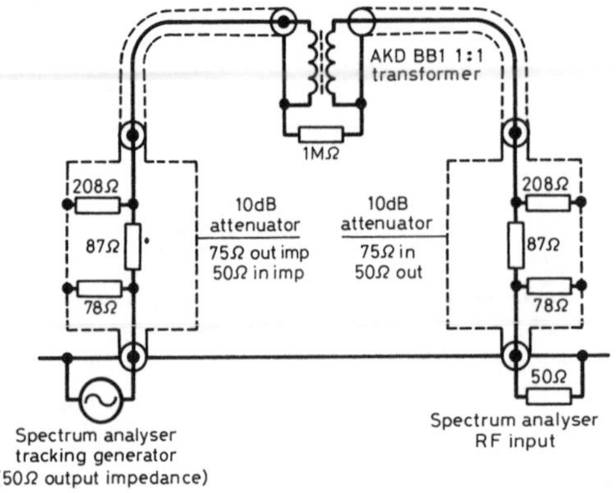

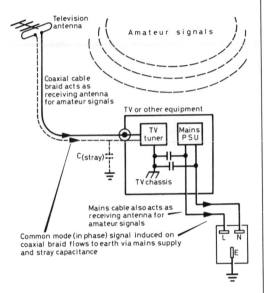

Fig A3.37. Illustration of common-mode signal pick-up

Fig A3.35. Differential-mode 75Ω filter test, floating source, 0dB reference

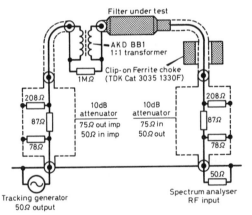

Fig A3.36. Differential-mode 75Ω filter test, floating source, measurement of filter loss

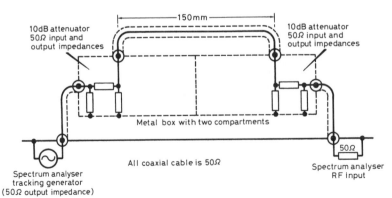

Fig A3.38. Common-mode filter test and ferrite choke test, 0dB reference

Test methods etc *(continued)*

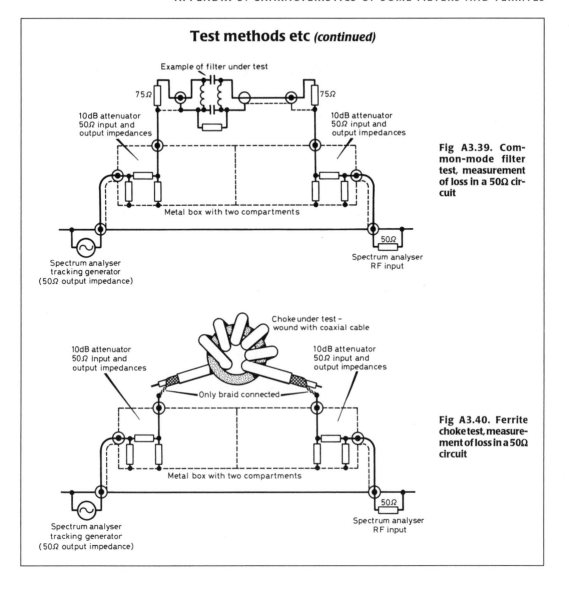

Fig A3.39. Common-mode filter test, measurement of loss in a 50Ω circuit

Fig A3.40. Ferrite choke test, measurement of loss in a 50Ω circuit

4 Notes on the European EMC standards

THESE NOTES have been prepared for radio amateurs and others who operate radio equipment in the domestic environment and want to have some idea of the EMC performance which they can expect from equipment designed for domestic use. Standards may cover many different products having widely different characteristics within a general product category. For this reason EMC test standards are often written in fairly broad terms and test procedures may be complicated, although limits are well defined.

The information given below is not definitive and is intended simply to give an idea of levels and measurement techniques. When definitive information is required reference should always be made to the relevant standard. Standards are available to the public and may be purchased from reference [1]. They may also be consulted free of charge at some of the larger public libraries. The titles used in these notes may not agree with the actual title as published. This is to enable easy identification; the official titles tend to be rather wordy.

Equipment being tested for compliance is often called the *Equipment Under Test* (EUT), and for convenience this abbreviation is used in these notes.

An overview

So far as the radio amateur is concerned, the EMC standards fall into two categories.

(a) *Immunity standards* which define the methods and conditions by which the equipment is tested for immunity to unwanted signals. In the case of domestic broadcast receivers and associated equipment, the permissible degradation of performance is defined by the standard. In other cases it is declared by the manufacturer.

(b) *Emission standards* which define the maximum level of interference which the equipment is permitted to generate.

Immunity standards

There are two types of immunity which are of interest – immunity to radiated fields of the EUT itself and immunity to signals which are picked up on external leads and fed into the EUT as an RF voltage or current. The ways in and out of the EUT are called *ports*, including the case itself which is known as the *enclosure port*.

The usual way to measure radiated immunity is to enclose the EUT in a *TEM cell* to measure or observe the performance while an electromagnetic field of the appropriate level is generated in the cell. 'TEM' stands for 'transverse electromagnetic', and the cell is really a development of a parallel-plate transmission line. Fig A4.1 shows the general arrangement. All the non-essential leads to the EUT are disconnected, and the remaining ones, such as antenna input and mains cable, are choked-off using ferrite rings.

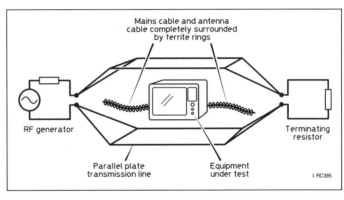

Fig A4.1. Radiated immunity testing in a TEM cell

Signals picked up on the various leads are known as *conducted* voltages or currents. Immunity is measured either by applying a specific RF voltage to the relevant input or output connector, or by injecting the required test signal using a specially designed clamp placed round the lead.

For radiated immunity the RF test voltages in the more recent standards are quoted prior to modulation being applied; usually 80% at a frequency of 1kHz. For products used in the domestic environment, a common level is 3V/m prior to modulation (giving a peak of 5.4V/m). In these notes 'modulated' always refers to 80% modulation at a 1kHz audio frequency. The most notable exception is the standard for domestic broadcast receivers (EN 55020) which includes TV sets. This calls up a variety of test signals due to the wide range of products covered and their different modes of operation.

The levels defined for conducted currents and voltages are also similar in the different standards. The common level in this case is 3V. This is also quoted prior to modulation at 80% at a frequency of 1kHz, giving a peak of 5.4V. Again, specifications like EN 55020 are not typical for the reasons already stated. It is interesting that the 3V of the conducted currents and voltages ties up with the 3V/m, implying that the voltage induced in a typical lead is numerically equal to the field strength. This may be true over a limited range of lead lengths and frequencies but it is reasonable to assume that much larger voltages could be caused by resonance effects on long leads.

Emission standards

The emission standards call for tests to be made for radiated emissions from the equipment itself (the enclosure port), and also for the level of *disturbance* voltage or current present on various leads such as mains or control leads. ('Disturbance' is the general term and so far as amateurs are concerned it can be taken to mean 'interference'.) Generally radiated emissions are measured at the higher frequencies, above 80MHz for instance, while conducted disturbances are measured at lower frequencies.

The permissible levels of emissions are high from the amateur's point of view. We could be looking at interference levels of S7 and more at quite long distances from the source. Fortunately, these high levels are only likely to be present on a few specific frequencies and this, combined with the fact that measurements are quasi-peak and made in a wide bandwidth (usually 9kHz for HF or 120kHz for VHF) means that things may not be as bad as the figures suggest. It is worth noting, however, that as digital systems become more common, broad-band noise over a wide bandwidth will become a major problem.

Some standards call for tests on discontinuous disturbances lasting relatively short times (clicks), though to avoid complication these are not included in these notes.

Conducted disturbances are usually measured with a suitable measuring receiver using a voltage probe, though in many cases no distinction is made between common-mode and differential signals. For some measurements a ferrite current transformer is used. Levels may be quoted as either quasi-peak or average; sometimes both are required. A quasi-peak measurement has a relatively fast charge and slow discharge, so that repetitive short pulses of interference indicate a higher figure than they would with an average detector. In general, conducted emissions are measured for lower frequencies, usually up to 80MHz, and typical quasi-peak levels are 56 to 66dBμV.

A closer look

This section takes a closer look at some of the standards from the radio amateur's view point.

The Generic Immunity Standard EN 50082-1

Part 1 – Residential, commercial and light industry

This is the standard which covers the immunity of equipment which is not subject to a specific standard. At the time of writing the standard is being updated. The proposed level for radiated immunity is 3V/m, 80% modulated at 1kHz, but this is only measured from 80 to 1000MHz. The proposed level for conducted immunity on AC power ports, signal and control lines and DC power ports is 3V (modulated). This is measured from 150kHz to 80MHz. The conducted immunity measurements are common-mode.

Immunity of broadcast receivers and associated equipment EN 55020

This standard is based on CISPR 20, and covers immunity of radio and television, and associated equipment. It includes items intended to be connected to sound and TV receivers, and also equipment for video or sound reproduction. In practice this covers a wide range of devices, and the complexity of the standard reflects this. The standard lists the types of equipment to which the various tests apply.

There are five main areas:

1. *Input immunity*. This is applied to TV and radio receivers, and is a measure of the ability to reject unwanted signals appearing at the antenna input. This is really a measure of the performance of the equipment as a receiver of radio signals. Inevitably it depends on the frequencies of the wanted and unwanted signals and is not easy to summarise.
2. *Radiated immunity*. This is the immunity to radio frequency fields of the actual unit itself, with all external leads disconnected or electrically isolated by means of ferrite chokes. Immunity is measured over a

frequency range of 150kHz to 150MHz. Levels vary considerably depending on frequency and type of equipment. A figure often quoted for domestic TV and VHF radio receivers is 125dB(μV/m). This is generally true for frequencies used by radio amateurs but notable exceptions are the 50MHz and 70MHz bands.

3. *Immunity to voltages injected into the mains and into speaker and headphone terminals.* This is of particular interest to radio amateurs. RF signals entering through the mains or speaker leads are a fairly common cause of interference to domestic entertainment equipment. The test voltage is 80% modulated at 1kHz and applied as a differential signal for headphones and speaker terminals, and as a common-mode signal for the mains. The required immunity decreases with frequency, being 130dBμV (3.16V) from 150kHz to 30MHz, 120dBμV from 30 to 100MHz, decreasing to 110dBμV at 150MHz.

4. *Immunity to voltages injected into the low-level audio input and output terminals.* The required immunity is considerably less than for the speaker/headphone terminals, presumably reflecting the fact that these terminals are likely to handle relatively small signals, and that leads connected to them can be expected to be fairly short or suitably screened. Again, the test voltage is applied as a differential signal, and is 80% modulated at 1kHz. The important levels are from 1.6 to 20MHz, 90 to 120dBμV; from 20 to 100MHz, 120dBμV, falling to 110dBμV at 150MHz. All the levels in this case are EMF.

5. *Immunity to conducted currents into the antenna terminals.* This is probably the most important parameter from the radio amateur's point of view. Unfortunately, tests only cover a frequency range of 26 to 30MHz. Although this is nominally a current measurement it is measured as an RF voltage applied to the braid of the coaxial cable under specified conditions. The limit is 126dBμV (EMF).

Immunity of household appliances, tools and similar apparatus EN 55104
This standard also includes electric toys. The radiated immunity is 3V/m modulated, measured over a frequency range of 80MHz to 1000MHz. The conducted immunity for the mains input and output ports is 3V (modulated), measured over a frequency range of 150kHz to 80MHz. The conducted immunity at other ports is generally 1V (modulated). There are a number of exemptions on certain ports, depending on length of lead, and for battery-operated appliances which cannot be connected to the mains when in use.

The Generic emission standard EN 50081-1

Part 1 – Residential, commercial and light industry
This standard covers emissions from equipment which is not subject to a product specific standard.

At the time of writing only radiated emissions and conducted disturbances via the mains leads are covered. Emission from other leads is under consideration.

Radiated emissions are 30dB(μV/m) from 30 to 230MHz, and 37dB(μV/m) from 230 to 1000MHz, measured at a distance of 10m. Disturbance voltages at the mains terminals over a frequency range of 500kHz to 30MHz are 56 to 60dBμV, quasi-peak.

Emissions from sound and television broadcast receivers and associated equipment EN 55013

This standard is based on CISPR 13, and covers emissions from radio and TV equipment. Like its immunity counterpart, EN 55020, it covers a wide range of equipment, including video and sound reproduction equipment.

At the time of writing limits on radiated emissions from the case and from the antenna port of radios, TVs and VCRs cover only local oscillators and their harmonics, and a number of specially protected spot frequencies.

Radiation from associated equipment (other than VCRs), is not measured directly, but the 'disturbance power' appearing on any leads longer than 25cm, including the mains lead, is measured using an absorbing clamp. The measurement is made over a frequency range of 30 to 300MHz, and the limits are 45 to 55dBpW (quasi-peak) depending on frequency.

Disturbance voltages at the mains terminals (quasi-peak) are measured over a frequency range of 150kHz to 30MHz. The levels are in the range 56 to 66dBμV depending on frequency. Measurements are made using an artificial mains network, more commonly known as a *LISN* (line impedance stabilisation network).

Emissions from Information Technology Equipment (ITE) EN 55022

As well as computers this standard covers a wide range of similar equipment including office machines, data processing equipment and electronic business equipment.

This is one of the most important standards from the amateur point of view. Interference from this type of equipment is becoming a major problem. It is noteworthy that the EMC performance of computers has improved markedly in recent years, mainly due to the existence of regulations.

Equipment is divided into two categories, Class A and Class B, the Class A requirements being less stringent than those for Class B. Class B equipment is intended primarily for use in the domestic environment. Class A is presumably intended to apply to commercial premises, but the standard does not actually say so and there is no restriction on sale of such equipment. Class A equipment is defined as satisfying the Class A limits but not the Class B limits. Class A equipment must have a warning about radio interference included in the instructions for use. If it is used in a domestic environment and causes interference, the user may be required to take measures to prevent the interference.

For Class B equipment, the limit for radiation from the case over a frequency range of 30 to 230MHz is 30dB(μV/m), and for 230 to 1000MHz is 37dB(μV/m) (quasi-peak), both measured at a distance of 10m. Limits of disturbance voltages at the mains port for Class B equipment, from 500kHz up to 30MHz, are between 56 and 60dBμV, quasi-peak, depending on frequency.

At the time of writing, limits on conducted emissions from the telecommunication ports are under consideration. It seems likely that these will be comparable to the levels for the mains port.

Emissions from household appliances EN 55014

This is another standard which is of particular interest to amateurs. It covers a wide range of equipment including household electrical appliances, electric tools and electric toys. Again, because of the wide range covered, the limits are complicated, depending of the type of equipment and also on the power rating

Radiation from associated equipment is not measured directly, but the 'disturbance power' appearing on any leads longer than 25cm, including the mains lead, is measured using an absorbing clamp. The measurement is made over a frequency range of 30 to 300MHz, and for household appliances and small tools the limits are 45 to 55dBpW (quasi-peak) depending on frequency. There are higher limits for tools rated over 700W.

Limits for conducted disturbances vary depending on the type of equipment and which leads are being tested. The limits for levels measured at mains terminals varies depending on the type and power of the equipment. For household appliances and small tools, over a frequency band from 500kHz to 30MHz, the range is 56 to 64dBμV quasi-peak.

Commercially available amateur radio equipment ETSI 300 684

This standard covers EMC performance of commercially available amateur equipment. It covers not only transceivers but also some ancillary products. The standard acknowledges the fact that amateur equipment is used by operators who have a reasonable degree of technical and operating knowledge, and is generally less rigorous than the standards covering non-amateur radio communications equipment. Oddly enough, though it deals with the actual equipment amateurs use, it will probably have less impact on amateur operation than the standards listed previously. Most commercially available amateur transceivers perform fairly well from the EMC point of view and the existence of a standard will just confirm this. It must be emphasised that the standard only applies to commercially available equipment. It does not apply to home-built amateur radio equipment. This has the distinction of being specifically exempt from the EMC directive. In addition the standard does not apply to second-hand equipment or such things as PMR transceivers modified as a 'one off' amateur activity. It would, however, apply to equipment subject to modification or remanufacture as part of a commercial operation. At the time of writing bona fide amateur radio kits (if put together according to the manufacturer's instructions) are exempt from the standard in the UK.

The standard gives limits for emissions from various ports, including the enclosure port, and the mains input. Probably the one of most interest is emissions from the antenna port. In effect these are the spurious emissions discussed in Chapter 6. Figures of 40 to 60dB are quoted depending on frequency. Immunity to unwanted signals at the various ports is also covered, though again this is not likely to lead to a noticeable change in practical amateur operation. Certainly it will not obviate the need for good station layout to avoid feed-back problems.

References
[1] British Standards Institution (BSI), 389 Chiswick High Road, London W4 4AL.

5 Good television and radio reception

This article by Martyn Culling, G8UCP, was written to encourage and promote good practice in domestic antenna installations. The author works for the BBC and acknowledges their assistance in the production of this article. All opinions expressed are those of the author and not necessarily those of the BBC.

I T IS probably true to say that something over half the television and radio antenna installations in this country leave at least something to be desired. It is not at all uncommon for someone with a television set costing over £1000 to have a television antenna costing about £5.

It is in the radio amateur's interest to ensure that his or her own radio and television installation is as good as possible. If your installation is demonstrably perfect, it is easier to convince someone else who suffers from breakthrough that theirs is not. Obviously under these circumstances the amateur should be a good neighbour and, at the very least, advise on what needs to done to improve matters.

The antenna

This is where a great many people come to grief. A properly designed Yagi antenna will have a balanced feedpoint impedance that varies with the number of elements. The dipole element taken in isolation has a balanced impedance of 300Ω. All television sets and television antenna cables have a characteristic impedance of 75Ω, unbalanced. It doesn't take much thought to realise that a balun (balanced-to-unbalanced transformer) is required to make everything match. If a balun is not present the antenna may have had its design modified to make it closer to 75Ω. If not, then a mismatch and an imbalance will be present between antenna and cable. In any event, an antenna without a balun will not give the gain or the performance that would be expected from a proper Yagi with the same number of elements. Compared with amateur practice the gain will always be lower due to the fact that the domestic antennas usually cover a far greater bandwidth.

One of the major problems with an imbalance is that the coaxial cable will not be able to do its job properly. Under normal circumstances the wanted signal travels down the cable between the inner conductor and the inside of the screen or braid. Seen from the outside, the braid should screen the wanted signal from external unwanted signals. A good general tip on identifying a television antenna without a balun is to examine the reflector when looking at it from the ground. If it is a flat metal plate it is reasonable to assume that it does not possess a balun (I've never yet seen one that did). If the reflector is a more convincing array of rods there is an increasing chance that there *may* be a balun inside. Obviously the only sure way is to look inside the connection box.

In the domestic market most reputable manufacturers quote their antenna gain in decibels relative to a dipole (dBd). Reference to an isotropic source (dBi) is rare. Additionally, reputable manufacturers check their antenna gains on a testing range rather than claim something that they cannot back up. This is where I cannot state strongly enough the importance of using an antenna from a reputable manufacturer as independent testers of antennas are almost unknown.

It is worth checking to see if the claimed antenna gains are believable when you are shopping for an antenna. Some claims are patently unreal. As a rough guide, peak gains for television antennas should be about 11dB for a 10-element Yagi, 15dB for a normal high-gain Yagi and 17dB for a large (chimney-breaking) high-gain Yagi. Band II antenna gains will be at most 3dB for a two-element and 5dB for a three-element array. Note these are peak figures and will not be maintained for the full bandwidth. Television antennas are usually designed to peak somewhere around the top end of their coverage to make up for the increased path and cable losses at the higher frequencies.

Television antennas
Apart from choosing a good antenna there are several other factors to consider. First, what antenna group is your local television transmitter? Local antenna installers and retailers should know or alternatively you can ring the BBC or ITC and ask them. In any event, make sure that the bandwidth of your antenna is wide enough to cover all the channels in use from your local television transmitting station.

Antenna Group A used to cover channels 21 to 34, Group B 39 to 53 and Group C/D 48 to 68. There is also a Group E defined as 39 to 68 but some reputable antenna manufacturers do not produce these, instead favouring a wide-band antenna to cover 21 to 68. Since the advent of Channel 5, all antenna manufacturers have widened Group A to cover 21 to 37 and Group B to cover 35 to 53. Also as a consequence another group which covers 21 to 48, Group K, is now being manufactured. Obviously it is important not to purchase old stock.

The Yagi. This is the most common type of television antenna, consisting of a central boom, a reflector (this counts as one element even though it may be a number of rods on a pair of arms arranged as a parabola) a dipole element and a number of directors. The most basic Yagi for television use is the 10-element type. This is suitable for areas with strong signals and no other problems. If well designed this type of antenna will have a front-to-back ratio of around 20dB; inferior antennas may be only 10dB although they will not advertise the fact. Yagi antennas are made in a number of sizes, 10 elements being the most common, with 14- and 18-element varieties also available. The 18-element type is sometimes referred to as a 'high-gain Yagi' although this term is best reserved for the following type of antenna.

The high-gain Yagi. This is similar in concept to the plain Yagi except that it possesses characteristic 'X'-shaped directors. In its most common sizes it may well have a gain of 14dB to 15dB, a front-to-back ratio of 25dB and a far superior polar diagram (compared to a plain Yagi) with much less pick-up at the sides. These antennas are used where more gain is required or there are unwanted signals coming from the sides (and to an extent the rear). This antenna can often be the best type to use when there is a 'ghosting' problem, except when the unwanted signal is coming from the rear.

The grid antenna. This looks rather like a bar-b-que grid with four 'X'-shaped dipoles in front of it. The dipoles are stacked vertically and phased together with an open wire balanced feeder. The major benefits are an excellent front-to-back ratio of around 28dB and the fact that it picks up signals from four different heights. This is *the antenna* if you have a tidal fading problem caused by looking at a transmitter across an estuary or the sea. Because of the dipole height differences, this antenna effectively has a measure of diversity reception. This is only appropriate if the transmitter is horizontally polarised which generally means main transmitting stations only. Very few relay transmitters are horizontally polarised, most of them being vertically polarised.

This antenna is often used as a 'anti-ghosting' antenna and this is correct if the problem signal is from the rear. If the reflection is arriving at the antenna at an angle of less than 90° compared to the wanted signal, a grid antenna is the wrong choice. Under these circumstances a high-gain Yagi is often a better choice, offering higher rejection of the unwanted signal.

Radio antennas

At one time, Band II (or FM antennas) covered a relatively narrow band from 88 to 96MHz when only the BBC used Band II. For many years antennas have been sold covering 88 to 108MHz but occasionally antennas which fail to give sufficient signal in the 96 to 108MHz region may be found in old installations.

Unless all-round reception is actually needed, the omnidirectional antennas should not be considered. If all-round reception is essential, a vertical dipole is the best choice, provided all the wanted signals are either vertically polarised or mixed polarised. The 'halo' for horizontal polarisation is 3dB down in gain compared to a dipole. This frequently leads to inadequate signals even in areas with good field strengths. Additionally problems are more likely to be encountered with multipath reception. This is the radio equivalent of ghosting with television reception. The cause is, as with ghosting on television, a direct signal and a reflected signal arriving at the antenna. Since the reflected signal has travelled a longer route it is time delayed compared to the direct signal. The audible effects of multipath reception are 'birdies' (little twittering noises), crashing distortion sounds on piano music and other similar effects.

If horizontal omnidirectional reception is essential, then you would be better employed putting your FM Yagi antenna on a rotator. With FM antennas the issue of a balun is still critical, possibly even more so than with television. The main problem with the absence of a balun in FM antennas is that of downlead pick-up. This can cause very similar effects to multipath distortion, and in a sense is multipath distortion within the antenna system. It is due to the mismatch causing signals to reflect within the system and travel a longer path before reaching the receiver. Another effect is signal cancellation, with signals picked up in the braid cancelling out those of the antenna. This can lead to a surprisingly low signal on some frequencies, while on other frequencies, the signal is higher than expected.

Most manufacturer's FM antennas look very similar and there is no easy way to tell if a balun is fitted without investigating the connection box attached to the dipole. The reflector is usually a single rod and only a few have multi-rod reflectors due to the fact that FM antennas are somewhat large. There are some antenna designs that look rather fanciful with gain claims that appear to defy the rules of physics. A three-element Yagi that covers 88 to 108MHz will have at most a gain of 5dB (a perfectly satisfactory antenna may even have slightly less). Some of the odder larger types have gain claims of 14dB or more. Whilst I am not going to into the technical arguments, I pose the question as follows. "Have you ever seen a 2m antenna of this or similar design?" Surely if it really worked someone would have scaled it down and produced a 2m antenna using the same principle. One 'explanation' I was given was that this particular antenna picked up both the horizontal and vertical components of a mixed polarised signal. If this were true, it could only work in good line-of-sight locations, since as soon as you get to an obscured location there will be path differences between the differently polarised components of the signal. More multipath interference.

A frequently asked question is: "Which polarisation should be used for the receiving antenna when the transmitting antenna is mixed polarised?" Generally the receiving antenna should be horizontal as this usually gives the best results. The only occasion when vertical mounting can be advantageous is at a distant location, obscured from the transmitter. Practical measurements taken by me and my colleagues have frequently given a significantly higher result for the vertical component than the horizontal component *under these conditions*. Normally I would expect to measure field strengths within 1 or 2dB for both polarisations. Note that you will have installation problems with vertical mounting because most poles available for mounting are steel or aluminium and will act as a spurious and misplaced element. Either procure a pole made of an insulating material or remake the antenna so that the mounting pole replaces the reflector. If any element has to be made too large to accommodate the mounting, the reflector is least likely to be a problem.

The cable

As a bare minimum this should be what is euphemistically termed 'low-loss' cable. 'Standard' quality usually possess so little copper in the screen that it cannot do its job properly and is frankly a waste of money. At all cost avoid the types that have a metallised mylar film as the only screen. There are cables that have braid and a mylar film which are sold for satellite use. They may be satisfactory for terrestrial use but do not use them for your satellite installation. If the cable run is long (20m) or more it is well worth using a proper satellite-type cable, for example CT100. This cable has a layer of copper foil between the braid and the centre insulator. Personally I am inclined to advocate the use of CT100 for normal domestic installations as the superior screening properties of CT100 are extremely desirable – and in an amateur's residence even more so. The cost is around 50% more than 'low loss' for this type of cable.

Domestic 75Ω cables are more easily damaged than the 50Ω cable often used in amateur and professional radio installations. This is because they are partially air spaced. This spacing is critical to retaining the characteristic impedance (and hence performance) so great care must be taken with the cable not to kink, crush or bend it through too tight a radius. A defect in the cable, whilst perhaps not immediately obvious in terms of loss, will almost certainly cause ghosting (more correctly called *delayed image interference* or DII). Even if a cable or connection defect does not cause noticeable ghosting on the picture it could still upset teletext reception.

The connectors

There are a great variety of domestic television and radio connectors. Some are good and others can be quite poor. There are some that have a little grub screw to clamp the inner conductor. Whilst it is easy to make a nice tight connection with this type, they are not a particularly good match to 75Ω. This has never been a problem to me but if you have other matching problems it will make them worse. The normal ones require you to get the soldering iron out to solder the inner wire to the pin, though very few people, even professionals, do it. This is most important as poor contact, often aggravated by tarnishing or corrosion, is a common source of problems. I would steer clear of the plastic-bodied types as it is not easy to get a nice positive braid connection.

The correct way to fit the cable does vary a little with the make of plug but the general principle is always the same. What you are trying to do is create a good mechanical fit that makes good electrical contact. I would always recommend the method shown in Fig 5.9(b) in Chapter 5. Based on having seen large numbers of domestic installations I would guess that as few as 5% of all domestic plugs are assembled properly.

Antennas in lofts

The best advice is don't do it! Although it can be made to work you will have problems. Not least of these is that some roof coverings will attenuate signals by as much as 20dB. Also metal objects in the loft will cause reflections and hence very closely spaced 'ghosts' – perhaps too close to be seen but frequently having disastrous effects on teletext. However, beware, some properties have restrictive covenants about antennas not being allowed outside. If you are trying to make an amateur antenna and a television antenna work at close quarters in a loft, you *will* have problems, and quite possibly your neighbours will as well. Although it probably isn't much help for your amateur antennas I do advise that you read your covenants carefully. Some carry a 'get-out clause' that allows outside antennas if *absolutely necessary*. Under these circumstances it may be not too difficult for it to be 'absolutely necessary'.

Combining antennas

It is possible to combine a television and a radio antenna into a single downlead but there are possible problems. Firstly any combiner will have loss, reducing the amount of signal received at the television set (or tuner). If possible I would advise that you keep television and radio signals apart and use separate feeders. If not, you will have loss both in the combiner and in the splitter that you will need near the receiving equipment to split the signals.

Combining television signals from two television antennas (two different transmitters) is more common but here the major constraint is that the antennas must be of different antenna groups. You cannot, for example combine Crystal Palace with Sandy Heath as they are both of the same antenna group (Group A). If the attempt is made, ghosting problems may occur and quite probably surprising losses of signal on some channel as the signals may come in via one antenna and leave by way of the other. The solution here is to use an antenna switch.

Combining different groups used to be quite simple – you just bought the appropriate combiner and connected everything up. Now that Group A extends to channel 37 there may be some problems with combining Group A and B.

Antenna amplifiers

The message here is *use sparingly*. There is no point in using an amplifier (frequently called *boosters* by householders) if a larger antenna would have provided enough signal. Most amplifiers are very broad-band with coverage from Band II to the top of the television band. The trouble is that 87 to 860MHz may include strong signals such as the various public services and private mobile radio (PMR), not to mention the 2m and 70cm amateur bands, dramatically increasing the risk of cross-modulation and breakthrough. If all you want to do is amplify your television signals, then do just that. You can buy what are referred to as *grouped amplifiers* that cover one antenna group only. Because these are narrower bandwidth they are much less likely to cause problems. It is also possible to buy (usually high-gain) amplifiers that have an internal gain control so that the correct amount of gain can be applied *and no more*. If you just want to amplify Band II signals then you are best advised to make your own amplifier. No manufacturer produces or imports to the UK a Band II-only amplifier. If you are reading this overseas, then ask your supplier – some are available in countries other than the UK.

Antenna amplifiers fall into three basic categories, *set-back, masthead,* and *distribution.* The set-back types which go between the antenna downlead and the set (hence the name) are best avoided. Apart from the fact that there are a lot of inferior models on the market there is something fundamentally wrong with the principle of amplifying a signal after you have lost some of it in the cable. With exactly the same antenna and downlead a masthead amplifier will yield a far higher signal-to-noise ratio at the television set than any amplifier could at the back of the set. The masthead amplifier of course requires a power supply. This is nearly always achieved by putting 12 to 18V DC up the downlead from a small power supply situated near the television set. The distribution amplifier is designed to feed a number of television sets from one antenna. Two-, four-, six- and eight-outlet types are commonly available. If you live in an area of strong signal strength then it may be possible to feed two sets from one antenna using a splitter. This is obviously less susceptible to breakthrough and can make for a cheaper and more reliable installation.

Digital television

This is very much in its infancy at the time of writing and there is little practical experience with either satellite or terrestrial digital television, especially with regard to EMC matters. However, what is definite is that any problem with digital television will be almost impossible to diagnose from inspection of the results on the screen. This is because digital television nearly always gives perfect pictures or no pictures at all. In between these states there is a very narrow area where intermittent frozen pictures or a square 'blocking' effect will be observed. However, this could arise as a result of a weak signal, extremely severe delayed image interference (which causes ghosting on analogue television) or an EMC problem; all of these could produce identical results. Digital television does not require anything like the carrier-to-noise figure that analogue television needs but since it is transmitted at lower powers than analogue it will not necessarily be more immune to EMC problems.

Other matters

A well-engineered system will be substantially more resistant to EMC problems. If you need to use a filter, the chances are that it will be more effective in a good installation since filters are designed to fit into a proper 75Ω system. The mechanical aspects should not be neglected and the cable should be neatly taped to the mounting pole to stop it moving around and getting damaged. Good-quality mountings will stop the antenna from moving in the wind. The type of bracket that screws to the barge board should be avoided if possible as these frequently work loose in the wind resulting in a damaged barge board (and antenna if it falls down!).

6 RF interference from computers

This appendix is taken from the EMC column in Radio Communication *for December 1996 and February 1997. Additional material has been provided by the author, David Lauder, G0SNO. It describes work he carried out to identify and remedy interference from personal computers.*

The discussion of the problems will be of interest to everyone involved with computers and radio. Investigations and modifications which involve opening the case should only be attempted by someone who has the proper technical expertise. Dangerous voltages exist in computers, particularly in monitors. Take heed of any warning notices on the case before proceeding.

Reducing VHF emissions

This section concentrates on reducing RF emissions from the case of a PC on the VHF bands, particularly 2m. The next section deals with RFI reduction on the HF bands, together with some tips on dealing with HF and VHF emissions from computer monitors. Many of the RFI reduction principles mentioned here are also applicable to other types of computers and to digital electronic equipment in general. Some of the measures described involve internal modification and are not recommended unless you own the computer and it is out of guarantee. Although the RFI levels from most CE-marked computers are a considerable improvement on older machines [1], there is still scope for improvement because the emission levels permitted by the EN 55022 Class B limits are large in relation to received amateur signal levels [2].

If amateur bands are affected by excessive RFI from a neighbour's computer, a diplomatic approach is recommended. Amateur radio is designated as an unprotected service, so the owner of the computer is not obliged to do anything to reduce the RFI unless it also affects a protected service such as FM radio broadcasting or UHF TV. If the neighbour is co-operative, any RFI reduction measures should be restricted to things which can be clipped on, plugged in or programmed by the owner without the need for you to touch the computer.

In the case of a computer in your radio shack, the antenna should obviously be as far from the computer as possible. The coaxial feeder should be well screened with good-quality woven braid. If a balanced antenna such as a dipole is used, it should be fed with a balun to minimise pick-up on the cable. It is also worth plugging a dummy load into the antenna socket to check that the RFI disappears and is not getting into the radio by some other route.

A computer may contain many different oscillators, for example on the main board, graphics card, disc drives, keyboard, mouse, etc. Most of these oscillators are divided down to lower frequencies which can in turn produce many other harmonics. Some frequencies commonly used in digital electronic equipment include 4, 6, 8, 12, 16 and 24MHz, all of which have harmonics at 144.000MHz.

Another frequency found in virtually all PCs, old or new, is 14.318MHz (±15kHz or so). This is four times the NTSC colour TV sub-carrier and may be used to synthesise other frequencies such as the CPU clock. Most 386 and 486 PCs up to 40MHz use an oscillator at twice the advertised CPU clock frequency so a 25MHz CPU has an oscillator at nominally 50MHz. In practice, this frequency can be synthesised by multiplying 14.318MHz by 7/2 to give 50.113MHz, which is 3kHz from the current 6m intercontinental calling frequency. Faster CPUs such as a 486DX2-66 and 486DX4-100 use a clock of nominally 33MHz which is multiplied by 2 or 3 on the CPU chip. Similar clock multiplication from 30 or 33MHz is also used by Pentium™ processors operating at frequencies such as 90, 100, 133, 166 or 200MHz etc.

Plugging leaks

Unwanted emissions from a computer or any other digital electronic device may escape via a number of routes so a step-by-step approach is normally required. It is best to monitor the level of RFI with an indoor antenna 2m to 3m from the computer, using an SSB receiver with an S-meter if possible.

A PC graphics card can be a significant source of RFI, particularly when displaying a graphics screen with a lot of fine detail rather than a DOS screen with only a C:\> prompt. The first test is to display an RF-noisy screen such as Windows Program Manager with plenty of icons then unplug the video lead from the computer and switch off the monitor. Next, unplug the keyboard, mouse and all other cables (except the mains!). If the computer is in a metal case, it should be fairly quiet now. Any remaining RFI is probably getting out through the case or from the power supply via the mains cable. The latter is more likely to affect the HF bands and will be mentioned later on.

On a CE-marked computer, the case normally has several features to improve screening as shown in Fig A6.1. Arrows A indicate lugs or 'pips' at intervals of about 50mm on the base or cover to ensure good electrical contact at many points. Holes for unused disc drive bays are usually filled with a metal blanking plate B. The wires to LEDs and switches on the front panel come through the metal case C which could cause a slight leak.

The keyboard and mouse

The keyboard socket on a PC is mounted on the main board and poor grounding here can cause leaks at VHF. Touch the metal shell of the keyboard DIN plug onto the metal shell of the DIN socket without actually plugging it in. If the RFI level increases, this indicates a *common-mode* emission source where RFI is getting out on to the screen of the keyboard cable.

The main board usually has six or more fixing holes but in the interests

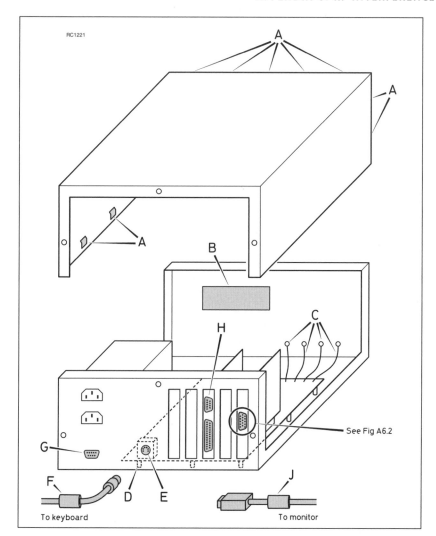

Fig A6.1. A typical PC case, showing features which can effect EMC

RC1221

To keyboard

To monitor

See Fig A6.2

of economy, most of these may be mounted on plastic pillars. The fixing hole nearest the keyboard socket ('D' in Fig A6.1), should be grounded via a metal pillar. CE-marked PCs normally ground the shell of the keyboard DIN socket directly to back of the case using four spring fingers ('E' in Fig A6.1) but this is not easy to add if it is not already fitted.

An alternative solution is a ferrite core on the cable ('F' in Fig A6.1). These are already moulded onto most keyboard cables but there is only one 'turn' so try threading the cable *twice* through a suitable clip-on ferrite core (such a Maplin BZ34M) as this gives up to four times as much impedance as one turn.

Next, plug the keyboard in properly and bring it near the receiving antenna to identify any significant emissions directly from the keyboard. The keyboard has its own microcontroller which normally has a ceramic resonator rather than a crystal. A fundamental frequency of 6MHz is commonly used but the frequency tolerance of a ceramic resonator could be about ±40kHz which puts the 24th harmonic around 144 ± 1MHz. A clip-on

187

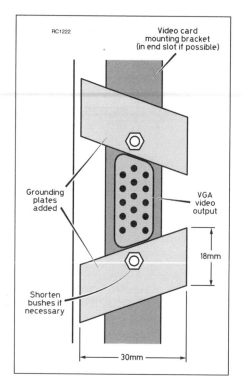

Fig A6.2. Improving the grounding of a PC video connector

ferrite choke with two turns close to the keyboard may help but is not very convenient. Some keyboards have provision for three chokes on the PCB in series with the cable but wire links may have been fitted instead. In this case, try 1mH chokes or two or three turns on a ferrite bead for VHF. It is not easy to screen a keyboard effectively so, if keyboard emissions are still a problem, the only solution may be to try another keyboard.

Next plug in the mouse and see whether the RFI increases. If it does, there are two possible reasons. An unscreened mouse cable can radiate any RFI which comes out of the computer's COM port or the mouse itself could be the source. One way to reduce emissions via the COM port is to wind the mouse cable or other serial cable through a clip-on ferrite core near the computer. Again a Maplin BZ34M clip-on core would be suitable. If possible, use two or three turns for VHF or five or six turns for HF.

Another approach is to add filtering to the serial port but this will only be effective at VHF if the shell of the connector on the PC is well grounded to the case. Point G in Fig A6.1 should be well grounded but point H may not be because it is on an expansion card. Filtered 'D' connectors have a 1nF ceramic feed-through capacitor built in to each pin but a nine-way socket is relatively expensive. A lower-cost alternative is to use a standard tin-plated 'D' socket and solder a 1nF or 4.7nF ceramic capacitor from each pin to the connector shell. The capacitors should have the shortest possible leads.

For a parallel printer port, similar considerations apply. Use screened cable with the screen solidly grounded to a metal connector shell at the PC end. The shell of the 'D' plug should have grounding 'dimples'.

The graphics card

It is also worth taking a look at the video output. With the monitor switched off, touch the shell of the connector on the monitor's video cable against the shell of the video output connector on the PC. If there is an increase in RFI, this indicates a common-mode source. The metal mounting bracket on the graphics card is grounded at the top but this does not mean that the connector shell is well grounded to the PC case at VHF. Fig A6.2 shows how grounding can be improved using two pieces of metal cut from a spare expansion slot blanking plate. If possible, the graphics card should be fitted in one of the end slots where grounding to the back panel is better. Some CE-marked PCs have spring fingers around all the expansion slots on the back panel to improve grounding.

Now plug the video lead in properly but do not turn the monitor on yet. If there is any increase in RFI, try a clip-on ferrite choke on the video cable ('J' in Fig A6.1) if one isn't fitted already. If there is one, try fitting another at the other end of the cable. By now, you probably have a very quiet computer at VHF until the monitor is switched on.

Reducing HF and monitor emissions

This section deals with computer RFI reduction at HF and monitor RFI reduction at HF and VHF. For the computer itself, it is worth paying particular attention to any unscreened interconnecting cables such as the mouse cable. If the computer has an internal modem, the unscreened telephone cable can radiate or pick up RF, especially if connected to an overhead telephone line. For BABT-approved telephone equipment, including modems, conducted RF emissions via the telephone line are tested but only up to 8MHz. Conducted RF emission tests via the telephone line are not yet required for a CE-marked modem. Quite a lot of non-BABT approved modems have been sold in the UK. If a mouse or modem cable radiates RFI, a clip-on ferrite core should be fitted to the cable near the computer using six turns for HF or three turns for VHF if possible. Suitable clip-on cores are available from Maplin Electronics (BZ34M), Farnell Components (535-904) and RS Components (779-813 or 779-863).

A computer contains a switch-mode power supply (SMPS) operating at around 30–40kHz or more. Harmonics of the switching frequency can extend through the LF, MF and HF bands, becoming weaker as frequency increases. They are not well-defined carriers but a large number of broad peaks at multiples of the switching frequency. In practice, the power supply of a CE-marked computer is likely to be fairly quiet on all amateur bands except those below 500kHz. Even before 1996, many computers were manufactured to meet German or US RFI limits. In the UK, however, some switch-mode power supplies in computers or monitors sold before 1996 had some of the mains filter components omitted. If you have a computer with a noisy power supply, a possible solution is to use a filtered mains plug although a new power supply may be cheaper! Filtered mains plugs are primarily intended to stop mains-borne RFI and spikes from getting into a computer and could also be useful for keeping mains-borne RF out of other equipment such as TVs or video recorders. They can reduce the amount of RFI which gets out from the computer into the mains but for maximum effectiveness in this application, the length of cable from the filtered plug to the computer should be kept to the absolute minimum, such as 15cm or so.

Mains plugs with a built-in 3A RFI filter are available from Maplin Electronics (KUI9V) or RS Components (239-567). RS Components also sell a filtered mains adaptor which does not need to be wired in (238-902). Note that ordinary surge-protecting mains plugs for computers only contain transient suppressors with no RF filtering.

A tale of two monitors

There are large variations in the amount of RFI emitted by different models of computer monitor. Fortunately, there are various ways of making a noisy monitor quieter. Some of these may only give one S-point improvement on some bands but every S-point counts and the combined effect of a number of different measures can be quite significant. A worthwhile improvement can often be achieved without any internal modifications. Where internal modifications are described, these should only be attempted by those with experience of such work and should be regarded as experimental due to the

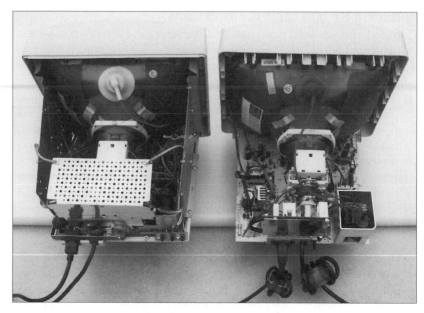

possibility of damaging the monitor. Note that ferrite is not an insulator and any ferrite cores should be fitted so as to avoid causing a short-circuit.

Photo A6.1 shows two 14in VGA/ SVGA computer monitors which I tested; a fairly quiet one and a fairly noisy one. The one on the left is an old Viglen model CA 1428A manufactured in 1991 which is solidly built, quite well screened and quite heavy at 14kg. It complies with the US FCC Rules and produces little RFI on any amateur band. The one on the right is a basic Korean monitor, a Xyst model FM370 manufactured in November 1994. It is significantly lighter (11kg), has little screening and does not claim to meet the US FCC Rules. It also generates far more RFI than the Viglen. I managed to achieve a worthwhile reduction in RFI from the Xyst monitor although it was still noisier than the Viglen.

For testing, I used an indoor wire antenna about 2.5m long with an ATU. The antenna was about 2m from the computer which gave a large enough S-meter reading (S7–8 in some cases) to give a clear indication of small changes in RFI level. The switching frequency for the power supply was synchronised to the line timebase frequency which made it difficult to distinguish between power supply harmonics and line timebase harmonics. Video amplifier harmonics are another possible source. On all bands, a bright graphics screen with a lot of detail was used for testing. Turning the brightness and contrast right down gave a large reduction in RFI. There are three possible reasons for this, reduced loading on the power supply, reduced loading on the line output stage and reduced output from the video amplifiers.

The switch-mode power supply has a mains filter on the PCB with space for additional filter components which are not fitted. Nevertheless, the IEC mains input connector is a filtered type in a metal can which is bolted to the 'chassis'. Adding further mains filtering did not give any improvement on any band. On most HF bands except 28MHz, the monitor produced more RFI when standing on top of the metal PC case than when lifted clear or placed on an insulating surface. Placing a hand under the case, near the power supply increased RFI because the power supply has no screening at all. I added an external screen underneath the monitor case using fine mesh to avoid obstructing the ventilation. As part of the monitor chassis was accessible at the back of the case, it was easy to ground the mesh to the chassis at this point.

An alternative is to cut away the sheath of the video cable carefully and make a ground connection to the braided screen. The mesh gave up to 8dB reduction on 1.8MHz and smaller improvements on 3.5MHz and 7MHz. On 14MHz and above it had no effect or could actually increase the RFI slightly. Fine expanded aluminium mesh is available by the metre from some hardware stores and also in small pieces from car accessory shops.

Gripping the video cable or mains cable tightly in both hands gave a noticeable reduction in RFI which suggests that RFI sources inside the monitor are radiating against these cables as ground radials. This effect can be reduced by means of ferrite rings on both cables. As the video cable is thick and inflexible, the only way to get enough turns for the HF bands is to use a large split ferrite yoke ring core from a scrap TV or monitor as shown in Photo A6.1. The cable was not long enough to allow more than five turns although 10 or more would have been better. For the mains cable, I used six turns on a small yoke ring core. These ferrite cores gave variable results with about 6dB reduction on 14MHz. Grounding the monitor chassis to the PC chassis using a short length of braid was not a good idea as it bypassed the ferrite chokes and increased the RFI level by 6dB on some bands.

The above measures produced a worthwhile improvement on the 1.8–14MHz bands but only a slight improvement on 28MHz. I found that the predominant source at 28MHz was harmonics from the line output stage. It seems that line output stages using modern plastic power transistors generate higher levels of 900th harmonic than older metal-can types such as BU208A. The collector of the line output transistor is directly connected to the 'hot' side of the line scan coils which can act as a radiating antenna. This point really is 'hot' with about 1500V peak. Note that the line output transistor is highly stressed and any overload can cause it to expire, taking one of the diodes in the power supply with it. It is difficult to filter the drive to the line scan coils because it is a high-current circuit where more than a few microhenrys of extra series inductance starts to reduce the picture width. Adding a shunt capacitor to ground is also not a good idea as it needs at least 2kV working voltage and could upset the delicate line output transistor. I found that the most effective way of reducing the high harmonics of the line timebase on 28MHz was by cutting the track to the collector of the line output transistor and putting in a series choke consisting of two turns on an FX 1115 ferrite bead. This gave about a 10dB improvement on 28MHz but had little effect on 14MHz and below.

Next, attention turned to the 144MHz band where harmonics from the monitor's unscreened switch-mode power supply were weak but detectable on an SSB receiver. These VHF harmonics were reduced by cutting the track to the collector of the main switching transistor in the power supply and inserting a series choke consisting of two turns on a ferrite bead.

Photo A6.2. A typical pair of amplified speakers for a multi-media PC

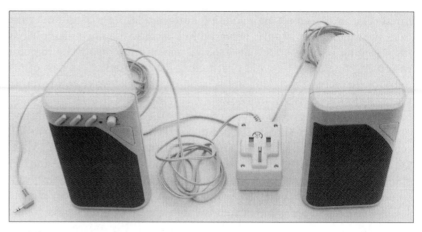

If the video amplifiers are radiating, displaying a screen with a lot of fine detail will produce more RFI than a plain screen of the same brightness. The video output transistors are nearly always mounted on the base of the CRT, on a small PCB with a tinplate screen. This screen should be grounded to the chassis by two short lengths of braid. The video cable from the computer should have its braid solidly grounded to chassis where it enters the monitor. Some CE-marked monitors have two large ferrite beads on the video cable, one each side of this ground point.

It would be possible to spray the whole inside of a monitor's case with nickel RF shielding spray but this is not recommended for several reasons. First, there are high voltages on the PCB which may flash over to any conductive coating inside the case. Secondly, the conductive layer may find its way through ventilation slots so that it can be touched from outside. This presents a shock hazard if part of the coating inside comes into contact with a high voltage. A third problem is that the coating may not adhere well to certain types of plastic and flakes could fall off and land on the PCB.

Even the software set-up of a PC can affect the emissions from a monitor. PC graphics cards can be programmed for many different operating modes which use various different pixel clock frequencies. Some of these modes are more EMC friendly than others! For example, many Cirrus Logic video cards in the 800 × 600 resolution modes use a pixel clock frequency of 36.088MHz or 72.176MHz. This produces a second or fourth harmonic at nominally 144.352MHz with sidebands either side. A VGA utility program such as CLMODE can be used to demonstrate the various graphics modes and identify any differences in RFI.

Multi-media speakers

There were very few reported cases of amateur transmissions affecting computers until multi-media PCs arrived. These have sound cards which can drive speakers or headphones directly but many users want increased power output and use amplified speakers such as those shown in Photo A6.2. One speaker box contains a stereo audio amplifier with on-off, volume and tone controls. The other box contains only a loudspeaker. Both boxes usually have a battery compartment but only one has any battery

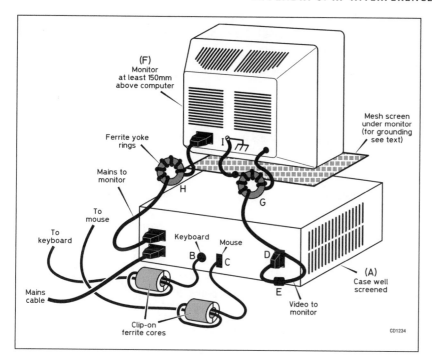

Fig A6.3. The RFI reduction measures shown in Table A6.1 overleaf

contacts. Alternatively, a mains-powered DC adaptor can be used. Predictably, some types of multi-media speaker (even CE-marked models) are lacking in RF immunity because they are classed as Information Technology Equipment (ITE) rather than audio equipment. These can be tested with an unmodulated carrier.

The first thing to do with breakthrough on multi-media speakers is to switch them off and unplug the mains power pack from the speaker. Switching off usually bypasses the amplifiers and connects the speakers directly to the output of the sound card. If breakthrough still occurs, a ferrite ring is required where the cable plugs into the sound card. To tackle RF breakthrough in the amplified speaker itself, a ferrite ring should be fitted to the audio input cable with another on the output cable leading to the other speaker. If breakthrough is still present, try running the speakers on batteries temporarily and if this helps, a ferrite ring may be required on the DC power cable.

References

[1] 'EMC' column, *Radio Communication* February 1991.
[2] 'EMC' column, *Radio Communication* June 1995.

Table A6.1. Summary of computer RFI reduction measures (see Fig A6.3)		
Key in Fig A6.3	RFI reduction measure	Frequencies where this is likely to give an improvement
For the computer itself		
A1	Ensure that the case is well screened	HF & VHF
A2	Ensure that the cover makes good contact at many points, that there are no large holes for unused disc drives etc and that there are no significant emissions from wiring to front-panel controls and indicators.	VHF
B1	Ensure good grounding of keyboard socket to back of case.	VHF
B2	Fit clip-on ferrite split bead to keyboard cable (3 turns or more).	VHF
C1	Ensure that serial and parallel port 'D' type connectors are well grounded to the case.	VHF
C2	Ensure that serial and parallel cables are well screened and that screen is well grounded to metal 'D' type connector shells. Ensure that the shells of the 'D' plug and socket have 'dimples' to make good contact.	
C3	For cables which cannot easily be screened (eg mouse or modem), fit a clip-on ferrite split bead core (3 turns for VHF, 6 turns for HF if possible).	HF & VHF
D	Ensure that video output connector is very well grounded to case (video card in end slot, possibly with additional grounding bar as shown in Fig A6.2).	VHF
For the monitor		
E	Ensure that a clip-on split ferrite bead is fitted to the monitor video cable near the 15-way 'D' connector.	VHF
F	Try raising the monitor 150mm (6in) above PC case or any other metal surface.	
G	Wind monitor video cable 7 or more turns through a split ferrite yoke ring core near the monitor.	HF
H	Wind monitor mains cable 7 or more turns through a split ferrite yoke ring core near the monitor.	HF
I	If the monitor is poorly screened, put a piece of sheet metal, mesh or foil under the monitor and ground it with a short wire or braid to the monitor chassis or to the video cable screen.	Lower HF bands (may increase emissions on other bands)

7 Useful data

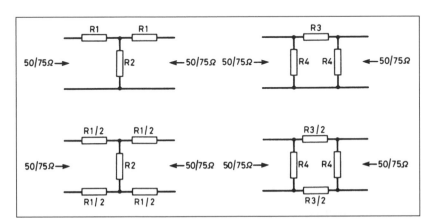

Fig A7.1. 50 and 75Ω attenuators

Table A7.1. 50 and 75Ω attenuators

| Attenuation (dB) | T pad | | | | π pad | | | |
| | 50Ω | | 75Ω | | 50Ω | | 75Ω | |
	R1	R2	R1	R2	R3	R4	R3	R4
1	2.9	433	4.3	647	5.8	870	8.6	1305
2	5.7	215	8.6	323	11.6	436	17.4	654
3	8.5	142	12.8	213	17.6	292	26.4	439
4	11.3	105	17.0	157	23.8	221	35.8	331
5	14.0	82	21.0	123.4	30.4	179	45.6	268
6	16.6	67	25.0	100	37.3	151	56.0	226
7	19.0	56	28.7	83.8	44.8	131	67.2	196
8	21.5	47	32.3	71	52.3	116	79.3	174
9	23.8	41	35.7	61	61.6	105	92.4	158
10	26.0	35	39.0	52.7	70.7	96	107	144
11	28.0	30.6	42.0	45.9	81.6	89	123	134
12	30.0	26.8	45.0	40.2	93.2	84	140	125
13	31.7	23.5	47.6	35.3	106	78.3	159	118
14	33.3	20.8	50.0	31.2	120	74.9	181	112
15	35.0	18.4	52.4	25.0	136	71.6	204	107
20	41.0	10.0	61.4	15.2	248	61	371	91.5
25	44.7	5.6	67.0	8.5	443	56	666	83.9
30	47.0	3.2	70.4	4.8	790	53.2	1186	79.7
35	48.2	1.8	72.4	2.7	1406	51.8	2108	77.7

Table A7.2. United Kingdom TV channel frequencies

	BAND IV Frequency (MHz)			BAND V Frequency (MHz)			Frequency (MHz)	
Channel	Vision	Sound	Channel	Vision	Sound	Channel	Vision	Sound
21	471.25	477.25	38	607.25	613.25	55	743.25	749.25
22	479.25	485.25	39	615.25	621.25	56	751.25	757.25
23	487.25	493.25	40	623.25	629.25	57	759.25	765.25
24	495.25	501.25	41	631.25	637.25	58	767.25	773.25
25	503.25	509.25	42	639.25	645.25	59	775.25	781.25
26	511.25	517.25	43	647.25	653.25	60	783.25	789.25
27	519.25	525.25	44	655.25	661.25	61	791.25	797.25
28	527.25	533.25	45	663.25	669.25	62	799.25	805.25
29	535.25	541.25	46	671.25	677.25	63	807.25	813.25
30	543.25	549.25	47	679.25	685.25	64	815.25	821.25
31	551.25	557.25	48	687.25	693.25	65	823.25	829.25
32	559.25	565.25	49	695.25	701.25	66	831.25	837.25
33	567.25	573.25	50	703.25	709.25	67	839.25	845.25
34	575.25	581.25	51	711.25	717.25	68	847.25	853.25
35	583.25	589.25	52	719.25	725.25			
36	591.25	597.25	53	727.25	733.25			
37	599.25	605.25	54	735.25	741.25			

EMC ASPECTS OF THE AMATEUR BANDS FROM 1810kHz TO 440MHz

The bands quoted are those allocated in the UK.

1810 to 2000kHz

Part of this band is shared with the Maritime Mobile Service and is allocated in the UK on the basis that no harmful interference is caused to that service. Breakthrough to cordless telephones on the CT1 system which use frequencies of about 1.7MHz (base transmit, handset receive) is a possibility. Image interference (tuneable breakthrough) to medium-wave broadcast receivers is common.

Harmonics

All harmonics up to the 15th fall into the HF band. Harmonics are unlikely to cause any problems in residential areas.

3500 to 3800kHz

This band is a shared band by several primary users of which the Amateur Service is one. Direct breakthrough to the video of TV sets and VCR playback amplifiers is fairly common.

Harmonics

All harmonics up to the eighth fall into the HF band. Harmonics are not likely to cause any problems in residential areas.

7000 to 7100kHz

This band is allocated exclusively to the Amateur Service on a world-wide basis.

Harmonics

Harmonics could be a problem in regions where VHF TV broadcasting on Band I (approximately 47 to 72MHz, depending on location) is still in use.

(TV broadcasting in Band I has declined over the years and has been discontinued completely in some countries, including the UK.)

10,100 to 10,150kHz

This is a shared band. The Amateur Service is the secondary user. Direct breakthrough into the 10.7MHz IF of VHF broadcast receivers is a possibility.

Harmonics

Harmonics could be a problem in regions where VHF TV broadcasting on Band I is still in use.

14,000 to 14,350kHz

This band is allocated exclusively to the Amateur Service on a worldwide basis.

Harmonics

Harmonics can be a serious problem in regions where VHF TV on Band I is still in use. It is possible that the seventh harmonic could cause interference to VHF radio broadcasting on Band II (88 to 108MHz).

18,068 to 18,168kHz

This band has been allocated to the Amateur Service on a primary basis.

Harmonics

Harmonics can be a serious problem in regions where VHF TV on Band I is still in use. The fifth harmonic falls into the lower part of VHF radio broadcast Band II (88 to 108MHz). The second harmonic (36MHz) could cause IF breakthrough to TV receivers.

21,000 to 21,450kHz

This band is allocated exclusively to the Amateur Service on a worldwide basis.

Harmonics

Harmonics can be a serious problem in regions where VHF TV on Band I is still in use. The fifth harmonic falls in the upper part of VHF radio broadcast Band II.

24,890 to 24,990kHz

This band has been allocated to the Amateur Service on a primary basis.

Harmonics

Harmonics can be a serious problem in regions where VHF TV on Band I is still in use. The fourth harmonic falls in the VHF radio broadcast Band II. The second harmonic could cause problems to low-power control and communication devices operating on frequencies around 49MHz.

28,000 to 29,700MHz

This band is allocated exclusively to the Amateur Service on a worldwide basis. Some low-power control devices such as radio door chimes etc operate on specific frequencies in the CEPT Citizens Band (26.96 to 27.4MHz). Breakthrough to such devices is a possibility.

Harmonics

Harmonics can be a serious problem in regions where VHF TV on Band I is still in use. The third harmonic of frequencies above 29.3MHz will fall into VHF radio broadcast Band II.

50.0 to 52.0MHz

This band has become available in the UK since the closing of VHF TV broadcasting. In some locations, care may be needed to avoid interference to TV in other countries. Breakthrough to CT1 cordless telephones operating near 47.5MHz or to low-power control and communication devices operating on frequencies around 49MHz is a possibility.

Harmonics

The second harmonic falls into the upper end of VHF radio broadcast Band II. Third harmonics could cause interference to mobile and other services operating between 150 and 156MHz.

70.0 to 70.50MHz

This is not an internationally allocated band. Available to amateurs in the UK on a secondary basis.

Harmonics

The second harmonic (140 to 141MHz) falls into a band used by various services depending on region. Includes aircraft, land mobile and space research. The third harmonic (210 to 211.5MHz) falls into the VHF TV Band III, which is no longer used for TV broadcasting in the UK.

144 to 146MHz

This band is allocated exclusively to the Amateur Service on a worldwide basis.

Harmonics

The second harmonic (288 to 292MHz) falls into a band allocated for fixed and mobile operation, the specific use depending on the region and country. The third harmonic falls into the 430 to 440MHz amateur band. The fourth harmonic (576 to 584MHz) could cause a problem to UHF TV (Band IV, channels 34 and 35 in the UK). The fifth harmonic (720 to 730MHz) could cause interference to UHF TV (Band V, channels 52 and 53 in the UK).

430 to 440MHz

In the UK this band is allocated to the Amateur Service on a secondary basis. There are also some special restrictions in certain locations. The lower end of UHF TV Band IV is not far above this band, so that breakthrough via TV antenna and normal receiving path is a likely possibility.

There is a CEPT ISM band centred on 433.92MHz. This is used for low-power devices including 'radio keys' for cars.

Harmonics

The second harmonic (860 to 880MHz) falls above the UK UHF Band V TV band but other countries use frequencies above 860MHz for broadcasting and in such cases second-harmonic interference to TV is likely. The third harmonic (1290 to 1320MHz) falls into the 1240 to 1325MHz amateur band but, since this band is shared by other services, third-harmonic interference to non-amateur services is possible. Third-harmonic breakthrough into the first IF of a satellite TV receivers is possible but not likely.

TECHNICAL TERMS AND ABBREVIATIONS

The meanings given are those normally used in informal technical discussion.

ADSL Asymmetric Digital Subscriber Line. A system of transmitting digital signals over telephone lines without affecting normal voice operation. The asymmetry refers to the fact that large amounts of data pass down to the customer in response to relatively short signals in the other direction.

Aerial Same as 'antenna'. Widely used in the UK in relation to domestic radio and TV etc. ('Antenna' is used for most engineering purposes.)

Antenna A radiator or collector of electromagnetic energy.

AMU Antenna matching unit. Same as ATU.

ASCII American National Standard Code for Information Interchange.

ATU Antenna (or aerial) tuning unit. Device to tune out the reactance of an antenna, and match the radiation resistance to the load or source – usually 50Ω.

Balun Balance-to-unbalance transformer. Often used to connect an unbalanced (coaxial) feeder to a balanced antenna.

BCI Interference to broadcast radio reception.

Beryllia Beryllium oxide. A white ceramic used in power transistors etc. Very toxic when in the form of fine particles.

Breakthrough Used (particularly by radio amateurs) to describe interference caused by the legitimate radiation from a transmitter entering a piece of equipment which has insufficient immunity.

Bond To connect together by a low-impedance path.

Braid The woven outer conductor of coaxial cables. The woven screen around screened cables. A woven (flat) conductor which gives a large conductor area and hence a low inductance.

Capture area The hypothetical area of space from which a receiving antenna can draw power.

CE mark The letters 'CE' in the form of an specific mark. The mark indicates that the product is manufactured to comply with the relevant regulations of the European Community. On almost all electronic equipment this includes the EMC regulations. In some cases the mark may be on the instructions for use or the packing instead of the item itself.

Characteristic impedance The resistive impedance presented to an RF signal by an infinitely long transmission line or by a transmission line terminated in a resistance equal to the characteristic impedance.

Choke An inductor used to restrict the flow of AC.

Code Often used by amateurs (particularly in the USA) as an abbreviation for Morse code.

Common-mode currents Currents flowing in one direction on two or more conductors, in contrast to the go-and-return differential signals.

Counterpoise A wire suspended some distance above the ground, insulated from earth, and connected to an antenna system in place of a true earth.

CW Short for 'continuous wave' telegraphy. Signalling by keying the carrier on and off. In amateur use it usually means Morse code.

Earth (radio) A conductor buried in the ground. Assumed to be at zero potential for radio frequencies.

Earth (mains) The protective conductor (at nominal earth potential).

EMC Electromagnetic compatibility. The ability of electronic devices and systems to operate without mutual interference.

EMC regulations (European) Regulations covering the EMC performance of products sold within the European Community.

EMI Electromagnetic interference.

EMP Electromagnetic pulse. A large pulse of electromagnetic energy caused by lightning or nuclear explosion.

ERP Effective radiated power. The power radiated in the direction of maximum radiation. The power supplied to the antenna multiplied by the gain.

Far field The field at a distance where the energy is no longer affected by the antenna. The electric and magnetic fields are at right-angles to one another, and to the direction of propagation. Also known as the 'radiation field'.

Feedthrough capacitor A capacitor which mounts directly onto a screen and has a lead passing through it.

Feeder A transmission line used to transfer the power from a transmitter or ATU to the antenna. Usually a coaxial cable or open-wire line.

Ferrite Magnetic material which can be manufactured with a wide range of properties. Usually it has a high electrical resistance.

Filter A circuit which allows some frequencies to pass with a small loss, while attenuating other frequencies.

Ground (radio) Same as earth.

Ground (signal) The path by which an unbalanced signal returns to its source.

Ground (system) Zero potential to which other potentials are referred. Chassis potential.

Ground, clean A ground connection reserved for small-signal operation. (Separate from the main ground).

Ground plane (of a circuit) A large area of copper comprising all or most of one side of a PCB. Effectively connects together points of nominal zero potential by a low-impedance path. The 0V power supply rail is usually connected to the ground plane.

Harmonic A spurious emission harmonically related to the carrier.

Image interference Interference caused by an unwanted signal, which is on the opposite side of the local oscillator to the wanted signal, beating with the local oscillator to give the IF.

Intermods Short for 'intermodulation products'. Outputs (usually unwanted) caused by two or more signals mixing in a non-linear circuit.

Instability Unwanted oscillation, or a tendency to oscillate.

ISM (industrial, scientific, medical) A radio band allocated for these purposes.

Mains The domestic electricity supply.

Mode conversion (in data transmission systems) The conversion of differential currents to common-mode currents due to imperfections in a nominally balanced system.

Near field The field relatively close to an antenna, where energy is exchanged between the field and the antenna. The relationship between the electric and magnetic fields is complex.

Parasitic oscillations An unwanted oscillation involving circuit conditions incidental to the main design aims.

Pass band The band of frequencies passed by a filter with small loss.

PCB Printed circuit board.

PCB Polychlorinated biphenyl: oil used at one time in certain types of transformers and capacitors etc. Highly toxic; can be absorbed through the skin.

PIPs Passive intermodulation products. Intermods caused by corroded contacts in passive metalwork such as masts and gutters.

PME Protective multiple earthing (see Appendix 1).

PMR Private mobile radio. Radio communication for business purposes.

Polarisation (of radio wave) The direction of the electric field. May be linear (eg horizontal or vertical), circular (rotating) or elliptical (a combination of linear and circular).

Primary user This is an official definition. So far as amateurs are concerned, it is the service which has the 'right of way' on a shared band.

Protected service So far as amateurs are concerned, this means a service which can expect official action to be taken against sources of interference. Amateur radio is not a protected service.

Radiation resistance A fictitious resistance which would dissipate the same power as that radiated by a particular antenna when transmitting or which would be the source resistance when receiving.

Radiation field Same as 'far field'.

Rail A power supply line, eg +5V rail; −12V rail; 0V rail etc.

RFI Radio-frequency interference.

SCART A 21-pin connector used on television receivers and similar equipment. It stands for 'Societé de Constructeurs d'Appareils Radio récepteur et Téléviseurs'. Also known a 'Peritel' or 'Euroconnector'.

Screen Conductive enclosure or partition. Sometimes used instead of 'braid' to describe a woven outer conductor.

Secondary user This is an official definition. So far as amateurs are concerned, it is the service which does not have 'right of way'. On a shared band, where the Amateur Service is a secondary user, amateurs must not cause interference to the primary user.

Second-channel interference An old name for image interference.

Selectivity The ability to reject unwanted, off-tune signals while receiving the wanted one.

Shield Same as screen.

Splatter Spurious emissions relatively close to the nominal carrier frequency. Caused by non-linearity (often due to overdriving) in an SSB transmitter.

Spurious Short for 'spurious emission'. Any radiation outside the normal bandwidth of the transmission.

Stop band Frequencies which are attenuated by a filter. Frequencies outside the pass band.

Transmatch Same as ATU.

Transmission line Conductors arranged to convey RF energy between different parts of an installation. Usually coaxial cable or open-wire line.

TVI Interference to TV reception.

VCR Video cassette recorder.

VDSL Very High Speed Digital Subscriber Line. A proposed system which would enable high-speed data to be passed over telephone lines.

White noise Noise which can be resolved into a continuous spectrum of component frequencies. The power in equal bandwidths at any part of the spectrum is the same. Called 'white' by analogy with white light which contains all colours.

0V (rail) Zero potential to which other potentials are referred. Normally the 0V terminal of the power supply is connected to this rail. Often used interchangeably with 'ground'.

Index